Consultants

Indiana
Purdue University
Mary Bouck, Mathematics Consultant

Michigan
Oakland Schools
Valerie Mills, Mathematics Education Supervisor

Mathematics Education Consultants:
Geraldine Devine, Dana Gosen

Ellen Bacon, Independent Mathematics Consultant

New York
University of Rochester
Jeffrey Choppin, Associate Professor

Ohio
University of Toledo
Debra Johanning, Associate Professor

Pennsylvania
University of Pittsburgh
Margaret Smith, Professor

Texas
University of Texas at Austin
Emma Trevino, Supervisor of
Mathematics Programs, The Dana Center

Mathematics for All Consulting
Carmen Whitman, Mathematics Consultant

D1081630

Reviewers

Michigan
Ionia Public Schools
Kathy Dole, Director of Curriculum
and Instruction

Grand Valley State University
Lisa Kasmer, Assistant Professor

Portland Public Schools
Teri Keusch, Classroom Teacher

Minnesota
Hopkins School District 270
Michele Luke, Mathematics Coordinator

Field Test Sites for CMP3

Michigan
Ann Arbor Public Schools
Tappan Middle School: Anne Marie Nicoll-Turner*

Portland Public Schools
Portland Middle School: Mark Braun,
Angela Buckland, Holly DeRosia, Holly Feldpausch,
Angela Foote, Yvonne Grant*, Kristin Roberts,
Angie Stump, Tammi Wardwell

Traverse City Area Public Schools
Traverse City East Middle School:
Ivanka Baic Berkshire, Brenda Dunscombe,
Tracie Herzberg, Deb Larimer, Jan Palkowski,
Rebecca Perreault, Jane Porath*, Robert Sagan,
Mary Beth Schmitt*

Traverse City West Middle School:
Pamela Alfieri, Jennifer Rundio,
Maria Taplin, Karrie Tufts*

Maine
Falmouth Public Schools
Falmouth Middle School: Sally Bennett,
Chris Driscoll, Sara Jones, Shawn Towle*

Minnesota
Minneapolis Public Schools
Jefferson Community School:
Leif Carlson*,
Katrina Hayek Munsisoumang*

Ohio
Clark-Shawnee Local Schools
Reid School: Joanne Gilley
Rockway Middle School: Jim Mamer*
Possum School: Tami Thomas

*Indicates a Field Test Site Coordinator

Contents

Moving Straight Ahead
Linear Relationships

Unit Planning

▼ Unit Overview

Unit Description

The primary goal of this Unit is for students to develop an understanding of linear relationships. Students recognize linear relationships by the constant rate of change between two variables in a contextual situation, a table, a graph, or an equation.

This idea is introduced in Investigation 1 with an experiment in which students determine their walking rates. This experiment is closely tied to the central idea of constant rate of change between two variables, and it provides a "walking rate" theme for the first two Investigations.

While identifying, representing, and interpreting linear relationships is the central idea in this Unit, students also work with inequalities and equivalent expressions in Investigations 3 and 4. Solving linear equations and writing equations for lines is also explored and will be revisited with more complexity in later Units—in particular, in *Thinking with Mathematical Models* and *Say It With Symbols*.

Summary of Investigations

Investigation 1: Walking Rates

The rates at which students walk and the amount of money per kilometer that sponsors donate for a walkathon are two contexts for this Investigation. Students look at the patterns of change for each relationship and the effect of that change on various representations. For example, they recognize that graphs of linear relationships are straight lines.

They begin to see that as the independent variable changes by a constant amount, there is a corresponding constant change in the dependent variable. For linear relationships, this pattern of change is a constant rate. At this point, some students will begin to recognize that rate of change is the coefficient of x in the general equation $y = mx + b$.

Investigation 2: Exploring Linear Relationships With Graphs and Tables

This Investigation continues the theme of walkathons and helps students deepen their understanding of patterns of change. The constant rate of change between the two variables in a linear relationship and the y-intercept of the graph of a linear relationship are formalized in this Investigation. Students interpret the y-intercept as a special point on a line, a pair of values in a table, or as the constant b in the equation $y = mx + b$. They find the constant rate, decide whether relationships are decreasing or increasing, and make connections among ordered pairs on a line, a pair of values in a row of a table, and the solution of a linear equation.

Investigation 3: Solving Equations

Students continue to make the connection between points on a line, pairs of data points in a table, and solutions to equations.

They represent pictorial situations symbolically and encounter equivalent expressions for a given situation. They use the Distributive Property to show that the two expressions are equivalent.

Students use the properties of equality for solving equations in pictorial form and then transition into solving equations in symbolic form. They add or subtract the same number or variable or multiply or divide by the same nonzero number or variable on both sides of an equation.

In Problem 3.5, students find the point of intersection of two lines (or the solution of a system of two linear equations) by setting the y-values equal and then solving for x. They also solve linear inequalities and use their solutions to answer questions about real-world contexts.

Investigation 4: Exploring Slope: Connecting Rates and Ratios

Students find the ratio of vertical change to horizontal change between two points on a line. The connection between this ratio and constant rate of change is made explicit. Students find the slope of a line given two points on the line and then find the y-intercept using either a table or a graph. They write an equation of the form $y = mx + b$, in which m is the slope and b is the y-intercept.

Students then explore the idea that lines with the same slope are parallel lines, and that two lines whose slopes are the negative reciprocals of each other are perpendicular lines. Graphing calculators help students explore the slopes of many lines before they make their conjectures.

Unit Vocabulary

- ccoefficient
- dependent variable
- equivalent expressions
- independent variable

- inequality
- linear relationship
- point of intersection
- properties of equality

- slope
- solution of an equation
- x-intercept
- y-intercept

Planning Charts

Investigations & Assessments	Pacing	Materials	Resources
Assessment: Unit Readiness	½ day		• Unit Readiness Assessment
1 Walking Rates	5 days	**Labsheet 1.2** Walking Rates **Labsheet 1.3** Pledge Plans **Labsheet 1ACE:** Exercise 4 (accessibility) **Labsheet 1ACE:** Exercise 6 (accessibility) **Labsheet 1ACE:** Exercise 12 (accessibility) • Generic Grid Paper • First-Quadrant Grid meter sticks, stopwatch, transparent grid, graphing calculators, poster paper	**Teaching Aid 1.2** Tables of Data **Teaching Aid 1.4** Ms. Chang's Class Account • Coordinate Grapher • Data and Graphs
Mathematical Reflections	½ day		
Assessment: Check Up 1	½ day		• Check Up 1 • Spanish Check Up 1
2 Exploring Linear Relationships With Graphs and Tables	4½ days	**Labsheet 2.2** Henri and Emile's Race **Labsheet 2ACE:** Exercise 5 (accessibility) • Generic Grid Paper • First-Quadrant Grid poster paper, sticky notes, graphing calculators	**Teaching Aid 2.4A** Alana's Pledge Plan **Teaching Aid 2.4B** Ali and Tamara's Graphs **Teaching Aid 2.4C** Graph of $y = 5x - 3$ **Teaching Aid 2.4D** Troy's Graphing Calculator • Coordinate Grapher • Data and Graphs
Mathematical Reflections	½ day		
Assessment: Partner Quiz	1 day	**Labsheet PQ:** Partner Quiz (accessibility)	• Partner Quiz • Spanish Partner Quiz

continued on next page

Planning Charts *continued*

Investigations & Assessments	Pacing	Materials	Resources
3 Solving Equations	6 days	**Labsheet 3.2** Pouch-and-Coin Situations **Labsheet 3.3** Pouch-and-Coin Equations **Labsheet 3ACE:** Exercise 1 (accessibility) **Labsheet 3ACE:** Exercise 41 (accessibility) **Labsheet 3ACE:** Exercise 54 (accessibility) **Labsheet 3ACE:** Exercise 59 (accessibility) • Blank Table and Graph (accessibility) poster paper	**Teaching Aid 3.1** Alana's Pledge Plan **Teaching Aid 3.2A** Pouches and Coins **Teaching Aid 3.2B** Pouch-and-Coin Strategies **Teaching Aid 3.2C** Nichole's Method **Teaching Aid 3.2D** Symbolic Representation Table **Teaching Aid 3.5A** Two T-Shirt Plans **Teaching Aid 3.5B** Fabian's Bakery • Coordinate Grapher • Data and Graphs • Algebra Tiles • Climbing Monkeys
Mathematical Reflections	½ day		
Assessment: Check Up 2	½ day		• Check Up 2 • Spanish Check Up 2

continued on next pag

Planning Charts *continued*

Investigations & Assessments	Pacing	Materials	Resources
4 Exploring Slope: Connecting Rates and Ratios	5 days	**Labsheet 4.1:** Stair Measurement Table and Grid (accessibility) **Labsheet 4.2:** Linear Relationships (accessibility) **Labsheet 4ACE:** Exercise 7 (accessibility) • Coordinate Grid **Labsheet 4.4:** Linear Logic Activity (accessibility) measuring tape in inches, large sheets of graph paper, poster paper, graphing calculators	**Teaching Aid 4.2A** A Set of Stairs **Teaching Aid 4.2B** Two Graphs and a Table **Teaching Aid 4.2C** Rate of Change Table **Teaching Aid 4.2D** Mary's Method **Teaching Aid 4.3** Pairs of Lines • Climbing Monkeys
Mathematical Reflections	½ day		
Looking Back	½ day		
Assessment: Unit Project	Optional		• **Labsheet** Wasted Water Experiment • **Labsheet** Ball Bounce Experiment
Assessment: Self-Assessment	Take Home	1 day	• Self-Assessment • Spanish Self-Assessment • Notebook Checklist
Assessment: Unit Test	1 day		• Unit Test • Spanish Unit Test • Unit Test Correlation
Total	27 days	**Materials for All Investigations** calculators, student notebooks, colored pens, pencils, or markers	

▶ UNIT
OVERVIEW   GOALS AND
STANDARDS   MATHEMATICS
BACKGROUND   UNIT
INTRODUCTION   UNIT
PROJECT

Block Pacing (Scheduling for 90-minute class periods)

Investigation	Block Pacing
1 Walking Rates	3 days
Problem 1.1	½ day
Problem 1.2	½ day
Problem 1.3	1 day
Problem 1.4	1 day
Mathematical Reflections	½ day
2 Exploring Linear Relationships With Graphs and Tables	2½ days
Problem 2.1	½ day
Problem 2.2	½ day
Problem 2.4	1 day
Problem 2.3	½ day
Mathematical Reflections	½ day

Investigation	Block Pacing
3 Solving Equations	4½ days
Problem 3.1	½ day
Problem 3.2	½ day
Problem 3.3	1 day
Problem 3.4	1 day
Problem 3.5	1 day
Mathematical Reflections	½ day
4 Exploring Slope: Connecting Rates and Ratios	3½ days
Problem 4.1	1 day
Problem 4.2	½ day
Problem 4.3	1 day
Problem 4.4	½ day
Mathematical Reflections	½ day

Parent Letter

- Parent Letter (English)
- Parent Letter (Spanish)

▼ Goals and Standards

Goals

Linear Relationships Recognize problem situations in which two variables have a linear relationship

- Identify and describe the patterns of change between the independent and dependent variables for linear relationships represented by tables, graphs, equations, or contextual settings

- Construct tables, graphs, and symbolic equations that represent linear relationships

- Identify the rate of change between two variables and the x- and y-intercepts from graphs, tables, and equations that represent linear relationships

- Translate information about linear relationships given in a contextual setting, a table, a graph, or an equation to one of the other forms

- Write equations that represent linear relationships given specific pieces of information, and describe what information the variables and numbers represent

- Make a connection between slope as a ratio of vertical distance to horizontal distance between two points on a line and the rate of change between two variables that have a linear relationship

- Recognize that $y = mx$ represents a proportional relationship

- Solve problems and make decisions about linear relationships using information given in tables, graphs, and equations

Equivalence Understand that the equality sign indicates that two expressions are equivalent

- Recognize that the equation $y = mx + b$ represents a linear relationship and means that $mx + b$ is an expression equivalent to y

- Recognize that linear equations in one unknown, $k = mx + b$ or $y = m(t) + b$, where k, t, m, and b are constant numbers, are special cases of the equation $y = mx + b$

- Recognize that finding the missing value of one of the variables in a linear relationship, $y = mx + b$, is the same as finding a missing coordinate of a point (x, y) that lies on the graph of the relationship

- Solve linear equations in one variable using symbolic methods, tables, and graphs

- Recognize that a linear inequality in one unknown is associated with a linear equation

- Solve linear inequalities using graphs or symbolic reasoning

- Show that two expressions are equivalent

- Write and interpret equivalent expressions

UNIT
OVERVIEW

▶ GOALS AND
STANDARDS

MATHEMATICS
BACKGROUND

UNIT
INTRODUCTION

UNIT
PROJECT

Standards

Common Core Content Standards

7.RP.A.2 Recognize and represent proportional relationships between quantities. *Investigation 1*

7.RP.A.2a Decide whether two quantities are in a proportional relationship, e.g., by testing for equivalent ratios in a table or graphing on a coordinate plane and observing whether the graph is a straight line through the origin. *Investigation 1*

7.RP.A.2b Identify the constant of proportionality (unit rate) in tables, graphs, equations, diagrams, and verbal descriptions of proportional relationships. *Investigations 1 and 2*

7.RP.A.2c Represent proportional relationships by equations. *Investigations 1 and 2*

7.RP.A.2d Explain what a point (x, y) on the graph of a proportional relationship means in terms of the situation, with special attention to the points $(0, 0)$ and $(1, y)$, where r is the unit rate. *Investigations 2 and 4*

7.EE.A.1 Apply properties of operations as strategies to add, subtract, factor, and expand linear expressions with rational coefficients. *Investigations 3 and 4*

7.EE.A.2 Understand that rewriting an expression in different forms in a problem context can shed light on the problem and how the quantities in it are related. *Investigations 3 and 4*

7.EE.B.3 Solve multi-step real-life and mathematical problems posed with positive and negative rational numbers in any form (whole numbers, fractions, and decimals), using tools strategically. Apply properties of operations to calculate with numbers in any form; convert between forms as appropriate; and assess the reasonableness of answers using mental computation and estimation strategies. *Investigations 1 and 2*

7.EE.B.4 Use variables to represent quantities in a real-world or mathematical problem, and construct simple equations and inequalities to solve problems by reasoning about the quantities. *Investigations 1, 2, 3, and 4*

7.EE.B.4a Solve word problems leading to equations of the form $px + q = r$ and $p(x + q) = r$, where p, q, and r are specific rational numbers. Solve equations of these forms fluently. Compare an algebraic solution to an arithmetic solution, identifying the sequence of the operations used in each approach. *Investigations 1, 2, 3, and 4*

7.EE.B.4b Solve word problems leading to inequalities of the form $px + q > r$ or $px + q < r$, where p, q, and r are specific rational numbers. Graph the solution set of the inequality and interpret it in the context of the problem. *Investigation 3*

Facilitating the Mathematical Practices

Students in *Connected Mathematics* classrooms display evidence of multiple Standards for Mathematical Practice every day. Here are just a few examples of when you might observe students demonstrating the Standards for Mathematical Practice during this Unit.

Practice 1: Make sense of problems and persevere in solving them.

Students are engaged every day in solving problems and, over time, learn to persevere in solving them. To be effective, the problems embody critical concepts and skills and have the potential to engage students in making sense of mathematics. Students build understanding by reflecting, connecting, and communicating. These student-centered problem situations engage students in articulating the "knowns" in a problem situation and determining a logical solution pathway. The student-student and student-teacher dialogues help students not only to make sense of the problems, but also to persevere in finding appropriate strategies to solve them. The suggested questions in the Teacher Guides provide the metacognitive scaffolding to help students monitor and refine their problem-solving strategies.

Students also demonstrate their perseverance when they work through real-world problems such as the one involving Chantal's birthday money in Problem 4.4, Question A. They may break the problem down into several smaller steps to find a solution.

Practice 2: Reason abstractly and quantitatively.

Students reason abstractly in Problem 1.3 when they represent linear relationships using equations and then examine the effect of adding a constant to the equation. They reason quantitatively as they show understanding of the meaning of the quantities involved and conclude that adding a constant does not affect the constant rate of change.

Practice 3: Construct viable arguments and critique the reasoning of others.

Students construct arguments when they solve the pictorial equations in Problem 3.2. They justify the steps they took to their classmates, and they evaluate the processes of other students who used different methods.

Practice 4: Model with mathematics.

Students model with mathematics in the Unit Project when they use a linear equation to find the amount of water dripping from a faucet. They will see that, while the linear model is a good approximation for this situation, factors such as measurement error have an impact on the accuracy of the model.

Practice 5: Use appropriate tools strategically.

Students begin Investigation 3 by using methods familiar to them—tables and graphs—to solve equations. Some students may use paper and pencil to construct their tables and graphs, and others may use graphing calculators. By Problem 3.4, students have transitioned to using symbolic methods to solve equations, employing paper and pencil to record their steps and strategies.

Practice 6: **Attend to precision.**

Students use precise definitions when they finally connect the three models they have used to represent linear relationships. In Problem 2.4, they use the definition of a solution of an equation clearly and apply the meaning of the solution to tables, graphs, and equations in order to solve problems.

Practice 7: **Look for and make use of structure.**

In Problem 4.3, students analyze the structure of equations of groups of lines. They also look for patterns in the graphs of these groups of lines. They will conclude that lines whose slopes are equal are parallel and that lines whose slopes are opposite reciprocals are perpendicular.

Practice 8: **Look for and express regularity in repeated reasoning.**

Students express regularity in repeated reasoning when they notice that the coefficient of the independent variable in a linear relationship determines the steepness of the line in Problem 1.3. They begin Investigation 1 by using rates to describe a comparison between two quantities. By Problem 1.3, they can express and compare constant rates of change (including horizontal lines) using verbal descriptions, tables, graphs, or equations.

Students connect the relationships in Problem 2.2 with the ones in Problem 2.3 to develop an understanding of how a constant rate of change and an initial value affect the equation of a linear relationship. They use this connection to express all linear relationships in the form $y = mx + b$.

Students identify and record their personal experiences with the Standards for Mathematical Practice during the Mathematical Reflections at the end of each Investigation.

▼ Mathematics Background

Linear Functions and Relationships

The goal of this Unit is to develop student understanding of linear functions and equations. A relationship between two variables is a *function* if each value of one variable (the independent variable) is related to exactly one value of the second variable (the dependent variable). If for each unit change in the independent variable *x* there is a constant change in the dependent variable *y*, the relationship is a *linear function*.

Throughout *Moving Straight Ahead*, students use tables, graphs, and equations to represent and explore linear functions. The pattern relating two variables in a linear function can be represented with an equation in the form $y = mx + b$. The coefficient *m* of the independent variable *x* indicates the constant *rate of change* of the dependent variable *y* and the *slope* of the straight-line graph of the function. The constant term *b* is the *y*-coordinate of the point (0,*b*) where the graph of the linear function intersects the *y*-axis. It is called the *y-intercept* of the graph. Understanding of those key linear function concepts—rate of change, slope, and *y*-intercept—is developed through exploration of their meaning in specific problem contexts and the patterns in context-free examples.

When a problem involving linear functions requires finding a value of *x* that corresponds to a specified value of *y*, the task is to solve a linear equation in the form $k = mx + b$. Problems in this Unit also develop the understanding and skills students need for success in such equation solving tasks. Students will learn how to inspect tables and graphs of the function $y = mx + b$ to find the required solutions. They will also learn how to use informal and symbolic algebraic reasoning for the same tasks.

The Common Core State Standards for Mathematics reserve introduction of the term *function* until Grade 8. Thus, throughout this Grade 7 Unit, we talk only about *linear relationships* between variables. The term *linear function* will be introduced early in CMP Grade 8 and used throughout that course. Linear relationships will be compared and contrasted with the different patterns of change produced by inverse variation, exponential functions, quadratic functions, and polynomials of higher degree.

Constant Rate of Change and Slope

In Problem 1.2, three students determine their walking rates. Alana walks 1 meter per second, Gilberto walks 2 meters per second, and Leanne walks 2.5 meters per second.

Each walking rate is the constant rate of change relating the variables distance and time. In each case, the dependent variable is the distance d that each person walks, and the independent variable is the time t. The patterns of movement generated by the three walking rates are illustrated by data in the following table.

Walking Rates

Time (seconds)	Distance (meters)		
	Alana	Gilberto	Leanne
0	0	0	0
1	1	2	2.5
2	2	4	5
3	3	6	7.5
4	4	8	10
5	5	10	12.5
6	6	12	15
7	7	14	17.5
8	8	16	20
9	9	18	22.5
10	10	20	25

In the table, the constant rate of change can be observed in the following patterns:

As t increases from 0 to 1 second, d increases by 1 meter for Alana, 2 meters for Gilberto, and 2.5 meters for Leanne. As t increases from 1 to 2 seconds, d increases again by 1 meter for Alana, 2 meters for Gilberto, and 2.5 meters for Leanne.

The patterns continue for each person—as t increases by one unit, d increases by a constant amount.

Each linear relationship can be represented by an equation. In each case, the constant rate of change is the coefficient of t.

$d = 1t$ (Alana)

$d = 2t$ (Gilberto)

$d = 2.5t$ (Leanne)

continued on next page

If we graph pairs of (*time, distance*) values, each graph is a straight line with slope equal to the corresponding constant rate of change.

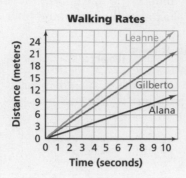

Walking Rates

The walking rate of 2.5 meters per second is represented by a linear graph with slope steeper than the lines representing the walking rates of 2 meters per second and 1 meter per second.

· ·

Students' understanding of linear situations is strengthened by examining both linear and nonlinear situations throughout the Unit. Most of these occur as tables or graphs like the ones below. Visit Teacher Place at mathdashboard.com/cmp3 to see the complete image gallery.

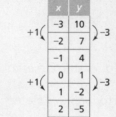

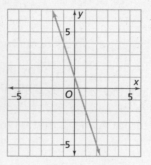

The pattern of change in this relationship is linear. The constant rate of change in the table is −3 and the *y*-intercept is 1. The equation for this pattern is $y = -3x + 1$.

In this Unit, students continue to develop their understanding of proportionality by looking at linear situations that are also proportional relationships. These relationships are represented by the equation $y = mx$. The constant *m* is both the constant rate of change for the linear relationship and the constant of proportionality for the proportional relationship. An equation of the form $y = mx$ can be written in the form $\frac{y}{x} = m$. Because *m* is a constant, *y* is proportional to *x*.

Students can determine whether a relationship is proportional by looking at a table or a graph for the relationship and observing whether the graph is a straight line through the origin. The constant rate of proportionality, or unit rate, is represented by the constant *m* in the equation or the point (1, *m*) on the graph of $y = mx$. Students can also determine whether a relationship is proportional by testing for equivalent ratios. If the ratios of the coordinates of every point (1, *m*) are equivalent, then the relationship is proportional.

Rate of Change, Ratio, and Slope of a Line

The constant rate of change for the linear relationship $d = 2t$ is shown in the table and graph below.

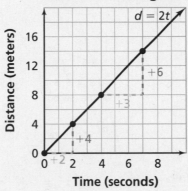

Gilberto's Walking Rate

Time (seconds)	Distance (meters)
0	0
1	2
2	4
3	6
4	8
5	10
6	12
7	14
8	16
9	18

In the table, the constant rate of change is illustrated by reading down both columns. For example, in the table above, the ratio of the change in the dependent variable to the corresponding change in the independent variable is 2 in every case.

In the graph, the constant rate of change is shown by the fact that the ratio of vertical change to horizontal change between any two points on the line is always 2. In this graphic context, the ratio is called the slope of the line. For any two points on the line,

$$\text{slope} = \frac{\text{vertical change}}{\text{horizontal change}}$$

In Investigations 1 and 2, linear relationships are characterized by the constant *rate of change* between the two variables. In Investigation 4, students are introduced to slope as a *ratio* of the vertical change to the horizontal change between two points on a line. The ratio concept of slope is connected to the constant rate of change between two variables.

Finding the Rate of Change, or Slope, of a Linear Relationship

The slope, or constant rate of change, of a line can be found directly from a verbal description of the problem context, a table of sample values for the independent and dependent variables, an equation for the relationship between the variables, or by finding the ratio of vertical to horizontal changes between two points on the line.

continued on next page

Finding the Slope From a Line on a Coordinate Grid

The points (1, 4) and (3, 10) lie on the line shown below.

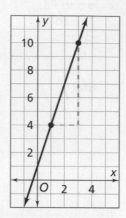

$$\text{slope} = \frac{\text{change in vertical distance}}{\text{change in horizontal distance}} = \frac{10 - 4}{3 - 1} = \frac{6}{2} = \frac{3}{1} = 3$$

Note the connection to constant rate of change. As x goes from 1 to 3, the (horizontal) change is 2. As y goes from 4 to 10, the (vertical) change is 6. That is, as x changes by 2 units, y changes by 6 units, or as x changes by 1 unit, y changes by 3 units.

Finding the Slope From a Table of Data

In a table, the relationship between two variables is linear if the ratio of change in the dependent variable to change in the independent variable is the same for every pair of (x, y) values.

Finding the Slope From an Equation

In the equation $y = mx + b$, m is the slope (or the rate of change).

Finding the Slope From a Context

In a context, such as a walkathon, the amount of money pledged by each sponsor is given. The amount of money pledged per kilometer walked is the constant rate of change (or slope of the line representing the relationship).

Suppose that a sponsor pledges to donate $5 plus $0.50 per kilometer walked. The relationship between the amount of money raised, A, and the distance walked in kilometers, d, can be represented by the equation $A = 5 + 0.5d$. The number of dollars pledged per kilometer, or 0.5, is the constant rate of change. It is also the coefficient of the independent variable, d, in the equation that represents this context.

UNIT
OVERVIEW

GOALS AND
STANDARDS

▶ MATHEMATICS
BACKGROUND

UNIT
INTRODUCTION

UNIT
PROJECT

Finding the *y*-Intercept and Equation for a Linear Relationship

In one of the problems in the Grade 6 Unit *Variables and Patterns*, students explored the cost of renting bikes for a group trip. The cost of the rental depends on the number of bikes and is represented by the equation $C = 150 + 10n$. The graph of $C = 150 + 10n$, is a straight line.

Cost of Bike Rental

Notice that the line does not pass through the origin. It crosses the *y*-axis at $150. The *y*-intercept is the constant term in the equation $C = 150 + 10n$. Students often refer to the *y*-intercept as the "starting point" from which they generate a table of data for a linear relationship. For example, in a table of the values for this equation, (0, 150) is the starting point. Students can then generate the table by repeatedly adding 1 to the values of the independent variable and 10 to the values of the dependent variable.

In general, to find an equation of the form $y = mx + b$ for a linear relationship, it is necessary to find the slope *m* and the *y*-intercept *b* of its graph.

Method 1: Finding an Equation Given Two Points on the Line

Suppose the two points are (1, 4) and (3, 10).

First, find the slope.

$$slope = \frac{10 - 4}{3 - 1} = \frac{6}{2} = \frac{3}{1} = 3$$

Then, substitute the slope into the equation $y = mx + b$ to obtain $y = 3x = b$.

The *x*- and *y* values of every point on the line satisfy the equation. Choose one point, such as (1, 4), and substitute it into the equation to get $4 = 3(1) + b$.

By solving for *b*, we find that $b = 1$.

Now substitute the value of *b* into the equation $y = 3x + b$ to get $y = 3x + 1$. This is the equation of the line passing through the points (1, 4) and (3, 10).

continued on next page

Method 2: Finding an Equation From a Table of Data

Consider the following table.

x	y
3	7
4	10
5	13
6	16
7	19

First, note that the data in the table represent a linear relationship because as x increases by 1 unit, y increases by 3 units. The constant rate of change, or slope, is 3.

Then, to find the y-intercept, you can follow the steps used in Method 1. Or, you can simply use the rate of change to work backwards in the table until $x = 0$. That is, as x decreases by 1 unit, y decreases by 3 units. This is repeated until $x = 0$.

x	y
0	−2
1	1
2	4
3	7
4	10
5	13

The y-intercept is −2. So the equation that represents the data in the table is $y = 3x - 2$.

Method 3: Finding an Equation From a Graph

First, find the y-intercept directly or by extending the line to intersect the y-axis. In the example pictured below, the y-intercept is 1, because the line crosses the y-axis at (0, 1).

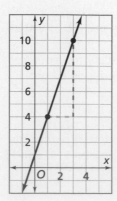

UNIT
OVERVIEW

GOALS AND
STANDARDS

▶ MATHEMATICS
BACKGROUND

UNIT
INTRODUCTION

UNIT
PROJECT

Then, find the slope by picking any two points on the line and applying the definition of slope. For example, in the graph above, the points (3, 10) and (1, 4) indicate a slope of 3.

Thus, the equation for the line is $y = 3x + 1$.

Linear Equations

Throughout this Unit, students use various representations (graphs, tables, equations, and verbal descriptions) to explore situations that involve linear relationships. They are asked to find information about one of the variables given information about the other. They can find this information from tables, from graphs, or by reasoning numerically. They can also apply properties of equality to solve a linear equation in one unknown symbolically.

Consider the equation $y = 5x - 10$. Suppose that the value of x is known to be 3. Then, to find the value of y, you can solve the equation $y = 5(3) - 10$. In this case, it is just a matter of applying arithmetic calculations to the expression $5(3) - 10$. This is more commonly called evaluating the expression $5x - 10$ when $x = 3$. Suppose that the value of y is known to be 15. You can find the value of x by solving the equation $15 = 5x - 10$, but it is not as straightforward.

Solving linear equations in one unknown involves finding information about one of the variables in a linear relationship. When students are asked to solve the equation $26 = 9 - 2x$, they can associate this equation in one unknown with the equation $y = 9 - 2x$ and look for values of x that correspond to $y = 26$.

Solving a Linear Equation

The key to solving equations symbolically is understanding equality. Many students think of the equal sign as a signal to "do something." For example, in elementary grades students encounter questions like these:

$6 + 15 = $ ■ $6 \cdot 13 + 15 = $ ■

As a consequence, they often come to think of an equation as a sequence of calculations on a set of numbers to get an answer. This can be a source of misconceptions. Instead, an equation is a statement that two quantities are equal. In this Unit, students develop an understanding of equality that can be thought of as a "balance." They learn how to write given equations in progressively simpler equivalent forms, which maintain the equality, or the balance, between two quantities.

continued on next page

In Investigations 1 and 2, students are frequently asked to find the value of one variable in a linear relationship when given information about the other variable. For instance, in the equation $A = 5 + 0.50d$, where A is the amount of money raised and d is the distance walked in kilometers, we might want to know how far a student would have to walk in order to raise $10. Answering that question requires solving a linear equation with one variable or "one unknown." Students can find the value of the variable by using various methods.

- Solve the equation using symbolic methods.

- Interpret the information from a table or a graph.

- Reason about the situation in verbal form—"There is a fixed pledge of $5 and then a donation of $0.50 per kilometer. By subtracting 5 from 10, we get $5 for the total amount donated based on the distance walked. If we divide this by 0.50, we get 10 kilometers."

Investigation 3 develops symbolic methods for solving equations. To solve an equation symbolically, we write a series of equivalent equations until we have one from which it is easy to read the value of the variable.

Equivalent equations have the same solutions. Equality or equivalence can be maintained by adding, subtracting, multiplying, or dividing the same quantity on both sides of the equation. For multiplication and division, the quantity must be nonzero. These properties are called the *properties of equality*.

· ·

Students explore the properties of equality informally by examining metaphorical equations that involve $1 gold coins and mystery pouches of coins. We assume that all pouches in an equation have the same number of coins and that both sides of the equality sign have the same number of coins. Visit *Teacher Place* at mathdashboard.com/cmp3 to see the complete video.

This provides a transition to the more abstract method of solving linear equations in one unknown. Students first find the number of coins using the pictures. Then, they translate each picture into a symbolic statement. For example, if x represents the number of coins in a pouch, then the preceding pictorial statement can be represented as $5 = 2x + 1$. Next, students apply the properties of equality to isolate the variable—that is, they solve the equation for x.

In this Unit, we solve equations with complexity like these examples:

$6 - 3x = 10$

$5 + 17x = 12x - 9$

$2(x + 3) = 10$

An understanding of integers was developed in *Accentuate the Negative*. An understanding of the Distributive Property was developed in *Prime Time*, *Accentuate the Negative*, and *Variables and Patterns*. Review of integers and the Distributive Property is also provided in the Connections section of the ACE Exercises.

Solving a System of Two Linear Equations

Students informally solve systems of linear equations throughout the Unit. They use graphs and tables to find the point of intersection of two lines. For example, in Problems 2.1 and 2.2, students compare walking rates of two brothers who are racing. In order to find the length of a race that will allow the younger brother to win in a close race, students are asked to determine when the brothers' distances from the starting point are equal.

The equations below represent the relationships between time and each brother's distance from the starting point. In eqch equation, *d* represents the distance, in meters, that each brother is from the starting point at time *t*.

$d_{Emile} = 2.5t$

$d_{Henri} = 45 + t$

To find the time at which Emile will catch up with Henri and their distances will be equal, students can use a table to find when the values of (*t*, *d*) are the same. Or, they can graph the equations and find the point of intersection of the two lines.

Later, students will learn how to solve the preceding system of equations symbolically. To find when Emile's distance equals Henri's distance, they would write $2.5t = 45 + t$ and solve for *t*. In Investigation 3, students learn that situations like this one can be represented by a system of linear equations. Thus, without calling attention to it, students have solved a linear system.

It is important that students understand what a solution to an equation means, whether they are dealing with a symbolic solution or a graphical solution. It is also important that they connect these two representations of a solution. In the preceding example, $t = 30$ is a solution of $2.5t = 45 + t$. It means that if Emile and Henri walk in their race for 30 seconds, they will be the same distance from the starting point. Graphically, the lines $y = 2.5x$ and $y = 45 + x$ intersect at (30, 75). This solution means that when the brothers each walk for 30 seconds, they are both 75 meters from the starting point. If the race were to end at this point, they would tie.

Inequalities

Investigations 1 and 2, ideas about inequality are informally explored by asking questions like this: "If $x = 4$, does Gilberto raise more or less money than Alana?" Students can answer this question by substituting 4 for x in $y = 2x$ and $y = 5 + 0.5x$ and then comparing the y-values.

In Investigation 3, solving linear inequalities using graphs evolves naturally from contexts such as Fabian's Bakery in Problem 3.5. In this Problem, the bakery's expenses for making and selling n cakes can be represented by the equation $E = 825 + 3.25n$. The bakery's income for selling n cakes is represented by the equation $I = 8.20n$.

In Question C, students apply their knowledge of how to solve a linear equation to find the break-even point, or the value of n, for which $E = I$ or $825 + 3.25n = 8.20n$.

In Question E, students are asked to find the number of cakes for which the bakery's expenses are less than \$2,400 and the number of cakes for which the bakery's income is greater than \$2,400. This requires students to use their knowledge of inequalities from *Accentuate the Negative* to find the solution set to the inequality statements $825 + 3.25n < 2,400$ and $8.20n > 2,400$. They can graph the associated equations and then find the values of n that satisfy the inequalities. Visit *Teacher Place* at mathdashboard.com/cmp3 to see the complete video.

$$825 + 3.25n < 2,400$$

$$\text{and}$$

$$8.2n > 2,400$$

$$292.7 < n < 484.6$$

$$293 \text{ cakes} \leq n \leq 484 \text{ cakes}$$

Equivalent Expressions

Two arithmetic expressions are equivalent if they have the same numerical value. For example, $7 - 8$ is equivalent to $7 + (-8)$. Two algebraic expressions are equivalent if they have the same numerical value regardless of the values of the variables involved. For example, $a - b$ is equivalent to $a + (-b)$.

Equivalent expressions were first introduced in Grade 6 using the Distributive Property—first as equivalent numerical expressions in *Prime Time* and then as equivalent algebraic expressions in *Variables and Patterns*. For example, the product of the two factors 3 and $(5 + 8)$ can be written as the sum of the two terms $3(5)$ and $3(8)$. That is, $3(5 + 8) = 3(5) + 3(8)$. Similarly, $3(x + 2) = 3(x) + 3(2)$. Area models were used to develop understanding of the Distributive Property.

The Distributive Property also provides a way to add "like terms." For example, $3x$ and $5x$ are like terms. They have the same variable(s); $3x + 5x$ is equivalent to $(3 + 5)x$ or $8x$.

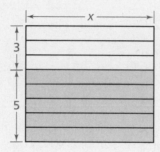

In this Unit, equivalent expressions arise in Problems 3.2 and 3.3 as students solve equations involving pouches filled with gold coins. (See the examples on the Mathematics Background page **Solving a Linear Equation**.) Visit *Teacher Place* at mathdashboard.com/cmp3 to see the complete video.

Method 1 :

$2x + 4 = 12$

Method 2 :

$2(x+2) = 12$

continued on next page

Equivalent expressions also surface in Problem 3.5. In Question A, students are given equations for the income *I* and the expenses *E* of a bakery. They are asked to find an equation for profit. Some students may write $8.2n - (825 + 3.25n)$ to represent the profit. Others may write $4.95n - 825$. The properties of numbers can be used to show that the two expressions are equivalent. See the discussion on the Mathematics Background page **Linear Inequalities** for further information about this Problem.

In Problem 4.4, students find an equation for perimeter *P* of Figure *n* made from square tiles.

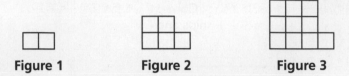

Figure 1   **Figure 2**   **Figure 3**

Students might find several equivalent expressions for the perimeter, such as $4n + 2$, $3n + (n - 1) + 3$, or even $2(n + 1) + 2n$. Properties of numbers can show that these expressions are equivalent.

One of the more important aspects of equivalent expressions is that they reveal different pieces of information about the context. Students who come up with the expression $4n + 2$ could be thinking of each figure as consisting of two squares, one that is $n \times n$ and another that is 1×1. Those who arrive at the expression $2(n + 1) + 2n$ could be thinking about the perimeter of a rectangle with dimensions $n + 1$ and *n*. The missing squares do not affect the perimeter. The expression $3n + (n - 1) + 3$ suggests looking at three sides of the figure of length *n* and then the remaining lengths are $(n - 1)$ and 3 (this represents the perimeter of the unit square at the right of each figure.)

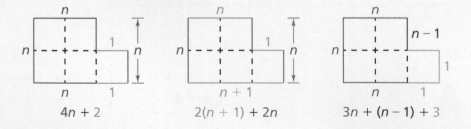

$4n + 2$ $2(n + 1) + 2n$ $3n + (n - 1) + 3$

Unit Introduction

Using the Unit Opener

Discuss the questions posed on the opening page of the Student Edition, which are designed to start students thinking about the kinds of questions and mathematics in the Unit. Don't look for "correct" answers at this time. Do, however, present an opportunity for the class to discuss the questions and to start to think about what they need to answer them. You may want to revisit these questions as students learn the mathematical ideas and techniques necessary to find the answers. Problems in contexts are used to help students reason informally about the mathematics of the Unit. The Problems are deliberately sequenced to provide scaffolding for more challenging problems. Contexts and models help students develop understanding of linear relationships and methods for writing, interpreting, and solving linear equations.

Using the Mathematical Highlights

The Mathematical Highlights page in the Student Edition provides information to students, parents, and other family members. It gives students a preview of the mathematics and some of the overarching questions that they should ask themselves while studying *Moving Straight Ahead*.

As they work through the Unit, students can refer back to the Mathematical Highlights page to review what they have learned and to preview what is still to come. This page also tells students' families what mathematical ideas and activities will be covered as the class works through *Moving Straight Ahead*.

▼ Unit Project

Introduction

As a final assessment in *Moving Straight Ahead*, you may administer the Unit Test or assign the Unit Project, Conducting an Experiment. This optional Unit Project provides students with an opportunity to further develop their understanding of linear relationships. You can formally assign the project near the end of the Unit. We recommend that students work on the project with a partner. Allow one class period for partners to collect their data. They can continue to investigate the task and draft their reports outside of class. Part of a second class period could be used for comparing results and finalizing reports. You may have students share their results in a class summary of the project.

The experiment in Project 1, the leaky faucet experiment, illustrates the relationship between time and amount of water lost. If the pressure of the water in the cup were constant, this relationship would be linear. However, the pressure decreases as the cup empties. Since the experiment is simulating a faucet dripping in which the pressure remains very nearly constant, you may want to suggest that water be added to the dripping cup to keep the height of the water in the cup somewhat constant. In trials, this experiment produced a graph that looks linear and permits convincing predictions.

In the experiment in Project 2, the relationship between the variables, original height and bounce height, is controlled by the fraction of the ball's energy that is lost on impact. This fraction is different for different balls but remains constant for individual balls. Student graphs should be linear, passing through the origin; but, because of measurement errors, students will not have exactly collinear points. The measurements should, however, be satisfactory enough for students to make confident predictions.

Assigning

The Unit Project is divided into two parts, Project 1 and Project 2. You can assign each part to a different group of students, or all students can complete both projects. For Project 1, students are asked to conduct an experiment simulating the water wasted by a leaky faucet so they can make predictions and use their data to answer questions. Project 2 involves an experiment in which students make predictions based on data they collect on the height of a bounce when a ball is dropped from different heights. These two experiments were chosen because the resulting graphs are convincingly linear in appearance. Samples of student projects and a suggested scoring rubric are provided.

Although students should be encouraged to be clever and creative, the emphasis of the project should be on mathematical content.

UNIT
OVERVIEW

GOALS AND
STANDARDS

MATHEMATICS
BACKGROUND

UNIT
INTRODUCTION

▶ UNIT
PROJECT

Providing Additional Support

If you have students who struggle with drawing their own tables and coordinate grids, you can give them **Labsheet: Wasted Water Experiment** and **Labsheet: Ball Bounce Experiment** to help them organize their data. Each labsheet provides students with a blank table and a blank first-quadrant grid. This can allow students to remain focused on the mathematics of the Unit Project while saving time.

Grading

Suggested Scoring Rubric

This rubric for scoring the project employs a scale that runs from 0 to 4, with a 4 + for work that goes beyond what has been asked for in some unique way. You may use the rubric as presented here or modify it to fit your district's requirements for evaluating and reporting students' work and understanding.

4+ Exemplary Response

- Complete, with clear, coherent explanations

- Shows understanding of the mathematical concepts and procedures

- Satisfies all essential conditions of the problem and goes beyond what is asked for in some unique way

4 Complete Response

- Complete, with clear, coherent explanations

- Shows understanding of the mathematical concepts and procedures

- Satisfies all essential conditions of the problem

3 Reasonably Complete Response

- Reasonably complete; may lack detail in explanations

- Shows understanding of most of the mathematical concepts and procedures

- Satisfies most of the essential conditions of the problem

2 Partial Response

- Gives response; explanation may be unclear or lack detail

- Shows some understanding of some of the mathematical concepts and procedures

- Satisfies some essential conditions of the problem

1   Inadequate Response

- Incomplete; explanation is insufficient or not understandable
- Shows little understanding of the mathematical concepts and procedures
- Fails to address essential conditions of problem

0   No Attempt

- Irrelevant response
- Does not attempt a solution
- Does not address conditions of the problem

Sample Student Work

Here is a sample of student data from Project 1.

Water Loss

Seconds	Amount of Water (ml)
5	5
10	9
15	14
20	18
25	22
30	26
35	30
40	33
45	36
50	39
55	43
60	46

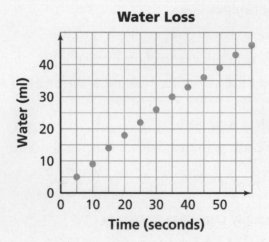

Water Loss

The table and graphs below show sample student data from Project 2. The balls used to collect this data were dropped on a sidewalk. The material the ball is made of will affect the bounce, as will the surface the ball bounces on. Another factor that can affect the results is the method students use to collect data. Some will collect several pieces of data for each bounce and average these. Some will use the top of the ball to indicate the drop and bounce height.

UNIT
OVERVIEW

GOALS AND
STANDARDS

MATHEMATICS
BACKGROUND

UNIT
INTRODUCTION

▶ UNIT
PROJECT

The data in this experiment are similar to the data students will collect for the bridge experiments in the Grade 8 Unit *Thinking With Mathematical Models*. Experiments like this are subject to measurement error and to other circumstances that may cause the data not to fit exactly on a straight line. However, the data should be very close to fitting on a line.

Ball Bounce Experiment

Drop Height (cm)	Bounce Height (cm)	
	Table-Tennis Ball	Tennis Ball
100	65	58
90	60	52
80	54	47
70	50	41
60	45	34

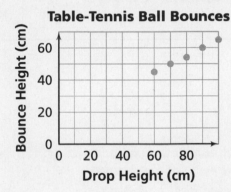

Table-Tennis Ball Bounces

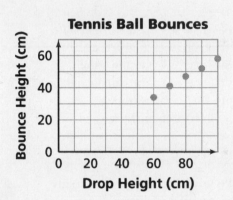

Tennis Ball Bounces

Looking Ahead

Grace's walking rate is 1.5 meters per second. Her house is 90 meters from the fountain. **How** many seconds will it take her to reach the fountain? It takes Allie 45 seconds to walk from Grace's house to the fountain. **What** is Allie's walking rate?

Grace's House

Forensic scientists can estimate a person's height by measuring the lengths of certain bones. **What** is the approximate height of a male whose tibia is 50.1 centimeters long?

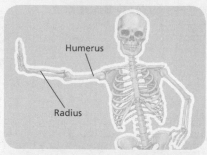
Humerus

Radius

Robert is installing a patio in his backyard. At 2:00 P.M., he has 120 stones laid in the ground. At 3:30 P.M., he has 180 stones in the ground. **When** will he be done?

Notes

All around you, things occur in patterns. Once you observe a pattern, you can use it to predict information beyond and between the data observed. The ability to use patterns to make predictions makes it possible for a baseball player to run to the right position to catch a fly ball or for a pilot to estimate the flying time for a trip.

In *Variables and Patterns*, you investigated relationships between variables. The relationships were displayed as verbal descriptions, tables, graphs, and equations. Some of the graphs, such as the graph of distance and time for a van traveling at a steady rate, were straight lines. Relationships with graphs that are straight lines are called *linear relationships.*

In this Unit, you will study linear relationships. You will learn about the characteristics of a linear relationship. You will determine whether a relationship is linear by looking at its equation or at a table of values. You will also learn how to solve linear equations. You will use what you learn about linear relationships to answer questions like those on the facing page.

Looking Ahead   3

Mathematical Highlights

Linear Relationships

In *Moving Straight Ahead*, you will explore properties of linear relationships and linear equations.

You will learn how to:

- Recognize problem situations that involve linear relationships

- Construct tables, graphs, and symbolic equations that represent linear relationships

- Translate information about linear relations given in a verbal description, a table, a graph, or an equation to one of the other forms

- Connect equations that represent linear relationships to the patterns in tables and graphs of those equations

- Identify the rate of change, slope, and *y*-intercept from the graph of a linear relationship

- Solve linear equations

- Write and interpret equivalent expressions as well as determine whether two or more expressions are equivalent

- Solve problems and make decisions about linear relationships using information given in tables, graphs, and equations

- Solve problems that can be modeled with inequalities and graph the solution set

When you encounter a new problem, it is a good idea to ask yourself questions. In this Unit, you might ask questions such as:

What are the variables in the problem?

Do the variables in the problem have a linear relationship to each other?

What patterns in the problem suggest that the relationship is linear?

How can the linear relationship in a situation be represented with a verbal description, a table, a graph, or an equation?

How do changes in one variable affect changes in a related variable?

How are these changes captured in a table, a graph, or an equation?

How can tables, graphs, and equations of linear relationships be used to answer questions?

Notes _____

_____

_____

Common Core State Standards
Mathematical Practices and Habits of Mind

In the *Connected Mathematics* curriculum you will develop an understanding of important mathematical ideas by solving problems and reflecting on the mathematics involved. Every day, you will use "habits of mind" to make sense of problems and apply what you learn to new situations. Some of these habits are described by the *Common Core State Standards for Mathematical Practices* (MP).

MP1 Make sense of problems and persevere in solving them.
When using mathematics to solve a problem, it helps to think carefully about

- data and other facts you are given and what additional information you need to solve the problem;
- strategies you have used to solve similar problems and whether you could solve a related simpler problem first;
- how you could express the problem with equations, diagrams, or graphs;
- whether your answer makes sense.

MP2 Reason abstractly and quantitatively.
When you are asked to solve a problem, it often helps to

- focus first on the key mathematical ideas;
- check that your answer makes sense in the problem setting;
- use what you know about the problem setting to guide your mathematical reasoning.

MP3 Construct viable arguments and critique the reasoning of others.
When you are asked to explain why a conjecture is correct, you can

- show some examples that fit the claim and explain why they fit;
- show how a new result follows logically from known facts and principles.

When you believe a mathematical claim is incorrect, you can

- show one or more counterexamples—cases that don't fit the claim;
- find steps in the argument that do not follow logically from prior claims.

Notes

MP4 Model with mathematics.

When you are asked to solve problems, it often helps to

- think carefully about the numbers or geometric shapes that are the most important factors in the problem, then ask yourself how those factors are related to each other;
- express data and relationships in the problem with tables, graphs, diagrams, or equations, and check your result to see if it makes sense.

MP5 Use appropriate tools strategically.

When working on mathematical questions, you should always

- decide which tools are most helpful for solving the problem and why;
- try a different tool when you get stuck.

MP6 Attend to precision.

In every mathematical exploration or problem-solving task, it is important to

- think carefully about the required accuracy of results; is a number estimate or geometric sketch good enough, or is a precise value or drawing needed?
- report your discoveries with clear and correct mathematical language that can be understood by those to whom you are speaking or writing.

MP7 Look for and make use of structure.

In mathematical explorations and problem solving, it is often helpful to

- look for patterns that show how data points, numbers, or geometric shapes are related to each other;
- use patterns to make predictions.

MP8 Look for and express regularity in repeated reasoning.

When results of a repeated calculation show a pattern, it helps to

- express that pattern as a general rule that can be used in similar cases;
- look for shortcuts that will make the calculation simpler in other cases.

You will use all of the Mathematical Practices in this Unit. Sometimes, when you look at a Problem, it is obvious which practice is most helpful. At other times, you will decide on a practice to use during class explorations and discussions. After completing each Problem, ask yourself:

- What mathematics have I learned by solving this Problem?
- What Mathematical Practices were helpful in learning this mathematics?

Notes

Notes

Conducting an Experiment

In many situations, patterns become apparent only after sufficient data are collected, organized, and displayed. Your group will be carrying out one of these experiments.

- In Project 1, you will investigate the rate at which a leaking faucet loses water.

- In Project 2, you will investigate how the drop height of a ball is related to its bounce height.

You will examine and use the patterns in the data collected from these experiments to make predictions.

Project 1: Wasted Water Experiment

In this experiment, you will simulate a leaking faucet and collect data about the volume of water lost at 5-second intervals. You will then use the patterns in your results to predict how much water is wasted when a faucet leaks for one month.

Read the directions carefully before you start. Be prepared to explain your findings to the rest of the class.

Materials:

- a watch or clock with a second hand

- a styrofoam or paper cup

- water

- a paper clip

- a clear measuring container (such as a graduated cylinder)

Notes

Directions:

Divide the work among the members of your group.

1. Make a table with columns for recording time and the amount of water lost. Fill in the time column with values from 0 seconds to 60 seconds in 5-second intervals (that is, 5, 10, 15, and so on).

2. Use the paper clip to punch a hole in the bottom of the paper cup. Cover the hole with your finger.

3. Fill the cup with water.

4. Hold the paper cup over the measuring container.

5. When you are ready to begin timing, uncover the hole so that the water drips into the measuring container, simulating the leaky faucet.

6. Record the amount of water in the measuring container at 5-second intervals for a minute.

Use this experiment to write an article for your local paper, trying to convince the people in your town to conserve water and fix leaky faucets.

In your article, include the following information:

- a coordinate graph of the data you collected;

- a description of the variables you investigated in this experiment and a description of the relationship between the variables;

- a list showing your predictions for:

  - the amount of water that would be wasted in 15 seconds, 2 minutes, in 2.5 minutes, and in 3 minutes if a faucet dripped at the same rate as your cup does;

  - how long it would take for the container to overflow if a faucet dripped into the measuring container at the same rate as your cup;

  Explain how you made your predictions. Did you use the table, the graph, or some other method? What clues in the data helped you?

- a description of other variables, besides time, that affect the amount of water in the measuring container;

- a description of how much water would be wasted in one month if a faucet leaked at the same rate as your paper cup (explain how you made your predictions);

- the cost of the water wasted by a leaking faucet in one month. (To do this, you will need to find out how much water costs in your area. Then, use this information to figure out the cost of the wasted water.)

Notes

Project 2: Ball Bounce Experiment

In this experiment, you will investigate how the height from which a ball is dropped is related to the height it bounces. Read the directions carefully before you start. Be prepared to explain your findings to the rest of the class.

Materials:

- a meter stick
- a ball that bounces

Directions:

Divide the work among the members of your group.

1. Make a table with columns for recording drop height and bounce height.

2. Hold the meter stick perpendicular to a flat surface, such as an uncarpeted floor, a table, or a desk.

3. Choose and record a height on the meter stick as the height from which you will drop the ball. Hold the ball so that either the top of the ball or the bottom of the ball is at this height.

4. Drop the ball and record the height of the first bounce. If the *top* of the ball was at your starting height, look for the height of the *top* of the ball. If the *bottom* of the ball was at your starting height, look for the height of the *bottom* of the ball. (You may have to do this several times before you feel confident you have a good estimate of the bounce height.)

5. Repeat this for several different starting heights.

Notes _____

_____

_____

After you have completed the experiment, write a report that includes the following:

- a coordinate graph of the data you collected;

- a description of the variables you investigated in this experiment and a description of the relationship between the variables;

- a list showing your predictions for:
  - the bounce height for a drop height of 2 meters;

  - the drop height needed for a bounce height of 2 meters;

- a description of how you made your prediction, whether you used a table, a graph, or some other method, and the clues in the data that helped you make your predictions;

- an explanation of the bounce height you would expect for a drop height of 0 centimeters and where you could find this on the graph;

- a description of any other variables besides the drop height, which may affect the bounce height of the ball.

Notes

Walking Rates

▼ Investigation Overview

Investigation Description

The rates at which students walk and the amount of money per kilometer that sponsors donate for a walkathon are two contexts for this Investigation. Students look at the patterns of change for each relationship and the effect of that change on various representations. For example, they recognize that graphs of linear relationships are straight lines.

They begin to see that as the independent variable changes by a constant amount, there is a corresponding constant change in the dependent variable. For linear relationships, this pattern of change is a constant rate. At this point, some students will begin to recognize that rate of change is the coefficient of x in the general equation $y = mx + b$.

Investigation Vocabulary

- dependent variable
- independent variable
- linear relationships

Mathematics Background

- Linear Functions and Relationships
- Constant Rate of Change and Slope
- Finding the Rate of Change, or Slope, of a Linear Relationship
- Finding the y-intercept and Equation for a Linear Relationship

Planning Chart

Content	ACE	Pacing	Materials	Resources
Problem 1.1	1–2, 15–18	1 day	**Generic Grid Paper** meter sticks stopwatch transparent grid	
Problem 1.2	3–5, 19–22, 30	1 day	**Labsheet 1.2** Walking Rates **Labsheet 1ACE:** Exercise 4 (accessibility) graphing calculators	**Teaching Aid 1.2** Tables of Data • Coordinate Grapher • Data and Graphs
Problem 1.3	6–9, 23–26, 31, 32	1½ days	**Labsheet 1.3** Pledge Plans **Labsheet 1ACE:** Exercise 6 (accessibility) • Generic Grid Paper transparent grid poster paper	• Coordinate Grapher • Data and Graphs
Problem 1.4	10–14, 27–29, 33	1½ days	**Labsheet 1ACE:** Exercise 12 (accessibility) • First-Quadrant Grid	**Teaching Aid 1.4** Ms. Chang's Class Account • Coordinate Grapher • Data and Graphs
Mathematical Reflections		½ day		
Assessment: Check Up 1		½ day		• Check Up 1

▼ Goals and Standards

Goals

Linear Relationships Recognize problem situations in which two variables have a linear relationship

- Identify and describe the patterns of change between the independent and dependent variables for linear relationships represented by tables, graphs, equations, or contextual settings

- Construct tables, graphs, and symbolic equations that represent linear relationships

- Identify the rate of change between two variables and the *x*- and *y*-intercepts from graphs, tables, and equations that represent linear relationships

- Translate information about linear relationships given in a contextual setting, a table, a graph, or an equation to one of the other forms

- Write equations that represent linear relationships given specific pieces of information, and describe what information the variables and numbers represent

- Make a connection between slope as a ratio of vertical distance to horizontal distance between two points on a line and the rate of change between two variables that have a linear relationship

- Recognize that $y = mx$ represents a proportional relationship

- Solve problems and make decisions about linear relationships using information given in tables, graphs, and equations

Mathematical Reflections

Look for evidence of student understanding of the goals for this Investigation in their responses to the questions in *Mathematical Reflections*. The goals addressed by each question are indicated below.

1. Describe how the dependent variable changes as the independent variable changes in a linear relationship. Give examples.

   Goals

   - Identify and describe the patterns of change between the independent and dependent variables for linear relationships represented by tables, graphs, equations, or contextual settings

   - Write equations that represent linear relationships given specific pieces of information, and describe what information the variables and numbers represent

   - Recognize that $y = mx$ represents a proportional relationship

2. How does the pattern of change between two variables in a linear relationship show up in

    a. a contextual situation?

    b. a table?

    c. a graph?

    d. an equation?

Goals

- Construct tables, graphs, and symbolic equations that represent linear relationships

- Identify the rate of change between two variables and the x- and y-intercepts from graphs, tables, and equations that represent linear relationships

- Translate information about linear relationships given in a contextual setting, a table, a graph, or an equation to one of the other forms

- Write equations that represent linear relationships given specific pieces of information, and describe what information the variables and numbers represent

- Recognize that $y = mx$ represents a proportional relationship

- Solve problems and make decisions about linear relationships using information given in tables, graphs, and equations

Standards

Common Core Content Standards

7.RP.A.2 Recognize and represent proportional relationships between quantities. *Problems 2 and 3*

7.RP.A.2a Decide whether two quantities are in a proportional relationship, e.g., by testing for equivalent ratios in a table or graphing on a coordinate plane and observing whether the graph is a straight line through the origin. *Problems 2 and 3*

7.RP.A.2b Identify the constant of proportionality (unit rate) in tables, graphs, equations, diagrams, and verbal descriptions of proportional relationships. *Problems 1, 2, and 3*

7.RP.A.2c Represent proportional relationships by equations. *Problems 1, 2, and 3*

7.EE.B.3 Solve multi-step real-life and mathematical problems posed with positive and negative rational numbers in any form (whole numbers, fractions, and decimals), using tools strategically. Apply properties of operations to calculate with numbers in any form; convert between forms as appropriate; and assess the reasonableness of answers using mental computation and estimation strategies. *Problems 1, 3, and 4*

7.EE.B.4 Use variables to represent quantities in a real-world or mathematical problem, and construct simple equations and inequalities to solve problems by reasoning about the quantities. *Problems 1 and 2*

7.EE.B.4a Solve word problems leading to equations of the form $px + q = r$ and $p(x + q) = r$, where p, q, and r are specific rational numbers. Solve equations of these forms fluently. Compare an algebraic solution to an arithmetic solution, identifying the sequence of the operations used in each approach. *Problems 3 and 4*

Facilitating the Mathematical Practices

Students in *Connected Mathematics* classrooms display evidence of multiple Common Core Standards for Mathematical Practice every day. Here are just a few examples of when you might observe students demonstrating the Standards for Mathematical Practice during this Investigation.

Practice 1: **Make sense of problems and persevere in solving them.**

Students are engaged every day in solving problems and, over time, learn to persevere in solving them. To be effective, the problems embody critical concepts and skills and have the potential to engage students in making sense of mathematics. Students build understanding by reflecting, connecting, and communicating. These student-centered problem situations engage students in articulating the "knowns" in a problem situation and determining a logical solution pathway. The student-student and student-teacher dialogues help students not only to make sense of the problems, but also to persevere in finding appropriate strategies to solve them. The suggested questions in the Teacher Guides provide the metacognitive scaffolding to help students monitor and refine their problem-solving strategies.

Practice 2: **Reason abstractly and quantitatively.**

Students reason abstractly in Problem 1.3 when they represent linear relationships using equations and then examine the effect of adding a constant to the equation. They reason quantitatively as they show understanding of the meaning of the quantities involved and conclude that adding a constant does not affect the constant rate of change.

Practice 8: **Look for and express regularity in repeated reasoning.**

Students express regularity in repeated reasoning when they notice that the coefficient of the independent variable in a linear relationship determines the steepness of the line in Problem 1.3. They begin Investigation 1 by using rates to describe a comparison between two quantities. By Problem 1.3, they can express and compare constant rates of change (including horizontal lines) using contextual situations, tables, graphs, or equations.

Students identify and record their personal experiences with the Standards for Mathematical Practice during the *Mathematical Reflections* at the end of the Investigation.

PROBLEM

1.1

Walking Marathons
Finding and Using Rates

▼ Problem Overview

> *Focus Question*   What equation represents the relationship between the time and the distance you walk at a constant rate? What are the dependent and independent variables?

Problem Description

This Problem introduces patterns of change between two variables in the context of a walkathon. Students determine their walking rates in meters per second as a ratio of distance to time. They answer questions about time and distance using their constant walking rates and write an equation that models the distance walked over time at their constant walking rates.

Problem Implementation

Students can work in groups of four.

Materials

• **Generic Grid Paper**

meter sticks (10 per group)
stopwatch
transparent grid (optional)

Using Technology

If you have access to a computer, you can use **Data and Graphs** to collect and display the walking rates for the entire class.

Vocabulary

• linear relationship

Mathematics Background

• Linear Functions and Relationships

At a Glance and Lesson Plan

- At a Glance: Problem 1.1 Moving Straight Ahead
- Lesson Plan: Problem 1.1 Moving Straight Ahead

▼ Launch

Launch Video

This animation depicts two characters discussing an upcoming walkathon and helping each other figure out their walking rates. You can use this animation to help students understand the context of the walkathon. You can also use it as a demonstration of the steps needed for students to find their walking rates. Visit Teacher Place at mathdashboard.com/cmp3 to see the complete video.

Connecting to Prior Knowledge

Tell a story about walkathons and ask the class if they know what their walking rates are in meters per second. Student predictions will likely be much higher than their actual walking rates. They may have some knowledge about walking rates if they have used a treadmill. On a treadmill, a person might set the walking speed at 4 miles per hour. One interesting thing about treadmills is that the rate of 4 miles per hour may also be reported as 15 minutes per mile. You might discuss why both these rates are reported or why treadmills do not report the rate in miles per minute or meters per hour.

Presenting the Challenge

Now tell students that they will have a chance to check their guesses. Describe the experiment.

The following suggestions for enriching the experiment might be interesting:

- Let the groups decide whether they want to calculate meters per second or seconds per meter.
- Ask one group to change their walking rate—maybe walk, jog, sprint, and so on.
- Ask some students to walk for 10 seconds rather than 10 meters.

Be sure to discuss these suggestions in the Summarize if you assign them here.

▼ Explore

Providing for Individual Needs

Give each group 10 meter sticks and a stopwatch or a clock with seconds. Students should do the experiment twice to get an accurate walking rate. They can choose either the rate they want or the average of the two. Make sure there is a person checking the time in each group. As the groups finish collecting their data, they can work on the questions in the Problem.

You could extend this Problem by asking some groups to record their data on a bar or line graph using **Generic Grid Paper**. Students may also record their graphs on transparent or electronic grids so that they can be used in the Summarize.

Look to see how students are recording their walking rates. Some may use unit rates, such as 2.5 meters per second, and some may use ratios, such as $\frac{2.5 \text{ m}}{1 \text{ s}}$. Discuss both of these ideas in the Summarize.

Planning for the Summary

What evidence will you use in the summary to clarify and deepen understanding of the Focus Question?

What will you do if you do not have evidence?

▼ Summarize

Orchestrating the Discussion

Ask for some rates. You could use **Data and Graphs** to display the frequencies of walking rates on a bar graph or on a line plot to quickly represent the class. You will find that they range from 1 meter per second to 3 or 4 meters per second. But most students will cluster around 2 to 2.5 meters per second. Use one or two of the more typical walking rates to answer the questions in the Problem. **Note:** The answer key uses 2 m/s as a walking rate.

Suggested Questions

If students record their walking rates as both a rate and a ratio, ask how they are the same. You might ask students to write their walking rates in seconds per meter. If so, you can then ask questions to relate back to concepts in *Comparing and Scaling*:

- What information does this rate tell you?(It tells you how long it takes a person to walk 1 meter.)

- When might you use this rate rather than meters per second? (If time were an important factor, then this rate would be helpful. For example, if you were going to walk for 15 seconds, you could find the number of meters you would walk.)

To discuss concepts from *Variables and Patterns*, ask:

• How does the equation show the relationship between the two variables? (The equation shows that the distance is the product of the walking rate and the time, or $d = rt$. The walking rate is the coefficient of the independent variable.)

• Explain what information the numbers and variables in your equation represent.(Take this opportunity to see how students interpret the term $2t$. They should say something like "If my walking rate is 2 meters per second, this is the distance that I walked after t seconds." Emphasize that $2t$ means 2 times the value of t.)

• Which variable in your equation is the independent variable, and which is the dependent variable? (Time is the independent variable, and distance is the dependent variable.)

• What does it mean to walk at a constant rate?(It means that you always walk the same distance for a set amount of time.)

• Suppose you do not walk at a constant rate for the walkathon. Which of the questions in Problem 1.1 can you still answer? Why? (It would be difficult to answer any of the questions since they all assume a constant walking rate. For Question A, you can find the total time it took to walk 10 meters and then compute the average rate.)

If some students made graphs during the Explore, display them for the class.

• How is the walking rate represented in these graphs? (The walking rate affects the steepness of the line. The person who walks fastest has the greatest walking rate and therefore the steepest line.)

Pick a typical equation from the class and ask students to use this equation to make a table.

• How does the walking rate show up in the table? (In the table, as the time increases by 1 second, the distance increases by a constant amount equal to the walking rate.)

Pick two different walking rates from the class.

• If these two students start walking at the same time, how far apart are they after 10 seconds? After $\frac{1}{2}$ hour? (Answers will vary. If one person walks at 2 meters per second, and the other walks at 3.5 meters per second, they will be 1.5 meters apart after 1 second. So, they will be 15 meters apart after 10 seconds and 2,700 meters apart after $\frac{1}{2}$ hour.)

The above questions on graphs and tables can be used to launch the next Problem.

Reflecting on Student Learning

Use the following questions to assess student understanding at the end of the lesson.

- What evidence do I have that students understand the Focus Question?
  - Where did my students get stuck?
  - What strategies did they use?
  - What breakthroughs did my students have today?
- How will I use this to plan for tomorrow? For the next time I teach this lesson?
- Where will I have the opportunity to reinforce these ideas as I continue through this Unit? The next Unit?

ACE Assignment Guide

- **Applications:** 1–2
- **Connections:** 15–18

Walking Rates and Linear Relationships
Tables, Graphs, and Equations

▼ Problem Overview

> *Focus Question* How can you predict whether a relationship is linear from a table, a graph, or an equation that represents the relationship?

Problem Description

Students explore the walking rates of three students. They look at the walking rate and its effect on various representations of the relationship between distance and time. This Problem introduces ways to represent linear relationships between two variables using tables, graphs, and equations. It is also the first time that students are asked to explain why a relationship is linear or to recognize a linear relationship from a table or an equation.

Problem Implementation

Students can work in groups of 2–4.

Labsheet 1.2: Walking Rates contains the table of walking rates in the Student Edition as well as a blank table and coordinate grid to record the results of the walkathon. You can give students this labsheet to let them focus on the mathematics of the situation and better organize their solutions.

You might have the class do Questions A and B, which involve the three students. Discuss these questions and then assign Question C as a follow-up to the discussion of Questions A and B.

You could collect some brochures for local walkathons to post in your room.

Materials

- **Labsheet 1.2:** Walking Rates (one per student/pair/group)
- **Labsheet 1ACE:** Exercise 4 (accessibility)
- **Teaching Aid 1.2:** Tables of Data

graphing calculator (optional)

Using Technology

If your students have access to computers, they can use **Coordinate Grapher** or **Data and Graphs** to plot points from a table on an interactive coordinate grid.

Vocabulary

There are no new glossary terms introduced in this Problem.

Mathematics Background

- Constant Rate of Change and Slope
- Finding the Rate of Change, or Slope, of a Linear Relationship

At a Glance and Lesson Plan

- At a Glance: Problem 1.2 Moving Straight Ahead
- Lesson Plan: Problem 1.2 Moving Straight Ahead

▼ Launch

Connecting to Prior Knowledge

In the last Problem, students determined their walking rates and represented them using equations.

Suggested Questions

- Can you recall another time that you studied the relationship between distance and time? (We studied rates of cars in *Variables and Patterns*. We used 50 mph, 55 mph, and 60 mph rates to examine the patterns between distance and time in tables, graphs, and equations.)

- Were any of these relationships linear? How do you know? (They were all linear because the graphs were all straight lines.)

In this Problem, they will explore a similar situation involving a walkathon.

Presenting the Challenge

Introduce the three students and their walking rates.

Suggested Questions

- What effect does a walking rate have on the relationship between time and distance walked? (If you increase the rate at which you walk, you can cover more distance in a given time. This is the same as saying that, if you increase the rate, then you will take less time to cover a given distance. Conversely, if the rate is decreased, then you can cover less distance in a given time, which is the same as saying you will take more time to cover a given distance.)

- As you change your walking rate to a faster rate, what effect does this have on the original equation? (The coefficient of *t* will increase.)

If you have graphs and tables from Problem 1.1, display them and ask:

- If you increased your walking rate, what effect would that have on your table or graph? (If you increase the rate at which you walk, you can cover more distance in a given time. The distance in each row of the table would increase, and the graph would be steeper. Similarly, if you walk faster, it takes less time to cover a certain distance.)

- If you increased the time you walk at a given rate, what effect would this have on your distance walked? (If you walk for a longer period of time at a given rate, you will cover more distance.)

Look for students to make conjectures at this time. Tell students that they will investigate the effect of the walking rate on the relationship between distance and time by looking at the walking rates of three students. They will be asked to make a table and a graph and to write an equation for each of the walkers. Students will examine these models to see how changing the walking rate affects each representation of the data.

Alternative Presentation

Pose the following situation:

Hillary and Bill used graphs to represent the relationship between distance they walked and time:

Hillary's Graph

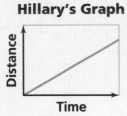

Bill's Graph

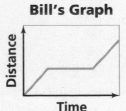

Suggested Questions

- Tell a story of a walkathon that could be represented by Hillary and Bill's graphs. (Sample answer: Hillary walked at a constant rate for the whole race. Bill stopped along the way to tie his shoes and drink some water. Then he continued walking. Bill walked at a faster rate than Hillary. You can tell this from the graph because the parts of the graph that show the rate he was walking are steeper than the line on Hillary's graph.)

- Does either of these graphs represent a linear relationship? (Students should agree that Hillary's graph shows a linear relationship. Some students will argue that pieces of Bill's graph are linear. This is okay as long as they emphasize that the total graph is not linear. This graph is called piecewise linear, which students will see in more detail in *Function Junction*.)

▼ Explore

Providing for Individual Needs

Students should each make their own tables and graphs, but they can discuss the questions in pairs. This will give you an opportunity to examine students' ability to make tables and graphs. If a student is having trouble getting started, you can pair the student temporarily with another student who seems to be on target to get started.

Suggested Questions

- Which axis should represent time? Which should represent distance? Explain. (The horizontal axis usually represents time (the independent variable), and the vertical axis represents distance.)

One of the issues that Question C raises is "Is every relationship linear?" If students are struggling to see the patterns in the table, you can suggest that they graph the data to see the pattern forms a straight line.

Check to see if students are picking up on the pattern in Elizabeth's table. It is linear, but the independent variable increases by 2 seconds each time. For each 2-second increase, distance is increasing by 3 meters. This data pattern represents a linear relationship, but the walking rate is 3 meters every 2 seconds, or *1.5 meters per second*—not 3 meters per second.

Planning for the Summary

What evidence will you use in the summary to clarify and deepen understanding of the Focus Question?

What will you do if you do not have evidence?

▼ Summarize

Orchestrating the Discussion

Suggested Questions

If you assign Questions A and B first, ask:

- How does the constant walking rate show up in the table, the graph, and the equation? (In the graph, it affects the steepness of the line. In the table, it is the number multiplied by t in the equation. In the table, it is the constant change in distance as time changes by 1 second.)

Recognizing the constant rate of change in tables is a bit more complex. See the following discussion as a model of how to help students see the patterns in a table.

Using a Table

For each unit change in time, there is a constant change in distance for a linear relationship. This constant rate should be explored in the different representations. It may be difficult for students to recognize the effect of changing the rate of walking when they use a table. Students can draw on what they learned in the Unit *Comparing and Scaling*.

- Gilberto walks at a rate of 2 meters per second. As the number of seconds he walks increases from 1 second to 2 seconds, how does his distance change? (The distance increases by 2 meters from 1 second to 2 seconds, from a total distance of 2 meters to a total distance of 4 meters.)

Students might think of this as a rate of increase of 2 meters for every second. They may instead use proportional reasoning to determine that, if the time doubles, then the distance should also double. Similarly, if the distance value is twice the time value after 1 second, it should continue to be twice the time value after 2 seconds. Remind students that this latter way of thinking about the situation works only if the distance is proportional to the time; that is, the point (0, 0) lies on the graph or the distance in the table is 0 meters when 0 seconds have passed. The walking rate is the constant of proportionality.

- If the number of seconds increases by 1, will Gilberto's distance always increase by 2 meters? (As long as Gilberto is walking at 2 meters per second, then in ANY 1-second interval, his distance increases by 2 seconds.)

Walking Rates

Time (seconds)	Distance (meters)		
	Alana	Gilberto	Leanne
0	0	0	0
1	1	2	2.5
2	2	4	5
3	3	6	7.5

- In the table, if the number of seconds increases by 2, what is the change in distance for Gilberto? (4 meters. Have the class illustrate this answer in the table. Students can see that a change from 1 second to 3 seconds produces a change of 4 meters in the distance.)

Note: Students tend to set up their tables using an interval of 1 second because that is what makes most sense to them. This means that they need to produce many pairs of data to get a sense of what is happening over a reasonable span of time. You may want to discuss the advantages and disadvantages of using other intervals, such as 2 seconds or 5 seconds.)

Using a Graph

It should be fairly easy for students to recognize the effect of changing the rate of walking when they use a graph—it changes the "steepness" of the line. Some students say that the line "goes up faster." These intuitive ideas are the goal at this time.

- What would a graph look like if someone walked 3 meters per second? $1\frac{1}{2}$ meters per second? $\frac{1}{2}$ meter per second? (The line that represents the distance a person walks at 3 meters per second will be a straight line and steeper than the graphs for Alana, Gilberto, and Leanne. The line for the person walking $1\frac{1}{2}$ meters per second will lie between the graphs for Alana and Gilberto. The line for the person walking $\frac{1}{2}$ meter per second will be less steep than any of the lines in Question A.)

- How would each of these walking rates appear in the table? (The Distance column would change for each walking rate. For each increase of 1 second, the distance will increase by 3 meters, $1\frac{1}{2}$ meters, and $\frac{1}{2}$ meter, respectively.)

- How would each of these walking rates change the equation? (The coefficient of time would change for each walking rate. The equations would be $d = 3t$, $d = 1t$, and $d = \frac{1}{2}t$, respectively.)

Pick two points on one of the graphs and ask students how the time and the distance change from one point to the next. This is an opportunity to connect the Problem to the unit rates in *Comparing and Scaling*. For example, for Leanne, two points are (3, 7.5) and (6, 15). For these points, time increases by 3 seconds and distance increases by 7.5 meters. To show that this is the same rate as 1 second to 2.5 meters, you can write:

1 second to 2.5 meters

2 seconds to 5 meters

3 seconds to 7.5 meters

4 seconds to 10 meters

5 seconds to 12.5 meters

6 seconds to 15 meters

Show the vertical and horizontal changes on the graph by drawing in dotted lines.

Using an Equation

Students may be able to recognize the effect of changing the rate of walking when they use the equation $d = rt$, or distance = rate × time. The rate (r) is the coefficient of t, the number by which time is multiplied. The word *coefficient* is defined in the next Investigation. At this point, students will say it is the rate at which people walk, which is "the number that time is multiplied by to get the distance." This is a good opportunity to discuss Question B, part (4) about proportionality. In the equation $d = rt$, r is the constant of proportionality.

Students may want to see the graphs of these equations on a graphing calculator or by using **Coordinate Grapher**. If you do this, then ask students to use the technology to answer questions similar to those above.

If you did not do so before, assign Question C. Be sure to discuss it and emphasize how a constant rate of change between time and distance is represented. The table of Elizabeth's time and distance represents a linear relationship, but students need to note that the time is not increasing by an interval of 1 second. Go back to the idea of writing the rate as a unit rate, as discussed earlier in this section.

- For those situations in Question C that could be linear, find two other pairs of data for the table. (Sample answer: For Elizabeth, two other pairs are (5, 7.5) and (12, 18). For Billie, two pairs are (1, 2.25) and (4, 10).)

As students determine two other pairs of data they could add to the table, watch and listen as they work to see how they are thinking about rate. They may be comparing the values for distance in George's and Elizabeth's tables, looking for an additive pattern instead of paying attention to both variables. A rate can be thought of as a single numerical quantity, especially when you are comparing rates. But a rate is also an internal comparison between two quantities.

- For those situations in Question C that are linear, compare the walking rates to those of the original three students. Who is the fastest? Who is the slowest? Which graph is the steepest? (Elizabeth walks 3 meters for every 2 seconds, or 1.5 meters per second. This is faster than Alana but slower than Gilberto. Billie walks 2.25 meters per second, which is faster than Alana and Gilberto but slower than Leanne. Since Leanne is still the fastest, her graph is the steepest.)

Pick one or two of the situations in Question C, and ask:

- What are the variables? (The variables for George are time in seconds and distance in meters. The variables for Bob are time t in seconds and walking rate r in meters per second. The variables for Elizabeth and Billie are distance and time.)

- Describe the patterns of change between the two variables. How did you find the pattern? (For Elizabeth, for every increase of 2 seconds, the distance increases by 3 meters. Each row of the table increases by the same number of seconds. For Billie, for every 1 second, the distance increases by 2.25 meters. The equation is in the form $d = rt$, so the walking rate is the same as the value of r. For George, distance increases with time, but there does not seem to be a pattern. For Bob, as rate increases, time decreases.)

- Describe what is happening in each situation. (According to the table, George is not walking at a constant rate. Elizabeth is walking at a constant rate and is using an interval of 2 seconds. Billie is also walking at a constant rate because the equation is similar to those for Alana, Gilberto, and Leanne. Bob is walking 100 meters, but the rate and time are not known. His walking rate may or may not be constant because the variables are time and rate, not time and distance.)

For all of the four situations in Question C, ask:

- After 5 seconds, who is ahead? (According to the table, George walks 25 meters in 5 seconds. In that time, Elizabeth walks 7.5 meters, and Billie walks 11.25 meters. (**Note:** Using the equation for Bob, a time of 5 seconds results in a rate of 20 m/s, which is not a realistic walking rate.)

• For which situation is the point (2, 3) on the line? Explain. (The point represents a distance of 3 meters for a time of 2 seconds, which is a row in the table for Elizabeth.)

Check for Understanding

If you need more examples of linear relationships in which the independent variable is changing in intervals other than 1, display **Teaching Aid 1.2: Tables of Data**. One misconception that students have is that in a table each value for x must be exactly 1 greater than the previous value.

• Does each table of data represent a linear relationship? Explain.

x	y
5	18
10	33
15	48
20	63

x	y
0	0
3	12
5	20
8	32
10	40

(Yes. In the first table, there is a constant difference of 5 for x. For y, the differences are $33 - 18 = 15$, $48 - 33 = 15$, and $63 - 48 = 15$. This means that for each change of 5 in x, there is a change of 15 in y. This is equivalent to saying that for a change of 1 in x, there must be a change of $15 \div 5 = 3$ in y.

In the second table, changes in x are not evenly spaced, so students need to be even more careful. Students can apply the reasoning that they developed in *Comparing and Scaling* to determine whether there is a constant rate. For the first two rows, we see that $12 - 0 = 12$. So for a change of 3 in x, we have a change of 12 in y. If the relationship is linear, then a change of 1 in x will result in a change of 4 in y. This pattern of change is true for any two rows of the table. For example, from (8, 32) to (10, 40) in the table is a change of 2 in x and a change of $40 - 32 = 8$ in y.)

If students are dubious about either table representing a linear relationship, have them graph each row as an ordered pair. Then have them re-examine the tables, looking for points they see on the lines but not in the tables.

Having students interpolate pairs of data for the table, extend the table, or produce pairs of data given an x-value or a y-value will allow you to assess how they are thinking of rate at this time.

You can make some quick sketches of graphs and ask whether they are linear. You might use some linear graphs, a piecewise linear graph (see the preceding Alternative Presentation), and some graphs with curves in them.

Conclude the discussion by asking:

- Was every relationship in this problem linear? Explain. (No; the data for George and Bob were not linear.)

- How can you tell if a graph does not represent a linear relationship? (A graph represents a linear relationship if it is one straight line. Therefore, if the graph is not a straight line, the relationship it models is not linear.)

- How can you tell if a table does not represent a linear relationship? (A table does not represent a linear relationship if for each unit change in the independent variable, there is not a constant change in the dependent variable.)

- How can you tell if an equation represents a linear relationship? (An equation represents a linear relationship if it can be written in the form $y = b + mx$.)

Reflecting on Student Learning

Use the following questions to assess student understanding at the end of the lesson.

- What evidence do I have that students understand the Focus Question?
  - Where did my students get stuck?
  - What strategies did they use?
  - What breakthroughs did my students have today?
- How will I use this to plan for tomorrow? For the next time I teach this lesson?
- Where will I have the opportunity to reinforce these ideas as I continue through this Unit? The next Unit?

ACE Assignment Guide

- **Applications:** 3–5
- **Connections:** 19–22
- **Extensions:** 30
- **Labsheet 1ACE:** Exercise 4 (accessibility)

Note: This labsheet is an example of a way to provide students with additional support for an ACE Exercise.

Raising Money
Using Linear Relationships

▼ Problem Overview

> *Focus Question* What is the pattern of change in a linear relationship?

Problem Description

A new situation involving collecting money from sponsors for the walkathon furthers students' understanding of constant rate of change between the two variables in a linear relationship. It also helps students generalize the constant rate of change across different linear situations. The rates in this Problem compare the amount of money donated (*A*) and the distance walked (*d*) for a walkathon. Students see linear relationships in a new context and interpret information using verbal descriptions, tables, graphs, and equations. They also informally explore the *y*-intercept.

Problem Implementation

Students can work in pairs or small groups, but each student should have their own tables, graphs, and equations.

You can give students **Labsheet 1.3: Pledge Plans** as they work through Question A, parts (1) and (2). The labsheet contains a blank table and coordinate grid to record the pledge plans of the three students. You can use the labsheet to make classroom time more efficient and let students focus on the relationship between amount of money raised and kilometers walked.

You could assign and discuss Questions A and B and then assign Question C to explore in class and discuss separately.

Materials

- **Labsheet 1.3:** Pledge Plans
- **Labsheet 1ACE:** Exercise 6 (accessibility)
- **Generic Grid Paper**

transparent grid

poster paper

Using Technology

If your students have access to computers, they can use **Coordinate Grapher** or **Data and Graphs** to plot points from a table on an interactive coordinate grid.

Vocabulary

- dependent variable
- independent variable

Mathematics Background

- Finding the Rate of Change, or Slope, of a Linear Relationship
- Finding the y-intercept and Equation for a Linear Relationship

At a Glance and Lesson Plan

- At a Glance: Problem 1.3 Moving Straight Ahead
- Lesson Plan: Problem 1.3 Moving Straight Ahead

▼ Launch

Connecting to Prior Knowledge

In the last two Problems, students looked at linear relationships that involved time as the independent variable and distance as the dependent variable. In this Problem, students will look at a relationship in which distance is the independent variable.

Pick one of the previous examples to review **dependent variables** and **independent variables**.

Presenting the Challenge

Many schools have walkathons or something similar to raise funds for charity. Ask students how they determined what to charge their patrons.

Suggested Questions

- What variables can affect the amount of money that a student raises? (The variables are the pledge amount for each sponsor, the distance a students walks, and the number of sponsors.)

- How can you use these variables to estimate the amount of money each student will collect? (If you know how much a sponsor pledges to donate and how far the student plans to walk, you can figure out how much each student might collect from each sponsor. For example, if the sponsor pledges to donate $4 for each kilometer walked, and the student plans to walk 5 kilometers, then you can estimate that the student will collect $4 \times 5 = \$20$ from each sponsor.)

- Will the amount of money raised be the same for each walker? Explain. (No; the amount of money raised might depend on the distance that each student walks, as well as his or her pledge plan, so the amount of money raised may not be the same for each walker.)

- Which variable is the independent variable? Which is the dependent variable? (Distance walked is the independent variable, and the amount of money raised from each sponsor is the dependent variable.)

Display the three pledge plans of Leanne, Alana, and Gilberto. Ask students to make tables, graphs, and equations to represent the relationship between distance and amount of money raised and answer the questions.

▼ Explore

Providing for Individual Needs

As you circulate, ask students for explanations. Look for students who have interesting ways to explain their thinking. Be sure to discuss these in the Summarize.

By this time, most students should have few problems making tables and graphs. Writing the equations may be difficult for some students. Encourage those students having trouble writing an equation to write out what the relationship is in words. Being able to write a verbal description of the relationship in each pledge plan is the first step to being able to write the same relationship algebraically. For example, a sponsor will donate $2 for each kilometer Gilberto walks. In other words, the sponsor donates two dollars times the number of kilometers he walks, or $A = 2 \times d$. Remind students that $2 \times d$ is often written $2d$, so the equation becomes $A = 2d$, where A is the amount the sponsor donates and d is the number of kilometers walked.

You may give different groups transparent or electronic grids or large poster paper to record their tables and graphs. These can be used during the summary.

Planning for the Summary

What evidence will you use in the summary to clarify and deepen understanding of the Focus Question?

What will you do if you do not have evidence?

▼ Summarize

Orchestrating the Discussion

Discuss Questions A and B. If you did not ask students to identify the dependent and independent variables in the Launch, ask them now.

Suggested Questions

The effect of the amount of money donated per kilometer on the total amount raised is very similar to the effect of a person's walking rate on the total distance traveled. Help students to see this similarity by asking:

- How is the amount of money donated per kilometer similar to a person's walking rate in meters per second? (The amount of money donated per kilometer affects how the amount of money increases as the distance increases, and the walking rate affects how the distance increases as time increases. The situation has changed, but both are constant rates, and both relationships can be represented as the graph of a straight line.)

- How can you recognize that the patterns in both situations (pledge plans and walking rates) are similar using a table, a graph, or an equation? (The graphs are both straight lines. Both tables have a constant change in the dependent variable for a constant change in the independent variable. One of the equations for the pledge plans is in the form $y = mx$, which is the same form as the equations for the walking rates in Problem 1.2. It is a proportional relationship. Another pledge plan equation has a similar form with another number added on. That is, it has a y-intercept that is not 0.)

Note: This is the first time that students have worked with a linear relationship that is not proportional; i.e., the y-intercept is not at the origin, (0, 0). In *Comparing and Scaling*, they observed that the rate tables relating cost of pizza to number of pizzas worked differently if a constant delivery charge was added. They noticed that there is a constant ratio of cost to number when there is no delivery charge, but not a constant ratio when there is a delivery charge. Here, students are learning about the specific details of linear relationships, in particular the y-intercept. Although students have not yet learned about the y-intercept, be sure to discuss this point on all three graphs and what information it represents in this context. The y-intercept will be explored more in subsequent Problems. This is a good opportunity to discuss which of these relationships are proportional.

One of the other equations has only a constant term and no x-term: $A = 10$. Show students that you could write this equation as $A = 10 + 0d$, which is a horizontal line with a constant rate of $0 per kilometer. Students may need help with horizontal lines. Pick two points in the table.

- What is the pattern of change between the two variables? Is it the same for two other points on the line? What rate of change is this? (Students may say that there is no rate, which is not correct. Look for answers that show the money donated increases by $0 for each kilometer walked, which is a rate of $0 per kilometer.)

If students have trouble making sense of a rate of $0 per kilometer, have them consider two situations:

- a person raising $10 plus $.10 per kilometer

- a person raising $10 plus $.05 per kilometer

Ask students what is happening to the rate.

- How is a constant rate of $0 per kilometer related to the graph of a horizontal line? (As the distance increases, the amount of money donated does not change. That is, between any two points, as the x-coordinate changes, the y-coordinate is not changing. (Make sure students illustrate this on the graph.))

- Describe another pledge plan whose graph is a horizontal line. What is its equation? How does the graph of this pledge plan compare to the graph of $A = 10$? (Answers will vary. Students' pledge plan should describe a rate of $0 per kilometer and involve an equation of the form $y = b$, where b is a constant. Sample answer: A sponsor will donate $4 regardless of how far you walk. The equation for this plan is $A = 4$, which is also a horizontal line and crosses the y-axis at (0, 4).)

Tell students to look at the graph and tables from Questions A and B. Pick some points from each of the three pledge plans. For each point:

- What information does this point represent? (The x-coordinate represents the number of kilometers the student walked, and the y-coordinate represents the amount of money the student raised from each sponsor.)

- Which graph does the point (4, 8) lie on? Explain. (Gilberto's graph; when Gilberto walks 4 kilometers, a sponsor donates $8.)

- How is this point related to the corresponding table and equation? (A distance of 4 kilometers and amount of $8 is a row in the table for this relationship. The ordered pair (4, 8) is a solution of the related equation where $d = 4$ and $A = 8$.)

- Write two questions that could be answered by locating this point. (How much money does Gilberto raise from each sponsor if he walks 4 km? How many kilometers does Gilberto need to walk if he wants to raise $8 from each sponsor?)

- What are the coordinates of the point where each graph intersects the *y*-axis? What information does this point represent? (Alana: (0, 5); Gilberto: (0, 0); Leanne: (0, 10). The points represent how much each student raises from a sponsor when they have walked 0 kilometers.)

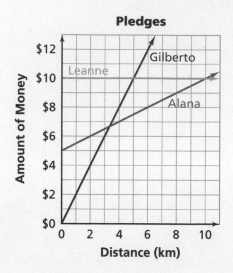

The three graphs intersect each other in pairs. Discuss the coordinates of the points of intersection.

- What information does each intersection point represent in the situation? (Each intersection point is where two of the plans raise an equal amount of money for the same distance. The coordinates represent equal distances and equal amounts donated.)

Direct students to the intersection of Alana's and Gilberto's lines. Pick two points to the left of the point of intersection, one on each line, with the same *x*-value.

- How are the two points similar? How are they different? How can you show the difference in money raised? (The two points represent the same distance walked, but they represent different amounts of money raised. For distances to the left of the point of intersection, Alana's graph is above Gilberto's, so Alana raises more money than Gilberto. You can show the difference in money collected by drawing a vertical line between Alana's and Gilberto's lines and measuring the distance. You can also find the difference in the *y*-coordinates to find the difference in the amount of money raised for that distance.)

Then, repeat the process for two points to the right of the point of intersection. (Now Gilberto's graph is above Alana's, so he raises more money for a given distance.)

- In part (1) of Question B, you found the money raised for each pledge plan if the student walked 8 kilometers. How is this information represented on the graph? (The amount of money raised for each student is the vertical distance between the *x*-axis and the point on the student's line with an *x*-coordinate of 8.)

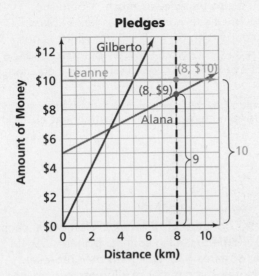

- In part (3) of Question B, you located the point (12, 11) on Alana's graph. Write a question that could be answered by locating this point. (Sample answers: What is the amount of money Alana raises from each sponsor if she walks 12 kilometers? How many kilometers does Alana need to walk if she wants each sponsor to donate $11?)

The preceding questions are designed to prepare students to solve equations symbolically. Later in this Unit, they will continue to relate coordinates of an ordered pair to specific information about the values of variables.

- Describe a pledge plan whose rate is greater than the three original pledge plans and one whose rate is less than the three plans. Compare the graphs of these two new pledge plans with the graphs of the original three pledge plans. (Answers will vary. Students will probably have an easier time designing a pledge plan with a greater rate. Since Leanne's plan has a rate of $0 per kilometer, a pledge plan with a lesser rate is a plan with a negative rate. Most students will say this does not make sense in the situation, but a few students might be able to think of a context that makes sense. Students should point out that the plan with the greater rate will be the steepest line, and the plan with the lesser rate will be the only line that shows a decrease.)

Discuss all of Question C. The purpose of this question is to introduce students to a negative *y*-intercept. Make sure students discuss the variables and numbers in the equation and connect where the information shows up in the graph, the table, and the equation.

At the end of this Problem, students will have had experiences with *y*-intercepts that are positive, negative, or zero. The term *y-intercept* is introduced in the next Investigation, but if your students are ready, you can name it at this point.

Compare the situation in this Problem to the walkathon in Problem 1.2. All the relationships are linear, but the graphs in this Problem do not all pass through the origin, so they are not all proportional relationships.

- In Problem 1.2, you noticed for Alana's rate of 1 m/s that if she walked twice as long, her distance would also be twice as much. Would the amount of money she raises double if she walks twice as far? Explain. (No; the equation for Alana's pledge plan is $A = 5 + 0.5d$, which is not a proportional relationship. The ratio between the money pledged and the distance walked is not constant even though the plan involves a constant rate of change.)

This idea will be revisited as students gain more experience with linear equations of the form $y = mx + b$.

Check for Understanding

Tell the class about a new pledge plan.

- If I walk 1 kilometer, each sponsor donates $1. If I walk 2 kilometers, each sponsor donates $4. If I walk 3 kilometers, each sponsor donates $9. If I walk 4 kilometers, each sponsor donates $16. Does this plan represent a linear relationship? Explain. (No; as the number of kilometers increases by 1 each time, the amount of money does not increase by a constant amount. (In fact, this plan seems to be a quadratic pattern.)

Reflecting on Student Learning

Use the following questions to assess student understanding at the end of the lesson.

- What evidence do I have that students understand the Focus Question?
  - Where did my students get stuck?
  - What strategies did they use?
  - What breakthroughs did my students have today?
- How will I use this to plan for tomorrow? For the next time I teach this lesson?
- Where will I have the opportunity to reinforce these ideas as I continue through this Unit? The next Unit?

ACE Assignment Guide

- **Applications:** 6–9
- **Connections:** 23–26
- **Extensions:** 31–32
- **Labsheet 1ACE:** Exercise 6 (accessibility)

Note: This labsheet is an example of a way to provide students with additional support for an ACE Exercise.

PROBLEM
1.4

Using the Walkathon Money
Recognizing Linear Relationships

▼ Problem Overview

> *Focus Question* How can you determine if a linear relationship is increasing or decreasing?

Problem Description

This Problem introduces negative rates of change (negative slope). It poses two situations involving a decreasing linear relationship. That is, for every unit change in the independent variable, the dependent variable decreases by a constant positive amount (which is equivalent to saying the dependent variable increases by a constant negative amount).

One situation uses a graphical representation, and the other uses a tabular representation. Students make a table of values from points on a graph, interpret and compare information from different representations, and build on skills recognizing linear relationships from various representations.

Problem Implementation

Students can work on this Problem in pairs and then share answers and strategies in larger groups.

Materials

- **Labsheet 1ACE:** Exercise 12 (accessibility)
- **Teaching Aid 1.4:** Ms. Chang's Class Account
- **First-Quadrant Grid**
- **Check Up 1**

Using Technology

If your students have access to computers, they can use **Coordinate Grapher** or **Data and Graphs** to plot points from a table on an interactive coordinate grid.

Vocabulary

There are no new glossary terms introduced in this Problem.

Mathematics Background

• Finding the *y*-intercept and Equation for a Linear Relationship

At a Glance and Lesson Plan

• At a Glance: Problem 1.4 Moving Straight Ahead
• Lesson Plan: Problem 1.4 Moving Straight Ahead

▼ Launch

Connecting to Prior Knowledge

Tell the students that they have been looking at linear relationships.

Suggested Questions

• How can you tell whether a relationship is linear? (Answers will vary and may not be polished at this point. Look for students to mention a constant rate of change and describe how to recognize a constant rate from different representations, including a table, a graph, an equation, or a verbal description.)

Presenting the Challenge

In this Problem, students will continue to work with linear relationships that are modeled by tables and graphs. Tell the first story of how one class is going to use the money they raised from the walkathon. Display **Teaching Aid 1.4: Ms. Chang's Class Account**.

Suggested Questions

• What do you think the graph of these data would look like? (Sample answer: The graph would look different from other graphs in this Investigation, because the dependent variable is decreasing.)

Use the above question to help students visualize that as *x* is increasing, *y* is decreasing. Some students may already be good at recognizing this trend, but most students need a chance to think about the question before they can make a graph. Eventually, the goal is for students to have a rough idea of what a graph of a linear relationship will look like without actually graphing it.

• Is this a linear relationship? (Answers may vary. Collect some conjectures and come back to them in the Summarize.)

▼ Explore

Providing for Individual Needs

This is the first time that students have encountered negative rates of change or negative slope. You can ask students why the line slants down or is decreasing from left to right.

Suggested Questions

- How can you represent this change in a table? (You can start with a row that shows the starting value is $144 and then for each new row, subtract $12 for each week.)

For Question B, students may need help finding the constant rate for the graph. Suggest that they make a table of values—this should help them find the constant rate.

Be sure to have students share their strategies in the summary.

Planning for the Summary

What evidence will you use in the summary to clarify and deepen understanding of the Focus Question?

What will you do if you do not have evidence?

▼ Summarize

Orchestrating the Discussion

The main goals in this Problem are for students to revisit constant rate and explore negative rates of change in the context of tables and graphs.

Suggested Questions

- For each class, how much money is being spent or withdrawn each week? (Ms. Chang's class: $12; Mr. Mamer's class: $10. For both classes, it is the constant rate of change or the difference in the amount of money between two consecutive weeks.)

- Compare the rates of change in this Problem with other rates that we have studied in this Unit. How do the rates in this Problem show up in a table? In a graph? In an equation? (These rates are negative, and the previous rates were positive (or zero). These tables show a constant decrease in the dependent variable as the independent variable increases. The graphs show lines that decrease from left to right, which is the opposite of the previous rates we studied. The coefficient of the independent variable in these equations is negative, while it was positive in previous Problems.

For each class:

- What are the coordinates of the point where the line intersects the *y*-axis? What information does this point represent? (Ms. Chang's class: (0, 144); Mr. Mamer's class: (0, 100). For both classes, this point represents the amount of money at the start.)

- What are the coordinates of the point where the line intersects the *x*-axis? What information does this point represent? (Ms. Chang's class: (12, 0); Mr. Mamer's class: (10, 0). For both classes, this point represents the week that the amount of money in the class's account reaches $0.)

If students are ready, you could introduce the terms *x-intercept* and *y-intercept*. You could go back to one of the other linear relationships and ask what the *x*-intercept means. For most of the previous relationships, unless the *x*-intercept is (0, 0), it does not mean much in the context. For example, for Alana's equation, $A = 5 + 0.5d$, the *x*-intercept is $(-10, 0)$, which does not have real-world meaning.

- Choose a pair of corresponding values in the table for Question A. What two questions could you answer using this pair of values? (Answers will vary. Sample answers use the pair (4, 96). Samples: In which week is the amount of money left in the account $96? How much money is in the account after 4 weeks?)

- Choose an ordered pair in the graph for Question B. What two questions could you answer using this pair of values? (Answers will vary. Sample answers use the pair (6, 40). Samples: In which week is the amount of money left in the account $40? How much money is in the account after 6 weeks?)

- Pick a point not on the graph for Mr. Mamer's class in Question B. Explain what this point means in terms of the class's account. (For example, the point (8, 60) is not on the graph for Mr. Mamer's class. The point represents an account that has $60 at the end of week 8, which is more than the amount of money in Mr. Mamer's class's account.)

- After how many weeks will each account be empty? (Ms. Chang's class: 12 weeks; Mr. Mamer's class: 10 weeks. (**Note:** This question was asked in a previous section about where the lines intersect the *x*-axis on each graph.))

- Which account has a graph that contains the point (0, 100)? (10, 24)? (12, 0)? (8, 20)? (The points (10, 24) and (12, 0) are on the graph of Ms. Chang's class. The points (0, 100) and (8, 20) are on the graph of Mr. Mamer's class.)

Check for Understanding

Introduce an equation for another class's account that represents the amount of money *A* in the account after *n* weeks: $A = 136 - 8.5n$. Ask:

- Explain what information the variables and numbers represent. (The variable *n* represents the number of weeks that have passed. The variable *A* represents the amount of money in the account after *n* weeks. The number 136 represents the starting balance of the account, and the number 8.5 represents the amount of money withdrawn each week.)

- Describe what the graph would look like. How does this graph compare to the other two graphs in this Problem? (It is a line that intersects the y-axis at (0, 136), which is between the intersection point for the two graphs in the Problem. This graph decreases from left to right. All three graphs decrease, and this graph is the least steep. (Ms. Chang's class's line is the steepest.)

- Describe a method for finding the number of weeks after which there is $0 in the account. (Sample answers: You could continue the graph until it intersects the x-axis; the x-coordinate of that point is the number of weeks. You could repeatedly subtract $8.50 from the starting balance until you reach $0; the number of times you subtracted is the number of weeks. You could substitute 0 for A in the equation that represents the account; the solution for n is the number of weeks it takes to empty the account.)

- Which of the following points lie on the graph for this account? (0, 136), (4, 102), (136, 0) ((0, 136) and (4, 102) lie on the line.)

- For each point above that lies on the graph, make up a question that could be answered using that point. ((0, 136): What is the amount of money the account had at the beginning? (4, 102): What is the amount left in the account after 4 weeks?)

- Mary asked whether you can write the equation as $A = -8.5n + 136$. Does this equation make sense? Explain. (Yes; $136 - 8.5n$ is equivalent to $136 + -8.5n$. Since addition is commutative, it is also equivalent to $-8.5n + 136$.)

Have students list several equations from this Investigation that represent linear relationships. Ask:

- Which relationship has the greatest rate of change? (Answers will vary. Look for students to choose the relationship that, when written in the form $y = b + mx$, has the greatest value of m.)

- Which relationship(s) has a graph that crosses the y-axis at a point with a positive y-coordinate? With a y-coordinate of zero? With a negative y-coordinate? (Answers will vary. Positive y-coordinate: Look for students to choose the relationship(s) that, when written in the form $y = b + mx$, has a positive value of b. Sample: The line that represents Alana's amount of money donated has a y-intercept of (0, 5). y-coordinate of zero: Look for students to choose a proportional relationship. Sample: Gilberto's pledge plan can be modeled by a line that passes through the origin. Negative y-coordinate: Look for students to choose the relationship(s) that, when written in the form $y = b + mx$, has a negative value of b. Sample: The line that represents Gilberto's pledge plan after purchasing a T-shirt for each sponsor.)

Note: ACE Exercises 27–29 give data for an experiment that involves looking at the relationship of the amount of water lost from a dripping faucet as time elapses. This real-world situation is the context for the Unit Project.

Reflecting on Student Learning

Use the following questions to assess student understanding at the end of the lesson.

- What evidence do I have that students understand the Focus Question?
  - Where did my students get stuck?
  - What strategies did they use?
  - What breakthroughs did my students have today?
- How will I use this to plan for tomorrow? For the next time I teach this lesson?
- Where will I have the opportunity to reinforce these ideas as I continue through this Unit? The next Unit?

ACE Assignment Guide

- **Applications:** 10–14
- **Connections:** 27–29
- **Extensions:** 33

Labsheet 1ACE: Exercise 12 (accessibility)

Note: This labsheet is an example of a way to provide students with additional support for an ACE Exercise.

▼ Mathematical Reflections

Possible Answers to Mathematical Reflections

1. In a linear relationship, as the independent variable increases by a constant amount, the corresponding dependent variable increases (or decreases) by a constant amount. For example, in the linear relationship that represents the distance Gilberto walked in t seconds, as the time he walked increased by 1 second, the distance he walked increased by 2 meters.

2. **a.** The pattern of change between two variables in a linear relationship is the rate in the contextual situation, sometimes given as a unit rate using the word *per*. For example, in the walkathon Gilberto walks at 2 meters *per* second, so this situation is linear.

   b. The linear pattern of change in a table is the constant increase or decrease in the dependent variable as the independent variable increases by a constant amount.

   c. In a graph, the linear pattern of change shows up as a straight line. The line may be increasing from left to right, decreasing, or show no change (horizontal line).

d. The pattern of change between two variables in a linear relationship shows up in the equation as the value of m when the equation is written in the form $y = mx + b$. If there is no number multiplied by x, the equation is of the form $y = x + b$, so the value of m is 1. If there is no term that includes the variable x, the value of m is 0, and the equation is of the form $y = b$.

Note to teacher: Look for examples of linear relationships. Be sure there are positive, zero, and negative rates of change as well as positive, zero, and negative y-intercepts.

Possible Answers to Mathematical Practices Reflections

Students may have demonstrated all of the eight Common Core Standards for Mathematical Practice during this Investigation. During the class discussion, have students provide additional Practices that the Problem cited involved and identify the use of other Mathematical Practices in the Investigation.

One student observation is provided in the Student Edition. Here is another sample student response.

> We observed that if you add a constant to a linear equation, the pattern of change is not affected. In Problem 1.3, the amount of money that Gilberto raises from each sponsor can be expressed by the equation $A = 2d$. If Gilberto buys each sponsor a T-shirt that costs $\$4.75$, the amount he raises from each sponsor is now represented by the equation $A = 2d - 4.75$. This equation still represents a linear relationship. The graph is a straight line that is parallel to the line $A = 2d$. The pattern of change is still 2 dollars per kilometer walked even though the y-intercept is different. This is similar to the Wump family in *Stretching and Shrinking*. Adding a constant to the variable term just shifts the graph up or down. The steepness of the line stays the same.
>
> **MP2: Reason abstractly and quantitatively.**

Walking Rates

In *Variables and Patterns*, you read about a bicycle touring business. You used contextual situations, tables, graphs, and equations to represent patterns relating variables such as cost, income, and profit. You looked at some linear relationships, like the relationship between cost and number of rental bikes represented in this graph:

A relationship between two variables for which all points lie on a straight line is called a **linear relationship.** From the graph, you see that the relationship between the number of bikes rented and the total rental cost is a linear relationship. In this Investigation, consider these questions:

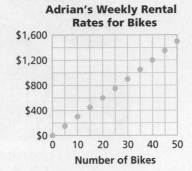

Adrian's Weekly Rental Rates for Bikes

- How can you determine whether a relationship is linear by examining a table of data or an equation?

- How do changes in one variable affect changes in a related variable? How are these changes captured in a table, a graph, or an equation?

Common Core State Standards

7.RP.A.2b Identify the constant of proportionality (unit rate) in tables, graphs, equations, diagrams, and verbal descriptions of proportional relationships.

7.RP.A.2c Represent proportional relationships by equations.

7.EE.B.4 Use variables to represent quantities in a real-world or mathematical problem, and construct simple equations and inequalities to solve problems by reasoning about the quantities.

Also 7.RP.A.2, 7.RP.A.2a, 7.EE.B.4a

Investigation 1 Walking Rates   7

Notes

1.1 Walking Marathons
Finding and Using Rates

Ms. Chang's class decides to participate in a walkathon. Each participant must find sponsors to pledge a certain amount of money for each kilometer the participant walks. Leanne suggests that they determine their walking rates in meters per second so they can make predictions.

- Do you know what your walking rate is?

- How can you determine your walking rate?

Notes

_____

_____

_____

Problem 1.1

One way to define your walking rate is the distance you walk for every second of walking time.

To determine your walking rate:

- Line up ten meter sticks, end to end (or mark off 10 meters), in the hall of your school.

- Have a partner time your walk.

- Start at one end and walk the length of the ten meter sticks using your normal walking pace.

A What is your walking rate in meters per second?

B Assume you continue to walk at this constant rate.

1. How long would it take you to walk 500 meters?

2. How far could you walk in 30 seconds? In 10 minutes? In 1 hour?

3. Describe in words the distance in meters you could walk in a given number of seconds.

4. Write an equation that represents the distance d in meters that you could walk in t seconds if you maintain this pace.

5. Use the equation to predict the distance you would walk in 45 seconds.

A C E Homework starts on page 16.

Notes

1.2 Walking Rates and Linear Relationships

Tables, Graphs, and Equations

Think about the effect a walking rate has on the relationship between time walked and distance walked. This will provide some important clues about how to identify linear relationships from tables, graphs, and equations.

Problem 1.2

Here are the walking rates that Gilberto, Alana, and Leanne found in their experiment.

A 1. Make a table showing the distance walked by each student for the first ten seconds. How does the walking rate appear as a pattern in the table?

Name	Walking Rate
Alana	1 meter per second
Gilberto	2 meters per second
Leanne	2.5 meters per second

   2. Graph the times and distances for the three students on the same coordinate axes. Use a different color for each student's data. How does the walking rate affect the graph?

   3. Write an equation that gives the relationship between the time t and the distance d walked for each student. How is the walking rate represented in the equations?

   4. How can you predict that the graph will be a straight line from the patterns in the table? In the equation? Explain.

   5. Are any of these proportional relationships? If so, what is the constant of proportionality?

B For each student:

   1. If time t increases by 1 second, by how much does the distance d change? How is this change represented in a table? In a graph?

   2. If t increases by 5 seconds, by how much does d change? How is this change represented in a table? In a graph?

   3. What is the walking rate per minute? The walking rate per hour?

Notes

Problem **1.2** *continued*

C Four other friends who are part of the walkathon made the following representations of their data. Could any of these relationships be linear relationships? Explain.

George's Walking Rate

Time (seconds)	Distance (meters)
0	0
1	2
2	9
3	11
4	20
5	25

Elizabeth's Walking Rate

Time (seconds)	Distance (meters)
0	0
2	3
4	6
6	9
8	12
10	15

Billie's Walking Rate

$$D = 2.25t$$

D represents distance
t represents time

Bob's Walking Rate

$$t = \frac{100}{r}$$

t represents time
r represents walking rate

A C E Homework starts on page 16.

1.3 Raising Money
Using Linear Relationships

In *Variables and Patterns*, you looked at situations that involved *dependent* and *independent* variables. In Problem 1.2, the distance walked depended on the time. This tells you that distance is the **dependent variable** and time is the **independent variable**. In this Problem, you will look at relationships between two other variables in a walkathon.

Each participant in the walkathon must find sponsors to pledge a certain amount of money for each kilometer the participant walks.

Notes _____

_____

_____

The students in Ms. Chang's class are trying to estimate how much money they might be able to raise. Several questions come up in their discussions:

- What variables can affect the amount of money that is collected?

- How can you use these variables to estimate the amount of money each student will collect?

- Will the amount of money collected be the same for each walker?

Each student found sponsors who are willing to pledge money according to the following descriptions.

- Leanne's sponsors will donate $10 regardless of how far she walks.

- Gilberto's sponsors will donate $2 per kilometer (km).

- Alana's sponsors will make a $5 donation plus 50¢ per kilometer.

The class refers to these as *pledge plans*.

Tables, graphs, and equations will help you predict how much money might be raised with each plan.

- What are the dependent and independent variables?

? Who will raise the most money after *d* kilometers?

  Problem 1.3

A **1.** Make a table for each student's pledge plan. Show the amount of money each of his or her sponsors would donate if he or she walked distances from 0 to 6 kilometers. What are the dependent and independent variables?

2. Graph the three pledge plans on the same coordinate axes. Use a different color for each plan.

Notes _____

_____

_____

Problem **1.3** *continued*

3. For each pledge plan, write an equation that represents the relationship between the distance walked and the amount of money donated. Explain what information each number and variable in the equations represents.

4. For each plan:

   a. What pattern of change between the two variables do you observe in the table?

   b. How does this pattern appear in the graph? In the equation?

   c. How can you determine if a relationship is linear from a table, a graph, or an equation?

   d. Does this relationship represent a proportional relationship?

B 1. Suppose each student walks 8 kilometers in the walkathon. How much money does each sponsor donate? Explain how you found your answer.

2. Suppose each student raises $10 from a sponsor. How many kilometers does each student walk? Explain.

3. On which graph does the point (12, 11) lie? What information does this point represent?

4. In Alana's plan, how is the fixed $5 donation represented in

   a. the table?

   b. the graph?

   c. the equation?

C Gilberto decides to give a T-shirt to each of his sponsors. Each shirt costs him $4.75. He plans to pay for each shirt with some of the money he raises from each sponsor.

1. Write an equation that represents the amount of money Gilberto raises from each sponsor after he has paid for the T-shirt. Explain what information each number and variable represents.

2. Graph the equation for distances from 0 to 5 kilometers. Compare this graph to the graph of Gilberto's pledge plan in Question A, part (2).

3. Is this relationship linear? Explain.

A C E Homework starts on page 16.

Notes

1.4 Using the Walkathon Money
Recognizing Linear Relationships

In previous Problems, you noticed that, as the independent variable changes by a constant amount, there is a pattern of change in the dependent variable. You can use this pattern of change to identify other linear relationships.

Ms. Chang's class decides to use their money from the walkathon to provide books for the children's ward at the hospital. The class puts the money in the school safe and withdraws a fixed amount each week to buy new books. To keep track of the money, Isabella makes a table of the amount of money in the account at the end of each week.

Week	Amount of Money at the End of Each Week
0	$144
1	$132
2	$120
3	$108
4	$96
5	$84

- What do you think the graph of this data would look like?

- Does this table represent a linear relationship? How did you decide?

 Problem 1.4

A 1. How much money is in the account at the start of the project? Explain.

2. How much money is withdrawn from the account each week?

3. Suppose the students continue withdrawing the same amount of money each week. Sketch a graph of this relationship.

4. Write an equation that represents the relationship. Explain what information each number and variable represents.

5. Is the relationship between the number of weeks and the amount of money left in the account linear? Explain.

Notes _____

_____

_____

Problem 1.4 *continued*

B Mr. Mamer's class also raised money from the walkathon. They use the money to buy games and puzzles for the children's ward. Keenan uses a graph to keep track of the amount of money in the account at the end of each week.

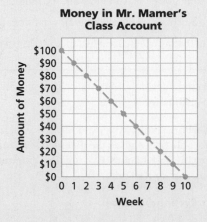

Money in Mr. Mamer's Class Account

1. What information does the graph represent about the money in Mr. Mamer's class account?

2. Make a table of data for the first 10 weeks. Explain why this table represents a linear relationship.

3. Write the equation that models the linear relationship. Explain what information each number and variable represents.

C 1. How can you determine whether a relationship is linear from a graph, a table, or an equation?

2. Compare the patterns of change for the linear relationships in this Problem to those in previous Problems in this Investigation.

A C E Homework starts on page 16.

Notes _____

Applications

1. Hoshi walks 10 meters in 3 seconds.

   a. What is her walking rate?

   b. At this rate, how long does it take her to walk 100 meters?

   c. She walks at this same rate for 50 seconds. How far does she walk?

   d. Write an equation that represents the distance d that Hoshi walks in t seconds.

2. Milo walks 40 meters in 15 seconds. Mira walks 30 meters in 10 seconds. Whose walking rate is greater?

For Exercises 3–5, Jose, Mario, Melanie, Mike, and Alicia are on a weeklong cycling trip. The table below gives the distance Jose, Mario, and Melanie each travel for the first 3 hours. Cycling times include only biking time, not time to eat, rest, and so on.

Cycling Distance

Cycling Time (hours)	Distance (miles)		
	Jose	Mario	Melanie
0	0	0	0
1	5	7	9
2	10	14	18
3	15	21	27

3. a. Assume that each person cycles at a constant rate. Find the rate at which each person travels during the first 3 hours. Explain.

   b. Find the distance each person travels in 7 hours.

   c. Graph the time and distance data for all three riders on the same coordinate axes.

   d. Use the graphs to find the distance each person travels in $6\frac{1}{2}$ hours.

   e. Use the graphs to find the time it takes each person to travel 70 miles.

Notes

f. How does the rate at which each person rides affect each graph?

g. For each rider, write an equation that can be used to calculate the distance traveled after a given number of hours.

h. Use your equations from part (g) to calculate the distance each person travels in $6\frac{1}{2}$ hours.

i. How does a person's cycling rate show up in his or her equation?

j. Are any of these proportional relationships? If so, what is the constant of proportionality?

4. Mike makes the following table of the distances he travels during the first day of the trip.

a. Suppose Mike continues riding at this rate. Write an equation for the distance Mike travels after t hours.

b. Sketch a graph of the equation. How did you choose the range of values for the time axis? For the distance axis?

c. How can you find the distances Mike travels in 7 hours and in $9\frac{1}{2}$ hours, using the table? Using the graph? Using the equation?

d. How can you find the numbers of hours it takes Mike to travel 100 miles and 237 miles, using the table? Using the graph? Using the equation?

Cycling Distance

Time (hours)	Distance (miles)
0	0
1	6.5
2	13
3	19.5
4	26
5	32.5
6	39

e. For parts (c) and (d), what are the advantages and disadvantages of using each model—a table, a graph, and an equation—to find the answers?

f. Compare the rate at which Mike rides with the rates at which Jose, Mario, and Melanie ride. Who rides the fastest? How can you determine this from the tables? From the graphs? From the equations?

5. The distance in miles Alicia travels in t hours is represented by the equation $d = 7.5t$.

a. At what rate does Alicia travel? Explain.

b. Suppose the graph of Alicia's distance and time is put on the same set of axes as Mike's, Jose's, Mario's, and Melanie's graphs. Where would it be located in relationship to each of the graphs? Describe the location without actually making the graph.

Notes _____

_____

_____

6. The graph below represents the walkathon pledge plans for three sponsors.

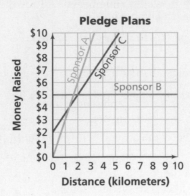

Pledge Plans

Money Raised — Sponsor A, Sponsor C, Sponsor B

Distance (kilometers)

a. Describe each sponsor's pledge plan.

b. What is the number of dollars per kilometer each sponsor pledges?

c. What does the point where the line crosses the y-axis mean for each sponsor?

d. Write the coordinates of two points on each line. What information does each point represent for the sponsor's pledge plan?

e. Does each relationship represent a proportional relationship?

7. The students in Ms. Chang's class decide to order water bottles that advertise the walkathon. Hyun obtains two different quotes for the costs of the bottles.

a. For each company, write an equation Hyun could use to calculate the cost for any number of bottles.

b. On the same set of axes, graph both equations from part (a). Which variable is the independent variable? Which is the dependent variable?

c. From which company do you think the class should buy water bottles? What factors influenced your decision?

d. For what number of water bottles is the cost the same for both companies? Explain.

4:45 PM

Edit

Water Bottle Cost Estimates

Fill It Up, Inc.
• $4 per bottle

Bottles by Bob, Co.
• $25 set-up fee
• $3 per bottle

18   Moving Straight Ahead

Notes _____

_____

8. **Multiple Choice** The equation $C = 5n$ represents the cost C in dollars for n caps that advertise the walkathon. Which of the following ordered pairs could represent a number of caps and the cost for that number of caps, (n, C)?

   A. $(0, 5)$ **B.** $(3, 15)$ **C.** $(15, 60)$ **D.** $(5, 1)$

9. The equation $d = 3.5t + 50$ gives the distance d in meters that a cyclist is from his home after t seconds.

   a. Which of the following ordered pairs represents a point on the graph of this equation? Explain your answer.

        i. $(10, 85)$ **ii.** $(0, 0)$ **iii.** $(3, 60.5)$

   b. What information do the coordinates tell you about the cyclist?

10. Examine the pattern in each table.

Table 1	
x	y
−2	3
−1	3
0	3
1	3
2	3

Table 2	
x	y
−3	9
−2	4
−1	1
0	0
1	1

Table 3	
x	y
0	10
3	19
5	25
10	40
12	46

Table 4	
x	y
0	−3
2	−6
4	−9
6	−12
8	−15

    a. Describe the similarities and differences in Tables 1–4.

    b. Explain how you can use each table to decide whether the data indicate a linear relationship between the two quantities.

    c. Sketch a graph of the data in each table.

    d. Write an equation that represents the relationship between the independent and dependent variables for each linear relationship. Explain what information the numbers and variables tell you about the relationship.

11. **a.** The temperature at the North Pole is 30°F and is expected to drop 5°F per hour for the next several hours. Write an equation that represents the relationship between temperature and time. Explain what information your numbers and variables represent.

    b. Is this a linear relationship? Explain your reasoning.

Notes _____

_____

_____

12. Jamal's parents give him money to spend at camp. Jamal spends the same amount of money on snacks each day. The table below shows the amount of money, in dollars, he has left at the end of each day.

Snack Money

Days	0	1	2	3	4	5	6
Money Left	$20	$18	$16	$14	$12	$10	$8

a. How much money does Jamal have at the start of camp? Explain.

b. How much money does he spend each day? Explain.

c. Is the relationship between the number of days and the amount of money left in Jamal's wallet a linear relationship? Explain.

d. Assume that Jamal's spending pattern continues. Check your answer to part (c) by sketching a graph of this relationship.

e. Write an equation that represents the relationship. Explain what information the numbers and variables represent.

13. Write an equation for each graph.

Graph 1   **Graph 2**

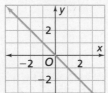   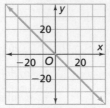

14. a. Describe a situation that involves a linear relationship between an independent variable and a dependent variable for which the rate of change is:

    i. positive.   **ii.** zero (no change).   **iii.** negative.

b. Write an equation that models each situation in part (a).

Notes

_____

_____

_____

Connections

15. Jelani is in a walking race at his school. In the first 20 seconds, he walks 60 meters. In the next 30 seconds, he walks 60 meters. In the next 10 seconds, he walks 35 meters. In the last 40 seconds, he walks 80 meters.

    a. Describe how Jelani's walking rate changes during the race.

    b. What would a graph of Jelani's walking race look like?

16. Insert parentheses in the expression on the left side of each equation to make each number sentence true.

    a. $2 + -3 \times 4 = -10$

    b. $4 + -3 \times -4 = -4$

    c. $-12 \div 2 + -4 = 6$

    d. $8 \div -2 + -2 = -6$

17. Which of the following number sentences are true? In each case, explain how you could answer without any calculation. Check your answers by doing the indicated calculations.

    a. $20 \times 410 = (20 \times 400) + (20 \times 10)$

    b. $20 \times 308 = (20 \times 340) - (20 \times 32)$

    c. $-20 \times -800 = (-20 \times -1,000) + (-20 \times 200)$

    d. $-20 + (300 \times 32) = (-20 + 300) \times (-20 + 32)$

18. Fill in the missing parts to make each number sentence true.

    a. $15 \times (6 + 4) = (15 \times \blacksquare) + (15 \times 4)$

    b. $2 \times (x + 6) = (2 \times \blacksquare) + (\blacksquare \times 6)$

    c. $(x \times 2) + (x \times 6) = \blacksquare \times (2 + 6)$

19. a. Draw a rectangle whose area can be represented by the expression $5 \times (12 + 6)$.

    b. Write another expression to represent the area of the rectangle in part (a).

Investigation 1   Walking Rates   21

Notes

20. Find the unit rate and use it to write an equation relating the two quantities.

    a. 150 dollars for 50 T-shirts

    b. 62 dollars to rent 14 video games

    c. 18 tablespoons of sugar in 3 glasses of Bolda Cola

21. The longest human-powered sporting event is the Tour de France cycling race. In a particular year, the average speed for the winner of this race was 23.66 miles per hour.

    a. In that same year, the race was 2,292 miles long. How long did it take the winner to complete the race?

    b. Suppose the winner had reduced his average cycling rate by 0.1 mile per hour. By how much would his time have changed?

22. **a.** In 1990, Nadezhda Ryashkina set the record for the 10,000 m race-walking event. She finished this race in 41 minutes 56.23 seconds. What was Ryashkina's average walking rate, in meters per second?

    b. In 2001, Olimpiada Ivanova set the record for the 20,000 m race-walking event. She finished the race in 86 minutes 52.3 seconds. What was Ivanova's average walking speed, in meters per second?

23. A recipe for orange juice calls for 2 cups of orange juice concentrate and 3 cups of water. The table below shows the amount of concentrate and water needed to make a given number of batches of juice.

Orange Juice Mixture Amounts

Batches of Juice (b)	Concentrate (c)	Water (w)	Juice (j)
1	2 cups	3 cups	5 cups
2	4 cups	6 cups	10 cups
3	6 cups	9 cups	15 cups
4	8 cups	12 cups	20 cups

The relationship between the number of batches of juice b and the number of cups of concentrate c is linear. The equation that represents this linear relationship is $c = 2b$. Are there other relationships in this table that are linear? Sketch graphs or write equations for any you find.

Notes _____

24. The table below shows the number of cups of orange juice, pineapple juice, and soda water needed for different quantities of punch.

Pineapple Punch Recipe

J (orange juice, cups)	P (pineapple juice, cups)	S (soda water, cups)
1	▪	▪
2	▪	▪
3	▪	▪
4	12	6
5	▪	▪
6	▪	▪
7	▪	▪
8	24	12

The relationship between cups of orange juice and cups of pineapple juice is linear. The relationship between cups of orange juice and cups of soda water is also linear.

a. Zahara makes the recipe using 6 cups of orange juice. How many cups of soda water does she use? Explain your reasoning.

b. Patrick makes the recipe using 6 cups of pineapple juice. How many cups of orange juice and cups of soda water does he use? Explain.

25. The graph at the right represents the distance John runs in a race. Use the graph to describe John's progress during the course of the race. Does he run at a constant rate during the race? Explain.

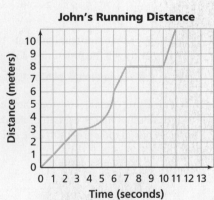

John's Running Distance

Notes

26. a. Does this graph represent a linear relationship? Explain.

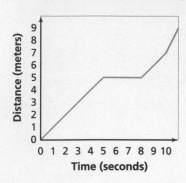

b. Could this graph represent a walking pattern? Explain.

For Exercises 27–29, students conduct an experiment to investigate the rate at which a leaking faucet loses water. They fill a paper cup with water, make a small hole in the bottom, and collect the dripping water in a measuring container, measuring the amount of water in the container at the end of each 10-second interval.

27. Students conducting the leaking-faucet experiment produce the table below. The measuring container they use has a capacity of 100 milliliters.

Leaking Faucet Experiment

Time (seconds)	10	20	30	40	50	60	70
Water Loss (milliliters)	2	5	8.5	11.5	14	16.5	19.5

a. Suppose the students continue their experiment. After how many seconds will the measuring container overflow?

b. Is this a linear relationship? Explain.

28. Denise and Takashi work together on the leaking-faucet experiment. Each of them makes a graph of the data they collect. What might have caused their graphs to look different?

Denise's Graph

Takashi's Graph
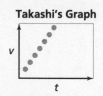

Notes

29. What might the graph below represent in the leaking-faucet experiment?

Extensions

30. **a.** The table below shows the populations of four cities for the past eight years. Describe how the population of each city changed over the eight years.

City Populations

Year	Population			
	Deep Valley	Nowhere	Swampville	Mount Silicon
0 (start)	1,000	1,000	1,000	1,000
1	1,500	900	1,500	2,000
2	2,000	800	2,500	4,000
3	2,500	750	3,000	8,000
4	3,000	700	5,000	16,000
5	3,500	725	3,000	32,000
6	4,000	900	2,500	64,000
7	4,500	1,500	1,500	128,000
8	5,000	1,700	1,000	256,000

b. Use the table to determine which relationships are linear.

c. Graph the data for each city. Describe how you selected ranges of values for the variables on the horizontal and vertical axes.

d. What are the advantages of using a table or a graph to represent the data?

Notes _____

31. In the walkathon, José asks his sponsors to donate $10 for the first 5 kilometers he walks and $1 per kilometer after 5 kilometers.

  a. Sketch a graph that represents the relationship between the money collected from each sponsor and the number of kilometers walked.

  b. Compare this graph to the graphs of the other pledge plans in Problem 1.3.

32. The cost C to make T-shirts for the walkathon is given by the equation $C = 20 + 5n$, where n is the number of T-shirts.

  a. Find the coordinates of a point that lies on the graph of this equation. Explain what information the coordinates represent in this context.

  b. Find the coordinates of a point above the line. Explain what information the coordinates represent in this context.

  c. Find the coordinates of a point below the line. Explain what information the coordinates represent in this context.

33. Reggie is looking forward to walking in a walkathon. He writes some equations to use to answer some questions he has about the walkathon. For each of parts (a)–(c), do the following two things:

  • Tell what information you think he was trying to find with the equation.

  • Write one question he could use the equation to answer.

  a. $y = 3x + 20$

  b. $y = 0.25x$

  c. $y = 4x$

Notes

Mathematical Reflections 1

In this Investigation, you began to explore linear relationships. You examined the patterns of change between two variables. The following questions will help you summarize what you have learned.

Think about these questions. Discuss your ideas with other students and your teacher. Then write a summary of your findings in your notebook.

1. **Describe** how the dependent variable changes as the independent variable changes in a linear relationship. Give examples.

2. **How** does the pattern of change between two variables in a linear relationship show up in

   a. a contextual situation?

   b. a table?

   c. a graph?

   d. an equation?

Notes

Common Core Mathematical Practices

As you worked on the Problems in this Investigation, you used prior knowledge to make sense of them. You also applied Mathematical Practices to solve the Problems. Think back over your work, the ways you thought about the Problems, and how you used Mathematical Practices.

Elena described her thoughts in the following way:

At the end of Problem 1.3, we noticed that the linear relationship with the greatest positive pattern of change had the steepest line. For example, $A_{Gilberto} = 2n$ and $A_{Alana} = 5 + 0.5n$. The line of Gilberto's equation is steeper since it has a greater rate of change.

This makes sense since as the number of kilometers increases by one unit, the money each sponsor donates to Gilberto increases by $2. The money each sponsor donates to Alana increases by $.50.

For Leanne, the equation is $A_{Leanne} = 10$, so the change is 0. As the number of kilometers increases by one unit, the money each sponsor donates to Leanne does not change. The graph is a horizontal line.

Common Core Standards for Mathematical Practice

MP8 Look for and express regularity in repeated reasoning.

- What other Mathematical Practices can you identify in Elena's reasoning?

- Describe a Mathematical Practice that you and your classmates used to solve a different Problem in this Investigation.

Notes _____

_____

_____

Exploring Linear Relationships With Graphs and Tables

▼ Investigation Overview

Investigation Description

This Investigation continues the theme of walkathons and helps students deepen their understanding of patterns of change. The constant rate of change between the two variables in a linear relationship and the *y*-intercept of the graph of a linear relationship are formalized in this Investigation. Students interpret the *y*-intercept as a special point on a line, a pair of values in a table, or as the constant *b* in the equation $y = mx + b$. They find the constant rate, decide whether relationships are decreasing or increasing, and make connections among ordered pairs on a line, a pair of values in a row of a table, and the solution of a linear equation.

Investigation Vocabulary

- coefficient
- solution of an equation
- *x*-intercept
- *y*-intercept

Mathematics Background

- Finding the Rate of Change, or Slope, of a Linear Relationship
- Finding the *y*-Intercept and Equation for a Linear Relationship
- Solving a System of Linear Equations

Planning Chart

Content	ACE	Pacing	Materials	Resources
Problem 2.1	1, 29–34, 42	1 day	• Generic Grid Paper poster paper sticky notes	
Problem 2.2	2–4, 6, 35–37, 43	1 day	**Labsheet 2.2** Henri and Emile's Race **Labsheet 2ACE:** Exercise 4 (accessibility) • Generic Grid Paper	• Coordinate Grapher • Data and Graphs
Problem 2.3	5, 7–14, 38, 39, 44, 45	1 day	• First-Quadrant Grid • Generic Grid Paper	
Problem 2.4	15–28, 40, 41	1½ days	graphing calculators	**Teaching Aid 2.4A** Alana's Pledge Plan **Teaching Aid 2.4B** Ali and Tamara's Graphs **Teaching Aid 2.4C** Graph of $y = 5x - 3$ **Teaching Aid 2.4D** Troy's Graphing Calculator • Coordinate Grapher
Mathematical Reflections		½ day		
Assessment: Partner Quiz		½ day	**Labsheet PQ:** Partner Quiz (accessibility)	• Partner Quiz

▼ Goals and Standards

Goals

Linear Relationships Recognize problem situations in which two variables have a linear relationship

- Identify and describe the patterns of change between the independent and dependent variables for linear relationships represented by tables, graphs, equations, or contextual settings

- Construct tables, graphs, and symbolic equations that represent linear relationships

- Identify the rate of change between two variables and the x- and y-intercepts from graphs, tables, and equations that represent linear relationships

- Translate information about linear relationships given in a contextual setting, a table, a graph, or an equation to one of the other forms

- Write equations that represent linear relationships given specific pieces of information, and describe what information the variables and numbers represent

- Make a connection between slope as a ratio of vertical distance to horizontal distance between two points on a line and the rate of change between two variables that have a linear relationship

- Recognize that $y = mx$ represents a proportional relationship

- Solve problems and make decisions about linear relationships using information given in tables, graphs, and equations

Equivalence Understand that the equality sign indicates that two expressions are equivalent

- Recognize that the equation $y = mx + b$ represents a linear relationship and means that $mx + b$ is an expression equivalent to y

- Recognize that linear equations in one unknown, $k = mx + b$ or $y = m(t) + b$, where k, t, m, and b are constants, are special cases of the equation $y = mx + b$

- Recognize that finding the missing value of one of the variables in a linear relationship, $y = mx + b$, is the same as finding a missing coordinate of a point (x, y) that lies on the graph of the relationship

- Solve linear equations in one variable using symbolic methods, tables, and graphs

- Recognize that a linear inequality in one unknown is associated with a linear equation

- Solve linear inequalities using graphs or symbolic reasoning

- Show that two expressions are equivalent

- Write and interpret equivalent expressions

Mathematical Reflections

Look for evidence of student understanding of the goals for this Investigation in their responses to the questions in *Mathematical Reflections*. The goals addressed by each question are indicated below.

1. **a.** Explain how the information about a linear relationship is represented in a table, a graph, or an equation.

   b. Describe several real-world situations that can be modeled by equations of the form $y = mx + b$ or $y = mx$. Explain how the latter equation represents a proportional relationship.

   Goals

   - Identify and describe the patterns of change between the independent and dependent variables for linear relationships represented by tables, graphs, equations, or contextual settings

   - Identify the rate of change between two variables and the x- and y-intercepts from graphs, tables, and equations that represent linear relationships

   - Translate information about linear relationships given in a contextual setting, a table, a graph, or an equation to one of the other forms

   - Recognize that $y = mx$ represents a proportional relationship

   - Recognize that the equation $y = mx + b$ represents a linear relationship and means that $mx + b$ is an expression equivalent to y

   - Recognize that linear equations in one unknown, $k = mx + b$ or $y = m(t) + b$, where k, t, m, and b are constants, are special cases of the equation $y = mx + b$

2. **a.** Explain how a table or a graph that represents a linear relationship can be used to solve a problem.

   b. Explain how you have used an equation that represents a linear relationship to solve a problem.

   Goal

   - Construct tables, graphs, and symbolic equations that represent linear relationships

   - Write equations that represent linear relationships given specific pieces of information, and describe what information the variables and numbers represent

   - Solve problems and make decisions about linear relationships using information given in tables, graphs, and equations

   - Recognize that finding the missing value of one of the variables in a linear relationship, $y = mx + b$, is the same as finding a missing coordinate of a point (x, y) that lies on the graph of the relationship

Standards

Common Core Content Standards

7.RP.A.2b Identify the constant of proportionality (unit rate) in tables, graphs, equations, diagrams, and verbal descriptions of proportional relationships. *Problems 1, 2, and 3*

7.RP.A.2c Represent proportional relationships by equations. *Problems 1, 2, and 3*

7.RP.A.2D Explain what a point (x, y) on the graph of a proportional relationship means in terms of the situation, with special attention to the points $(0, 0)$ and $(1, r)$, where r is the unit rate. *Problems 1, 2, and 3*

7.EE.B.3 Solve multi-step real-life and mathematical problems posed with positive and negative rational numbers in any form (whole numbers, fractions, and decimals), using tools strategically. Apply properties of operations to calculate with numbers in any form; convert between forms as appropriate; and assess the reasonableness of answers using mental computation and estimation strategies. *Problems 3 and 4*

7.EE.B.4 Use variables to represent quantities in a real-world or mathematical problem, and construct simple equations and inequalities to solve problems by reasoning about the quantities. *Problems 2 and 3*

7.EE.B.4a Solve word problems leading to equations of the form $px + q = r$ and $p(x + q) = r$, where p, q, and r are specific rational numbers. Solve equations of these forms fluently. Compare an algebraic solution to an arithmetic solution, identifying the sequence of the operations used in each approach. *Problems 1, 2, 3, and 4*

Facilitating the Mathematical Practices

Students in *Connected Mathematics* classrooms display evidence of multiple Common Core Standards for Mathematical Practice every day. Here are just a few examples of when you might observe students demonstrating the Standards for Mathematical Practice during this Investigation.

Practice 1: **Make sense of problems and persevere in solving them.**

Students are engaged every day in solving problems and, over time, learn to persevere in solving them. To be effective, the problems embody critical concepts and skills and have the potential to engage students in making sense of mathematics. Students build understanding by reflecting, connecting, and communicating. These student-centered problem situations engage students in articulating the "knowns" in a problem situation and determining a logical solution pathway. The student-student and student-teacher dialogues help students not only to make sense of the problems, but also to persevere in finding appropriate strategies to solve them. The suggested questions in the Teacher Guides provide the metacognitive scaffolding to help students monitor and refine their problem-solving strategies.

Practice 6: **Attend to precision.**

Students use precise definitions when they finally connect the three models they have used to represent linear relationships. In Problem 2.4, they use the definition of a solution of an equation clearly and apply the meaning of the solution to tables, graphs, and equations in order to solve problems.

Practice 8: **Look for and express regularity in repeated reasoning.**

Students connect the relationships in Problem 2.2 with the ones in Problem 2.3 to develop an understanding of how a constant rate of change and an initial value affect the equation of a linear relationship. They use this connection to express all linear relationships in the form $y = mx + b$.

Students identify and record their personal experiences with the Standards for Mathematical Practice during the Mathematical Reflections at the end of the Investigation.

PROBLEM 2.1

Henri and Emile's Race
Finding the Point of Intersection

▼ Problem Overview

> *Focus Question*   When is it helpful to use a graph or a table to solve a problem?

Problem Description

Students look at the context of a young boy challenging his older brother to a race. Students explore the question, "How long should the race be so that the younger brother wins in a close race?" This Problem introduces the idea of students finding the point of intersection of two linear relationships using a graph, a table, or numeric reasoning. The Problem also assesses what students have learned about linear relationships and their representations from Investigation 1.

Problem Implementation

Let the class work in groups of 2 to 3.

Students may want to record information in a table or a graph using **Generic Grid Paper**. Students may also record their graphs on poster paper in order to present their solutions and arguments on poster paper to use in the Summarize.

Materials

• **Generic Grid Paper**

poster paper

sticky notes

Vocabulary

• x-intercept

Mathematics Background

• Solving a System of Linear Equations

At a Glance and Lesson Plan

- At a Glance: Problem 2.1 Moving Straight Ahead
- Lesson Plan: Problem 2.1 Moving Straight Ahead

▼ # Launch

Launch Video

In this animation, Henri and Emile are preparing for a walking race against each other. The video illustrates why Henri would need a head start in order for the race to be close. Emile considers a few options, decides to give Henri a 45-meter head start, and poses Question A from the Student Edition: How long should the race be so that Henri will win in a close race? Visit Teacher Place at mathdashboard.com/cmp3 to see the complete video.

Connecting to Prior Knowledge

If you did not pose the following questions at the end of the Summarize for Problem 1.4, ask them now. Begin by having students list several equations from Investigation 1 that represent linear relationships.

Suggested Questions

- Which relationship has the greatest rate of change? (Answers will vary. Look for students to choose the relationship that when written in the form $y = b + mx$ has the greatest value of m.)

- Which relationship(s) has a graph that crosses the y-axis at a point with a positive y-coordinate? With a y-coordinate of zero? With a negative y-coordinate? (Answers will vary. Positive y-coordinate: Look for students to choose the relationship(s) that when written in the form $y = b + mx$ has a positive value of b. Sample: The line that represents Alana's pledge plan. Zero y-coordinate: Look for students to choose a proportional relationship. Sample: Gilberto's pledge plan can be modeled by a line that passes through the origin. Negative y-coordinate: Look for students to choose the relationship(s) that when written in the form $y = b + mx$ has a negative value of b. Sample: The line that represents Gilberto's pledge plan after purchasing a T-shirt for each sponsor.)

You can tell students that they will continue to look at linear relationships in this Problem.

Presenting the Challenge

Tell the story of the race between Emile and his younger brother, Henri. This Problem is intended to show what knowledge students already have concerning linear relationships. Problem 2.2 will serve as a summary of this Problem.

Because the Problem asks "how long" the race should be, some students will choose to focus on length and some will focus on time.

Note: An alternative version of the Problem is to challenge the class to decide on both the head start and the length of the race. For this situation, you would give the rates at which the two brothers walk and tell the class that Emile wants his brother to win, but he wants the race to appear close.

Suggested Questions

- What should Emile do? (Sample answer: Give a head start to his brother.)

- What head start should he give his brother, and how many meters long should the race be? (Answers will vary. Sample answer: The race cannot be so short that it's obvious Henri will win. The head start will depend on how long the race is in order to make it a close race.)

- Is giving his little brother a head start sufficient to guarantee that Henri will win? (No; Emile will eventually catch up because his walking rate is greater than Henri's.)

- What strategy do you need to ensure that the younger brother is still ahead at the end of the race? (Answers will vary. Sample answer: The race needs to be long enough to look like it is a close race but not long enough for Emile to catch up.)

This is a nontrivial insight: that, given an appropriate domain, the faster rate or the steeper slope will always overtake the lesser rate.

Students may suggest that once Emile is about to catch up to Henri, he can slow his walking rate so that Henri maintains the lead until the race is finished. If students give this suggestion, you can tell them to assume that each walking rate remains constant.

▼ Explore

Providing for Individual Needs

Circulate and ask groups to explain their thinking. Put the emphasis on what evidence the group will use to justify their conclusion. Encourage all groups to listen to each member in order to reach a consensus on a single answer or to agree that more than one choice is reasonable and explain why.

Some students might use a guess-and-check method to find the answer. Others may use a graph or a table. Look to see if they are choosing reasonable scales for the graphs or intervals for the tables. Some might use an equation, but this may not be as common.

Look for other interesting strategies. For example, one group may look at the distance between the two brothers after t seconds. At the start of the race, they are 45 meters apart. Since the difference in their walking rates is $2.5 - 1 = 1.5$ meters per second, Emile is 1.5 meters closer each second. After 5 seconds, for example, they are 37.5 meters apart. Students who use this method may make a table and find the time it takes for the distance between the brothers to be 0. They essentially are solving the equation $45 + t - 2.5t = 0$, or they are finding the x-intercept of the graph of the linear relationship $y = 45 + t - 2.5t$.

Note: This line has a negative rate of change. Its graph is a line that is decreasing from left to right and connects back to Problem 1.4.

Going Further

Test students' understanding of how the length of the race depends on the head start and both brothers' walking rates.

- Suppose Henri has a different head start. How would this affect your answer? (If Henri has a bigger head start, the race would need to be longer so that it would still be a close race. Similarly, if Henri has a smaller head start, the race would need to be shorter so that Emile does not catch up.)

- Suppose Henri or Emile has a different walking rate. How would this affect your answer? (If the head start is still 45 meters and one or both of the walking rates change, then the time it takes Emile to catch up to Henri will also change. Sample answer: If Emile walks faster, the race would need to be shorter so that Henri still wins.)

Planning for the Summary

What evidence will you use in the summary to clarify and deepen understanding of the Focus Question?

What will you do if you do not have evidence?

▼ Summarize

Orchestrating the Discussion

If you have student work on poster paper, put it up and give students a few minutes to examine the work. They can leave sticky notes on the posters with questions or comments.

Suggested Questions

Collect some strategies from the class. Encourage students to explain their reasons for the choices they make. The process of making such decisions is very important.

- How did your group interpret the Problem? What strategy did you use? (Answers will vary. Possible answers are provided below.)

Students may have informal ways of thinking about the Problem. These informal methods can enhance their appreciation and understanding of what the more formal mathematical processes can tell them. This transition to using more formal processes should proceed slowly. Students need to develop their intuitions about the Problem. Encourage them to explain their reasons for the decisions they make. The process of making such decisions and being able to explain them is very important.

Possible Student Explanations

- Some students in one class made a table in intervals of 10 seconds, recorded data until Henri and Emile had the same distance, and then chose the distance for one second before they met.

Distance From Starting Line

Time (seconds)	Henri's Distance (meters)	Emile's Distance (meters)
0	45	0
10	55	25
20	65	50
30	75	75
40	85	100

- Some students may guess at a length for the race, check it, and then make adjustments as necessary. Others may guess a time, check it, and make adjustments.

- A few students may write equations to represent the situation: $d_{Henri} = 45 + t$, $d_{Emile} = 2.5t$. They may graph both lines to find the point of intersection. Then they might select a suitable coordinate pair to represent the time and length of the race. Although any distance less than 75 meters or time less than 30 seconds will ensure Henri wins, choosing a time such as 25 seconds or distance such as 70 meters will make a close race.

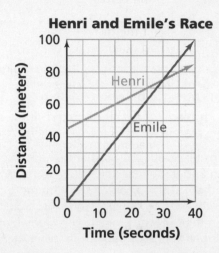

Henri and Emile's Race

- Another group of students chose to look at the difference in rates. After each second, Emile is another 1.5 meters closer to catching up to Henri: after 1 second, he is 43.5 meters away from Henri; after 2 seconds he is 3 meters closer, or 42 meters away, from Henri. Informally, they are finding when $d = 0$ in the equation $d = 45 - 1.5t$. This value of t represents when Emile catches up to Henri, similar to the example given in the Explore.

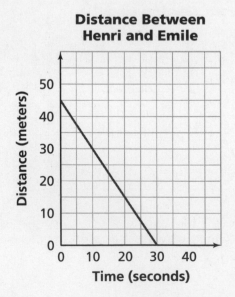

**Distance Between
Henri and Emile**

Be sure to have the class verify the lengths (or times) of the race if different lengths (or times) are suggested. For each suggested answer, ask:

- How did you determine what the length (or time) of the race should be? (Sample answers: We found the distance (or time) when the race would be a tie, and then we made the race 1 meter (or 1 second) shorter. Henri will win this race.)

- Why is that distance (or time) reasonable? (We wanted Henri to win the race and for the race to be close. If the race is 29 seconds long, Henri will be a greater distance from the starting point than Emile will be.)

If no group comes up with the strategy of looking at the distance between the brothers decreasing over time, use the following question to wrap up your discussion.

- One group of students looked at the distance between the brothers at the start of the race and every 5 seconds. How might this method help them find the answer? (Sample answer: The distance between them is less as time passes. If you can find the number of seconds it takes Emile to catch up to Henri, you can make the time of the race less than that time.)

Use the Summarize to launch the next Problem. If some students used a table, show this table to transition into the next Problem. Problem 2.2 is a more formal presentation of this Problem. Students will use a table, a graph, and an equation for each brother. They will look at the pattern of change in all three representations and use these representations to answer questions about the race.

Reflecting on Student Learning

Use the following questions to assess student understanding at the end of the lesson.

- What evidence do I have that students understand the Focus Question?
  - Where did my students get stuck?
  - What strategies did they use?
  - What breakthroughs did my students have today?
- How will I use this to plan for tomorrow? For the next time I teach this lesson?
- Where will I have the opportunity to reinforce these ideas as I continue through this Unit? The next Unit?

ACE Assignment Guide

- **Applications:** 1
- **Connections:** 29–34
- **Extensions:** 42

Crossing the Line
Using Tables, Graphs, and Equations

▼ Problem Overview

> *Focus Question* How does the pattern of change for a linear relationship appear in a table, a graph, or an equation?

Problem Description

Students compare data from Problem 2.1 using tables, graphs, and equations. The younger brother has a head start, which sets up questions about the point where the graph crosses the *y*-axis for a situation that is not proportional. Although the *y*-intercept is not named until the next Problem, students make meaning of the point where the graph of a line intersects the *y*-axis. This Problem focuses on the essential features of a linear relationship and how they are represented in a graph, a table, and an equation. Students connect walking rates to the constant rate of change between two variables that have a linear relationship. They also continue to interpret a graph, a table, or an equation to determine specific information about a situation. For example, if the value of one variable is known, they find the corresponding value of the second variable.

Problem Implementation

Students can work in groups of 2–4.

Labsheet 2.2: Henri and Emile's Race contains the information about both brothers from the Student Edition. You can give this labsheet to students to help them organize their solutions to Question A, parts (1) and (2). This can optimize class time and allow students to focus on the mathematics of the situation.

Materials

- **Labsheet 2.2:** Henri and Emile's Race
- **Labsheet 2ACE:** Exercise 4 (accessibility)
- **Generic Grid Paper**

Using Technology

- Coordinate Grapher
- Data and Graphs

Vocabulary

There are no new glossary terms introduced in this Problem.

Mathematics Background

- Finding the Rate of Change, or Slope, of a Linear Relationship
- Finding the *y*-intercept and Equation for a Linear Relationship
- Solving a System of Linear Equations

At a Glance and Lesson Plan

- At a Glance: Problem 2.2 Moving Straight Ahead
- Lesson Plan: Problem 2.2 Moving Straight Ahead

▼ Launch

Connecting to Prior Knowledge

Use the Summarize of Problem 2.1 to launch this Problem. Depending on the richness of the summary of Problem 2.1, this Problem may go quite quickly, particularly Question A. If your students did not use a table, a graph, or an equation to solve Problem 2.1, discuss with them that it is sometimes useful to look at other ways to solve the Problem.

Presenting the Challenge

Review the questions posed in Problem 2.1. Ask students how they can use a table, a graph, or an equation to answer these questions. Remind students that once they have tables, graphs, and equations for each relationship, they can answer other questions about the race.

Students should make their own table, graph, and equation for each brother, but they can discuss the strategies for using them to find information with other students in their group.

▼ Explore

Providing for Individual Needs

As you circulate, ask additional questions about features of the graph or table. Some students may have trouble recognizing 1 as the coefficient of t in the equation for Henri.

Suggested Questions

- How do you represent Henri's walking rate of 1 meter per second in an equation? (The walking rate is the coefficient of the variable t. Since the walking rate is 1, you do not need to write it because $1t$ is equivalent to t. The equation for Henri can be written as $d_{Henri} = 45 + t$.)

- For the graphs of the two lines, why are the points where the lines cross the y-axis different? (Henri gets a head start, which means that at the start of the race, he is 45 meters from the starting point. The point $(0, 45)$ represents his starting distance at a time of 0 seconds. The origin $(0, 0)$ represents Emile's distance at a time of 0 seconds.)

- What does the vertical (up and down) difference between the two lines on the graph tell you? (The vertical difference tells you how far apart the brothers are at that moment in time. It shows that the difference is 45 meters at $t = 0$ and that the distance between them gets smaller as Emile catches up to Henri.)

- Can you tell from a table how far Henri is from the starting point at 7 seconds? Explain your reasoning. (You can find the row of the table where $t = 7$. The distance that corresponds to a time of 7 seconds is 52 meters.)

- Is either relationship linear? Explain. (They are both linear since they both walk at a constant rate. The graphs that represent the relationships are both straight lines.)

Going Further

- How can you use the equations for the brothers to find the length of the race? (You can use the equations to find the time when the brothers are the same distance from the starting line. Since $d = 2.5t$ for Emile and $d = 45 + t$ for Henri, then you want to solve for t when $2.5t = 45 + t$. You can solve this equation using guess and check or fact families.)

Students have done some solving of equations in *Variables and Patterns*. They are more likely to be able to write the equation $2.5t = 45 + t$ than they are to be able to solve it. This equation is a bit more complicated than the ones they solved in *Variables and Patterns* because it involves two steps and has variables on both sides of the equation. They might be able to use a guess-and-check strategy or use fact families. They will learn how to solve these equations algebraically in Investigation 3.

Planning for the Summary

What evidence will you use in the summary to clarify and deepen understanding of
the Focus Question?

What will you do if you do not have evidence?

▼ Summarize

Orchestrating the Discussion

Suggested Questions

- How can you tell how long the race should be using the graph? Using
  the table? (In the graph, the brothers are at the same place at the point
  where the two lines cross. In the table, this is the row for which the times
  and distances are equal. The race needs to be to the left of the point of
  intersection on the graph, so it should be shorter than 30 seconds or
  75 meters for Henri to win a close race.)

The previous question is beginning to lay the foundation for linear inequalities.
You could also pick points to the right of the intersection point and ask questions
about those distances, such as "When t is greater than 30, who wins the race?
When $t = 35$, how far ahead is Emile?".

- Is either relationship linear? Explain. (They are both linear. Both brothers
  walk at constant rates, the graphs are straight lines, and the equations are
  in the form $y = mx + b$.)

Ask questions about various points from the graph and table:

- What information does the point (20, 50) represent in the situation?
  Would this be a data point for Henri or for Emile? How does it relate to
  a table, a graph, and an equation for this situation? (This pair of values
  represents someone who is 50 meters from the starting point after a time
  of 20 seconds. It is a data point for Emile. It is a pair of values for one of
  the rows in the table, a point on the line of Emile's graph, and it is a pair
  of values (t, d) that makes the equation for Emile true.)

- What does the pair of values (10, 55) mean in this situation? Would this
  be a data point for Henri or for Emile? (This pair of values represents a
  distance of 55 meters from the starting line after 10 seconds. It is a data
  point for Henri. This pair of values cannot represent a time and distance
  for Emile since Emile has only walked 25 meters in 10 seconds. However,
  in 10 seconds Henri walks 45 meters plus 10 additional meters, which
  corresponds to the distance of 55 meters.)

- How does the pair of values (10, 55) from the table show up on the
  graph? How is it related to the equation? (The ordered pair appears as
  a point on the graph for Henri. It is also a pair of values that make the
  equation for Henri true because (55) = 45 + (10).)

Understanding how an ordered pair appears in each representation of a linear relationship and what the values mean for the situation is fundamentally very important. From this understanding, students can build a connection between every pair of values in a table to corresponding points on the graph and to pairs of values that satisfy (or solve) the equation.

- Pick a point on the graph of one of the brothers and write a question that can be answered using this point. (Answers will vary. Possible answer: The point (25, 70) lies on the graph for Henri. You can ask the question "How far from the starting point will Henri be after 25 seconds?")

- Describe the behavior of the two graphs. How can you tell from the graphs who is ahead? (Henri's graph is a straight line that starts at (0, 45) and increases over time. Emile's graph is a straight line that passes through the origin and is steeper than Henri's graph. The two lines intersect at the point (30, 75). For Henri to win the race, Henri's graph must be higher than Emile's graph, which is true to the left of the intersection point. To the right, Emile is ahead because Emile's line is above Henri's line.)

Question B serves as a preliminary introduction to solving equations. At this stage, students can answer them using a table, a graph, or by reasoning about the situation.

Question C refers to the "steepness" of a line. You might need to discuss what steepness means. You can use riding a bike up or down a hill for reference. (Be careful if you do use the steepness of a hill because the rate of the bike rider will typically be less for a very steep hill. In this context the rate of the rider and the rate at which the hill rises are two different things.) This question is foreshadowing the concept of slope, which is addressed later in this Unit.

In the next Investigation, students will find the point of intersection by setting the two equations for distance equal to each other.

$$d_{\text{Henri}} = d_{\text{Emile}} \text{ or } 45 + t = 2.5t$$

Note: Some students may suggest using a graphing calculator to find the point of intersection. If you use the graphing calculator, you may have to give the class suggestions for finding the appropriate viewing window. You can also have students use **Coordinate Grapher** to display each equation.

Check for Understanding

A friend joins Emile and Henri's race. The equation for the friend is $30 + 1.5t = d$. Your class decided that the race had to be shorter than 30 seconds or 75 meters for Henri to win. Suppose the race ends after 25 seconds or 70 meters.

- What information do the variables and numbers represent? (The number 30 is the head start the friend gets: 30 meters. The coefficient of t is the walking rate of the friend: 1.5 meters per second. The variables t and d still represent time and distance, respectively.)

- If the friend starts at the same time as Emile and Henri, who wins the race? (At 25 seconds (the time we agreed on for the race), the distance each person is from the starting point can be found by substituting 25 for t in each equation and solving for d. Emile is 62.5 meters from the starting point, Henri is 70 meters from the starting point, and the friend is 67.5 meters from the starting point. Henri still wins this race.)

- Another friend enters the race such that his equation is $d = 30 + t$. Would he overtake Emile or Henri during the race? Explain. (No; this friend starts ahead of Emile, and Emile overtakes the friend after 20 seconds. The friend also starts behind Henri and walks at the same constant rate, so he will never catch up to Henri.)

Reflecting on Student Learning

Use the following questions to assess student understanding at the end of the lesson.

- What evidence do I have that students understand the Focus Question?
  - Where did my students get stuck?
  - What strategies did they use?
  - What breakthroughs did my students have today?
- How will I use this to plan for tomorrow? For the next time I teach this lesson?
- Where will I have the opportunity to reinforce these ideas as I continue through this Unit? The next Unit?

ACE Assignment Guide

- **Applications:** 2–4, 6
- **Connections:** 35–37
- **Extensions:** 43
- **Labsheet 2ACE:** Exercise 4 (accessibility)

Comparing Costs
Comparing Relationships

▼ Problem Overview

> *Focus Question* How can you decide if a table or an equation represents a linear relationship?

Problem Description

Students explore constant rate and *y*-intercept in a new context. They solve problems and make decisions about linear relationships using information given in tables, in graphs, and in equations. This Problem formally introduces the words *coefficient and y-intercept*. The *y*-intercept is named and students interpret it as a point on a line, an entry in a table, or as the constant *b* in the equation $y = mx + b$. The constant rate of change is emphasized as the coefficient of the independent variable. Students learn to recognize a linear relationship within a contextual situation, from an equation, from a table, or from a graph. This is the first time students have to decide if an equation or a table represents a linear relationship.

Problem Implementation

Let the class work in pairs. You can have them record any tables or graphs on **Generic Grid Paper** or **First-Quadrant Grid** and then move into larger groups to share answers and strategies.

You could let the class work on Question A and then summarize it and then assign Question B.

Materials

- **First-Quadrant Grid**
- **Generic Grid Paper**

Vocabulary

- coefficient
- solution of an equation
- *y*-intercept

Mathematics Background

• Finding the *y*-intercept and Equation for a Linear Relationship

At a Glance and Lesson Plan

• At a Glance: Problem 2.3 Moving Straight Ahead
• Lesson Plan: Problem 2.3 Moving Straight Ahead

▼ Launch

Connecting to Prior Knowledge

You can start by showing the equations from Problem 2.2.

$$d_{\text{Henri}} = 45 + t \text{ and } d_{\text{Emile}} = 2.5t$$

Suggested Questions

• What information do the variables and numbers represent in each equation? (The variable *t* represents time, and the variable *d* represents each brother's distance from the starting line. The number 45 represents Henri's head start, and the number 2.5 represents how many meters Emile walks per second. Henri's rate of 1 m/s is the assumed coefficient of *t*.)

Display a graph and a table for each of the two equations.

• Where do the lines cross the *y*-axis? (The line for Henri crosses the *y*-axis at the point (0, 45), and the line for Emile crosses the *y*-axis at the point (0, 0).)

• Why is the name **y-intercept** a good name for these points? (This is the point where each line intersects, or intercepts, the *y*-axis.)

Go over the definition of **coefficient** with students. Then ask:

• How does the walking rate show up in the equations? (The walking rate of each brother is the coefficient of *t* in the equation for each relationship. In Henri's equation, the coefficient is 1, which is not written, but assumed.)

Define the **solution of an equation** using the explanation in the student book. Tell students that a solution of the equation $d = 45 + t$ is a pair of values that makes the equation true, or an ordered pair that lies on the graph of the line.

• Is (0, 45) a solution of this equation? Explain. (Yes; if $t = 0$ and $d = 45$, $45 = 45 + 0$ is a true equation.)

• What would the value of *d* be if (48, *d*) is a solution? Explain. (93 meters; if (48, *d*) is a solution, then $d = 45 + 48$, or $d = 93$; $93 = 45 + 48$ is a true equation.)

- What would the value of *t* be if (*t*, 50) is a solution? Explain. (5 seconds; if (*t*, 50) is a solution, then $50 = 45 + t$, or $t = 5$; $50 = 45 + 5$ is a true equation.)

- What is the *y*-intercept of this equation? Are the coordinates of the *y*-intercept a solution of the equation? Explain. (The graph of the equation has a *y*-intercept of (0, 45), which is a solution of the equation.)

Presenting the Challenge

Once the class is comfortable with how to read these equations, tell the story of the cost plans offered by two T-shirt companies. The goal for students is to recognize which equations represent linear relationships and interpret the characteristics of these two linear relationships from the equations.

▼ Explore

Providing for Individual Needs

Look for interesting strategies. Call on these students in the summary to share their strategies. Be sure to have a representative sample of the strategies presented. Students may choose to use numerical reasoning, tables, graphs, or equations. Be sure to look at what methods students are using to find when the two cost plans are equal.

In Question A, make sure students explain how they found their answers. Ask:

- How do the solutions to Question A, part (2) and part (3) show up in the graph and in the table? (For the first question in part (2), the ordered pairs (12, 61) and (12, 54) are the answers. These ordered pairs are the coordinates of a point on each graph and are also entries in the table of data for each equation. For part (3), the coordinate pairs that relate to a cost of $120 are (71, 120) and (26, 117). The point (71, 120) lies on the line of the graph of $C_{\text{Mighty}} = 49 + n$, and its coordinates are an entry in the table of data for C_{Mighty}. In the table of data for the equation $C_{\text{No-Shrink}} = 4.5n$, there is no entry with a *C*-value of 120. This is because, in order to spend exactly $120, the school would have to buy $26\frac{2}{3}$ T-shirts, which is impossible. The school cannot spend more than the amount of money they have, so you would look for the entry in the table with a whole number of T-shirts and a cost just under $120. This gives you the coordinates (26, 117), which correspond to a point that lies on the graph of $C_{\text{No-Shrink}}$.)

Planning for the Summary

What evidence will you use in the summary to clarify and deepen understanding of the Focus Question?

What will you do if you do not have evidence?

▼ Summarize

Orchestrating the Discussion

The main goals in this Problem are for students to revisit constant rate in the context of an equation, to interpret information from an equation, and to use linear equations to answer questions.

Suggested Questions

- What is the cost per T-shirt under each plan? (The cost per T-shirt is $1 for Mighty Tee and $4.50 for No-Shrink Tee.)

- Compare these costs per T-shirt with other rates that you have studied so far in this Unit. (The cost per T-shirt represents the constant rate of change for each linear relationship. It is the coefficient of the independent variable, the number of T-shirts. It is similar to the rates at which Henri and Emile walk. The Mighty Tee's equation is similar to the equation for Henri but with different y-intercepts. The No-Shrink equation is similar to Emile's equation but with different coefficients of the independent variables.)

- How would this rate show up in a table? In a graph? (As the value in the column for the number of T-shirts increases by 1, the value for cost increases by $1 for Mighty Tee and $4.50 for No-Shrink Tee. The graph of the line for No-Shrink Tee is much steeper than the graph of the line for Mighty Tee.)

- What information does the y-intercept represent in each equation? (The y-intercept represents the cost of 0 T-shirts. It is the starting cost for each company.)

- How could you use a table to find the cost of producing 100 T-shirts? How could you use a graph? How could you use an equation? (You can find the value in the table for cost that corresponds to the entry for 100 T-shirts purchased. You can trace the graph to find the y-coordinate of the point on the line that has an x-coordinate of 100. You can substitute 100 for n in the equation to solve for the value of C.)

- Which representation seems most convenient for solving this Problem? (Answers will vary. Students may give reasons for each representation. At this stage in their development, they might say that equations are most convenient because the row you need to answer a question might not be in the table, or the point on the line you need might not be shown on a graph. They may also explain that graphs can be easily traced to find the missing value of an ordered pair. Finally, they may point out that tables usually require no calculations to find pairs of values.)

Problem 2.3 Summarize   119

Ask students the following questions without graphing either equation.

- Does the point (50, 99) lie on the line for either company's graph? Explain. (The point lies on the graph for Mighty Tee. The cost is $49 plus $1 per T-shirt, which is $49 + $50, or $99.)

- How is this point related to the equation of the cost plan? (This point means that 50 T-shirts costs $99, which is true for $C_{Mighty} = 49 + n$. The point is a solution of the equation for Mighty Tee.)

Review Question A, part (4) by asking:

- For what number of T-shirts are the two costs equal? How did you find that number? (14 T-shirts; students may have made a table and found the row for which the two costs are equal, constructed a graph and identified the intersection point, or used a method involving guess and check.)

To review Question A, part (5), you can ask:

- What would the value of C be for each equation if (5, C) is a solution? Explain. ($C_{Mighty} = 54$ and $C_{No\text{-}Shrink} = 22.5$. In each equation, substitute 5 for n and solve for C.)

- What would the value of n be for each equation if (n, 50) is a solution? Explain. ($n = 1$ for Mighty Tee. $n \approx 11$ for No-Shrink Tee. In each equation, substitute 50 for C and solve for n.)

You could ask students to find the value of n when $C_{No\text{-}Shrink} = 50$. This provides an opportunity to discuss whether the ordered pair (11.1, 50) can be a solution for No-Shrink Tee. Some students may specify that the greatest number of T-shirts you can buy for $50 is 11 (for $49.50). Other students may point out that there is no real-world number of T-shirts you can buy for exactly $50, so it is not a solution. This can lead to a discussion about whether it is more appropriate to graph this relationship as a line or as a series of points (for whole-number x-coordinates only).

Be sure to discuss Question B, which will help you determine what your students know about linear relationships.

- Write an equation that represents the costs of the new company. ($C_{Big\ T} = 34 + 2.5n$)

- What information do the variables and numbers represent? (The variables n and C still represent the number of T-shirts and the cost for n T-shirts, respectively. The number 34 represents the starting cost, and the number 2.5 represents the cost per T-shirt.)

- In a linear situation, describe how you can find a value of a variable if the value of the other variable is known. (Answers will vary. Sample answer: For an equation, if the independent variable is known, you can substitute its value into the equation and then evaluate the resulting expression. If the dependent variable is known, you can substitute its value into the equation and then solve the equation to find the corresponding value of the independent variable.)

Ask questions that check students' understanding of the meaning of *coefficient* and *y-intercept*. You might use situations from Investigation 1 or Problem 2.2.

You can also ask questions about which equation in the Problem represents a proportional relationship. These questions provide an opportunity to reinforce understanding of proportional relationships and to distinguish linear relationships that are proportional from ones that are not.

- Mitch said that you can find the cost of 40 T-shirts at No-Shrink Tee by doubling the cost of 20 T-shirts. Is he correct? Explain. (Yes; since the equation is of the form $y = mx$, the cost at No-Shrink Tee is proportional to the number of T-shirts. So, if you double the number of T-shirts, you also double the cost.)

- Will the same strategy work for Mighty Tee? Explain your reasoning. (No; the equation for Mighty Tee is of the form $y = mx + b$, which is not a proportional relationship. Even though the cost increases by a constant rate per T-shirt, the relationship is not proportional.)

Reflecting on Student Learning

Use the following questions to assess student understanding at the end of the lesson.

- What evidence do I have that students understand the Focus Question?
  - Where did my students get stuck?
  - What strategies did they use?
  - What breakthroughs did my students have today?
- How will I use this to plan for tomorrow? For the next time I teach this lesson?
- Where will I have the opportunity to reinforce these ideas as I continue through this Unit? The next Unit?

ACE Assignment Guide

- **Applications:** 5, 7–14
- **Connections:** 38, 39
- **Extensions:** 44, 45

▼ Problem Overview

> *Focus Question* How are solutions of an equation of the form $y = b + mx$ related to the graph and the table for the same relationship?

Problem Description

Students investigate various pledge plans from sponsors of the walkathon. The plans are represented by equations. In this Problem, students identify the constant rate of change from various representations. They decide whether the graph of a linear relationship is decreasing, increasing, or staying the same from different representations of the relationship. They also begin to make the connections among the points on a line, the pairs of data in a row of a table, and a solution of an equation of the form $y = b + mx$. This latter goal provides a transition to solving equations using algebraic methods.

Problem Implementation

Students can work on this Problem in pairs and then share answers and strategies in larger groups.

Materials

- **Teaching Aid 2.4A:** Alana's Pledge Plan
- **Teaching Aid 2.4B:** Ali and Tamara's Graphs
- **Teaching Aid 2.4C:** Graph of $y = 5x - 3$
- **Teaching Aid 2.4D:** Troy's Graphing Calculator
- **Partner Quiz**
- **Labsheet PQ:** Partner Quiz (accessibility)

graphing calculator

Using Technology

- Coordinate Grapher

Vocabulary

There are no new glossary terms introduced in this Problem.

Mathematics Background

- Finding the Rate of Change, or Slope, of a Linear Relationship

At a Glance and Lesson Plan

- At a Glance: Problem 2.4 Moving Straight Ahead
- Lesson Plan: Problem 2.4 Moving Straight Ahead

▼ Launch

Launch Video

This animation shows a teacher sorting through his students' walkathon pledge plans. One of the plans has no name, and he needs to identify its owner. To do so, he must analyze the information on the plan and then find an equation, a table, or a graph from one of his students that matches the data on the plan. You can use this animation to start a discussion about how one could determine whether a pair of numbers belongs to a given representation of a linear relationship—either an equation, a table, or a graph. Visit Teacher Place at mathdashboard.com/cmp3 to see the complete video.

Connecting to Prior Knowledge

Remind students about the three students and their pledge plans from Investigation 1. Display **Teaching Aid 2.4A: Alana's Pledge Plan**.

Suggested Questions

- Write a question that could be answered using the point (14, 12). (Sample answers: How far did Alana walk if a sponsor donates 12 dollars? How much money would Alana raise from each sponsor if she walked 14 kilometers?)

- How can you use the equation for Alana's plan to check the answer to the question you wrote? (The equation for Alana's plan is $A = 5 + 0.5d$. For the first question, if you substitute 12 for A in the equation and solve for d, you will find the number of kilometers. For the second question, if you substitute 14 for d in the equation and solve for A, you will find how much each sponsor pledges.)

- How can you use a graph to find the number of kilometers that Alana walked if each sponsor donated $17? (You can find 17 on the y-axis and move horizontally until you reach a point on the line. Then, you move vertically down until you hit the x-axis. The value on the x-axis is the number of kilometers walked.)

Ask the class to show how the questions relate to solving the equation
$A = 5 + 0.5d$ when the value of one variable is known. Students are
substituting one value into the equation and solving for the other.

$A = 5 + 0.5(14)$ to solve for A if $d = 14$.

$12 = 5 + 0.5d$ to solve for d if $A = 12$.

Discuss how a graph or a table could be used to find solutions of these
two equations.

Pick 2 or 3 other points on the line and repeat the preceding questions. Students
should begin to see that there is an infinite number of coordinate pairs that
are solutions of $A = 5 + 0.5d$. When they are solving a linear equation in one
"unknown," they are looking for the missing coordinate of an ordered pair that is a
solution of the linear equation.

Presenting the Challenge

Now pose the challenge in the Problem. Tell students they need to decide
whether an equation represents a reasonable pledge plan for the walkathon if the
idea is to raise money for charity. They will decide which points are solutions of
the equation and whether the *y*-values increase, decrease, or stay the same as the
x-values increase.

You might have students use a graphing calculator or **Coordinate Grapher**.
Review graphing calculators, if necessary. Students may find a graphing calculator
helpful for answering questions like those in the Problems in this Investigation.
When they use a graphing calculator, they need to make decisions about the
range of values and the scale interval for each axis. These values are called window
settings because they determine what part of the graph will be displayed in the
calculator's window.

Suggested Questions

- How far would a student have to walk to raise $8.50 from each sponsor
  under Alana's plan? (7 kilometers)

Display **Teaching Aid 2.4B: Ali and Tamara's Graphs**. Tell students that Ali and
Tamara are using graphing calculators to answer questions about Alana's pledge
plan. They both enter the equation $Y_1 = 5 + 0.5X$. Ali uses Window 1 for his graph,
and Tamara uses Window 2. Both students use TRACE to find the solution.

Window 1 (Ali's Graph)

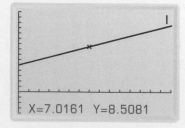

X=7.0161   Y=8.5081

Window 2 (Tamara's Graph)

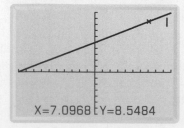

X=7.0968   Y=8.5484

- What does the X-value displayed at the bottom of each window mean? What does the Y-value mean? (The X-value is the x-coordinate of the point that is marked on the line. The Y-value is the y-coordinate.)

- How could you interpret the information displayed in the windows to determine how far you need to walk to raise $8.50 from each sponsor? (This point represents the number of kilometers walked to raise $8.50 from each sponsor. It appears to be about 7 kilometers.)

- How could you check your answer? (Sample answer: Since it appears that $x = 7$ may be the solution, you can check your answer by entering 7 while in TRACE mode. You can press ENTER and the screen will show the value of y for $x = 7$. Or, you can try the values $A = 8.50$ and $d = 7$ into the equation for Alana's pledge plan, to see if they satisfy or solve the equation.)

▼ Explore

Providing for Individual Needs

Look for interesting explanations of what information each equation represents and discuss these in the Summarize.

For Question C, some students may discard Plan 3 because the equation does not have a solution with a y-value of 8. Students may mistakenly reject Plan 2 for the same reason if they are only looking in the first quadrant. If they look in the second quadrant, they will find that the equation has a solution with a y-value of 8: $(-2, 8)$. Although the equation for Plan 2 has the solution $(-2, 8)$, remind students that the solution corresponds to walking -2 kilometers, which may not make sense in this real-world situation. Some students might find some interesting ways to interpret $y = -x + 6$ in this context. However, this equation can represent many situations, and $(-2, 8)$ might well make sense for a different situation. It is a solution for this equation, but does not make sense within the context.

You might ask students to use their graphing calculators to explore the idea that $y = 5x - 3$ relates values of x and y for all values of x and y, and $8 = 5x - 3$ is one instance. However, with real-world situations it makes sense to sometimes restrict the answers to ones that make sense for the situation. The following questions might help:

Suggested Questions

- Which relationship has a graph you can use to find a value of x that makes $5 = 5x - 3$ true? Explain. (Plan 1; the equation for Plan 1 is $y = 5x - 3$. You can find the value of x that makes the equation $5 = 5x - 3$ true by finding the x-coordinate of the point on the graph that has a y-coordinate of 5.)

- What point represents the solution for the equation $5 = 5x - 3$? What question could you answer using this point? $((\frac{8}{5}, 5)$; Sample answer: How many kilometers does the person need to walk to raise $5 from each sponsor?)

- Which relationship has a graph you can use to find a value of x that makes $5 = -x + 6$ true? Explain. (Plan 2; the equation for Plan 2 is $y = -x + 6$. You can find the value of x that makes the equation $5 = -x + 6$ true by finding the x-coordinate of the point on the graph that has a y-coordinate of 5.)

- What point represents the solution for the equation $5 = -x + 6$? What question could you answer using this point? ((1, 5); Sample answers: How make kilometers does the person need to walk to raise $5 from each sponsor? How much money was raised from each sponsor if the person walked 1 kilometer?)

Students may need help with the negative coefficient in the equation for Plan 2. You can ask students to explain why the line slants down or why the relationship is decreasing.

- Does the table help you decide whether the graph of the relationship is increasing or decreasing? (Yes; you can use the table to see how the dependent variable changes as the independent variable increases. If the dependent variable decreases, then the line will slant down. If the dependent variable increases, then the relationship is increasing and the line will slant up.)

- Pick a point on this line. Can you find this point in the table? Explain. (Answers will vary. Sample answers: Yes; the point (2, 4) is also an entry in the table where the value of x is 2 and the value of y is 4. No; the point (6, 0) is not a row in the table that I made, but if I extended the table, it would be there.)

- How do you know the ordered pair you picked is a solution to the equation? (It makes the equation $y = -x + 6$ true, because, for the point (2, 4), $4 = -2 + 6$.)

Planning for the Summary

What evidence will you use in the summary to clarify and deepen understanding of the Focus Question?

What will you do if you do not have evidence?

▼ Summarize

Orchestrating the Discussion

One goal of this Problem is for students to revisit constant rate in the context of equations and connect the rate to tables and graphs of linear relationships.

Suggested Questions

What is the amount raised per kilometer under each plan? (Plan 1: $5 per kilometer; Plan 2: −1 dollar per kilometer; Plan 3: $0 per kilometer)

- How does each rate appear in a table? In a graph? In an equation? (In a table, the rate is the constant change in the amount of money raised when the number of kilometers increases by 1. In a graph, the rate is the steepness of the line. In an equation, the rate is the coefficient of x.)

- What information does the y-intercept represent in each plan? (The y-intercept represents the amount of money a sponsor donates for 0 kilometers walked. If the person did not walk at all, he or she would still raise an amount of money equal to the y-intercept.)

- Do the plans make sense? Explain. (Answers may vary. Sample answers: Plan 1 makes sense because the walker is asking each sponsor to donate $5 per kilometer and then gives the sponsor something that costs $3 (such as a T-shirt). Plan 2 does not make sense because the amount of money raised should not decrease as the number of kilometers walked increases. Plan 3 makes sense because the walker raises $2 from each sponsor regardless of the distance walked, which is similar to Leanne's plan in Problem 1.3.)

Let students share their ideas with the main focus on the rate, intercepts of the graphs, and solutions of the equations. Most students will say that the negative rate does not make sense. It means you give money back. However, students are very creative and may suggest something plausible. Another suggestion could be that the walker for Plan 2 collects $6 and promises to walk 15 kilometers. If she does not walk the 15 km, then she will pay back $1 for each kilometer she does not walk. In this case, it is necessary to change what the variable x represents to the number of kilometers *not* walked.

Be sure to go over the answers to Questions B, C, and D. Check to make sure students understand the relationship between the points on a line and the solutions of the equation for that line. Have students share their solutions and their strategies for each part of the Problem. Ask for explanations.

Students should be making the connection between a specific solution of an equation and the more general relationship between two variables for the related equation. They should see the relationship between equations, such as $y = 5x - 3$ and the following equations: $12 = 5x - 3$, $-8 = 5x - 3$, and $27 = 5x - 3$.

- How are the equations $12 = 5x - 3$, $-8 = 5x - 3$, and $27 = 5x - 3$ related to $y = 5x - 3$? (In each equation, you are given the value of y and are looking for the corresponding value of x for that solution.)

- How can you find the missing value of x? (You can use a table or a graph to find the y-value of that row of the table or the y-coordinate of that point on the line.)

If needed, you can repeat some of the questions from the Explore that help students sort out the solutions of an equation.

You may want to draw the line and then label several points with their coordinates. Display **Teaching Aid 2.4C: Graph of $y = 5x - 3$**. Put the corresponding equation next to the coordinates to show that it is a true statement for these particular values of x and y.

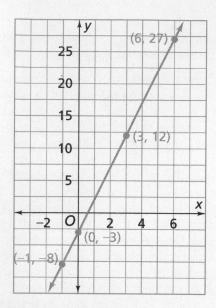

For example, in Question B, part (1):

- For which equation is (2, 4) a solution? Explain your answer. (Plan 2; if you substitute 2 for x and 4 for y in the equation for Plan 2, it makes the equation true.)

- How is the solution (2, 4) related to a table and a graph of Plan 3? (The values $x = 2$ and $y = 4$ are a solution of the equation. The ordered pair (2, 4) represents the coordinates of a point on the graph of the equation and an entry in the table.)

Check for Understanding

Display **Teaching Aid 2.4D: Troy's Graphing Calculator**. Troy is working with the equation $y = 100 - 3x$. He is trying to find a value of x that corresponds to $y = 22$. He writes the following question: "What is x if $100 - 3x = 22$?"

- Explain how Troy can use the following table or graph to answer this question.

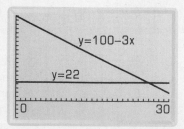

He can trace the graph to find where it intersects the graph of $y = 22$. The corresponding x-value of the intersection point is the answer to his question. He can identify 22 in the y-column and see that the corresponding x-value is 26.

Reflecting on Student Learning

Use the following questions to assess student understanding at the end of the lesson.

- What evidence do I have that students understand the Focus Question?
  - Where did my students get stuck?
  - What strategies did they use?
  - What breakthroughs did my students have today?
- How will I use this to plan for tomorrow? For the next time I teach this lesson?
- Where will I have the opportunity to reinforce these ideas as I continue through this Unit? The next Unit?

ACE Assignment Guide

- **Applications:** 15–18
- **Connections:** 40, 41

▼ Mathematical Reflections

Possible Answers to Mathematical Reflections

1. **a.** The coefficient m in the equation, $y = mx + b$, that represents the linear relationship is the rate of change between the independent variable and the dependent variable. It controls the slant of the line that represents the relationship. Greater positive values of m mean there is a greater rate of change in the situation, so the lines are steeper. Negative values of m give lines that slant down. The value of b gives the y-intercept of the line. It is represented as the point $(0, b)$ on the line or the pair of values in a table. In a table, the y-intercept is the value where the x-value is 0, and the rate of change is the difference in consecutive values of the dependent variable for constant increments in the independent variable.

    b. The relationships between the distances that Emile and Henri walked over time are two examples of linear relationships. In Problems 2.1 and 2.2, $d_{Henri} = 45 + t$, and $d_{Emile} = 2.5t$. The equation for Emile also represents a proportional relationship. The relationship between the cost of buying T-shirts and the number of people is also a linear relationship. In Problem 2.3, $C_M = 49 + n$, and $C_N = 4.5n$. The equation for No-Shrink Tee is also a proportional relationship. The pledge plans in Problem 2.4 are also examples of linear relationships. In addition, there are several examples in the ACE.

Note: For an equation of the form $y = mx$, you can write the equivalent equation $\frac{y}{x} = m$, so y is proportional to x. This will be developed further in Investigation 4 when slope is defined.

2. **a.** Any ordered pair (point) that lies on the graph of a linear relationship can be used to find the solution to a problem. The ordered pair (x, y) represents specific values of the variables. If the value of one of the variables is known, then the graph can be traced to find the corresponding value of the other variable. Similarly, any ordered pair in a table for a linear relationship can be used to find the solution to a problem.

b. You can also use the equation for a linear relationship to solve a problem. You substitute the value given in the problem into the equation and solve the equation for the unknown variable. For example, in Problem 2.3, the equation $C_M = 49 + n$ represents the relationship between cost, C, and number of T-shirts, n. If you know the number of T-shirts you want to buy from Mighty Tee is 30, then you can solve for the cost: $C_M = 49 + (30)$; $C_M = 79$. Likewise, if you know the cost at Mighty Tee is $100, then you can solve for the number of T-shirts: $100 = 49 + n$; $n = 51$.

Possible Answers to Mathematical Practices Reflections

Students may have demonstrated all of the eight Common Core Standards for Mathematical Practice during this Investigation. During the class discussion, have students provide additional Practices that the Problem cited involved and identify the use of other Mathematical Practices in the Investigation.

One student observation is provided in the Student Edition. Here is another sample student response.

> We noticed in Problem 2.3 that the two equations, $C_{Mighty} = 49 + n$ and $C_{No\text{-}Shrink} = 4.5n$, are similar to the equations for Henri and Emile's race, $d_{Henri} = 45 + t$ and $d_{Emile} = 2.5t$. The numbers 49 and 45 are the starting cost for Mighty Tee and the starting position for Henri. They are also the y-intercepts of the graphs. For No-Shrink Tee and for Emile, the starting amount and y-intercept of the graph is 0. The coefficient of the independent variable in all four equations represents the rate of change. It is either the walking rate in meters per second or the cost per shirt. All four graphs are straight lines that show a constant rate of change.
>
> **MP8: Look for and express regularity in repeated reasoning.**

Investigation 2

Exploring Linear Relationships With Graphs and Tables

In the last Investigation, you examined linear relationships. For example, the distance, d, a person walks at a constant rate depends on the amount of time, t, the person walks. Also, the amount of money, A, a person raises from each sponsor depends on the distance, d, walked in the walkathon. Both of these relationships are linear. You might have written the following equations to represent these two relationships for Alana.

$$d = 1t$$
$$\text{and}$$
$$A = 5 + 0.5d$$

In this Investigation, you will continue to solve problems involving walking rates and other linear relationships.

Common Core State Standards

7.RP.A.2b Identify the constant of proportionality (unit rate) in tables, graphs, equations, diagrams, and verbal descriptions of proportional relationships.

7.RP.A.2c Represent proportional relationships by equations.

7.EE.B.3 Solve multi-step real-life and mathematical problems posed with positive and negative rational numbers in any form (whole numbers, fractions, and decimals), using tools strategically. Apply properties of operations to calculate with numbers in any form; convert between forms as appropriate; and assess the reasonableness of answers using mental computation and estimation strategies.

7.EE.B.4 Use variables to represent quantities in a real-world or mathematical problem, and construct simple equations and inequalities to solve problems by reasoning about the quantities.

Also 7.RP.A.2d, 7.EE.B.4a

Notes

2.1 Henri and Emile's Race
Finding the Point of Intersection

 In Ms. Chang's class, Emile found out that his walking rate is 2.5 meters per second. That is, Emile walks 2.5 meters every 1 second. When he gets home from school, he times his little brother Henri as Henri walks 100 meters. He figures out that Henri's walking rate is 1 meter per second. Henri walks 1 meter every second.

Problem 2.1

Henri challenges Emile to a walking race. Because Emile's walking rate is faster, Emile gives Henri a 45-meter head start. Emile knows his brother would enjoy winning the race, but he does not want to make the race so short that it is obvious his brother will win.

A How long should the race be so that Henri will win in a close race?

B Describe your strategy for finding your answer to Question A. Give evidence to support your answer.

A C E Homework starts on page 38.

2.2 Crossing the Line
Using Tables, Graphs, and Equations

Your class may have found some very interesting strategies for solving Problem 2.1, such as:

- Making a table showing time and distance data for both brothers

- Graphing time and distance data for both brothers on the same set of axes

- Writing an equation for each brother representing the relationship between time and distance

? How can each of these strategies be used to solve the Problem?

Notes

STUDENT PAGE

Problem 2.2

A For each brother in Problem 2.1:

1. Make a table showing the distance from the starting line at several different times during the first 40 seconds. How can the table be used to find the length of the race?

2. Graph the time and the distance from the starting line on the same set of axes. How can the graph be used to find the length of the race?

3. Write an equation representing the relationship between time and distance. Explain what information each variable and number represents.

4. How does the walking rate of each brother show up in the graph, the table, and the equation?

B 1. How far does Emile walk in 20 seconds?

2. After 20 seconds, how far apart are the brothers? How is this distance represented in the table and on the graph?

3. Is the point (26, 70) on either graph?

4. When will Emile overtake Henri? Explain.

C How can you determine which of two lines will be steeper from

1. a table of the data?

2. an equation?

D 1. At what points do Emile's and Henri's graphs cross the *y*-axis?

2. What information do these points represent in terms of the race?

3. How can these points be found in a table? In an equation?

A C E Homework starts on page 38.

Investigation 2   **Exploring Linear Relationships With Graphs and Tables**   31

Notes _____

2.3 Comparing Costs
Comparing Relationships

All of the linear relationships you have studied so far can be written in the form $y = mx + b$, or $y = b + mx$. In this equation, y depends on x.

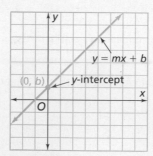

In Problem 2.2, you found the points at which Emile's and Henri's graphs cross the y-axis. These points are called the *y-intercepts*. The **y-intercept** is the point where the line crosses the y-axis, or when $x = 0$. The coordinates of the y-intercept for the graph shown above are $(0, b)$. To save time, we sometimes refer to the number b, rather than the coordinates of the point $(0, b)$, as the y-intercept.

Notes

A **coefficient** is the number that multiplies a variable in an equation. The m in $y = mx + b$ is the coefficient of x, so mx means m times x.

- You can represent the distance d_{Emile} that Emile walks after t seconds with the equation, $d_{\text{Emile}} = 2.5t$. The y-intercept is $(0, 0)$, and the coefficient of t is 2.5. You multiply Emile's walking rate by the time t he walks. He starts at a distance of 0 meters.

Emile

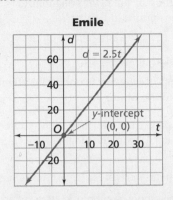

- You can represent the distance d_{Henri} that Henri is from where Emile started with the equation, $d_{\text{Henri}} = 45 + t$, where t is the time in seconds. The y-intercept is $(0, 45)$, and the coefficient of t is 1.

Henri

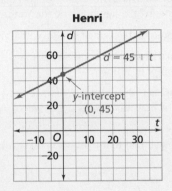

A **solution of an equation** is an ordered pair that makes the equation true and lies on the graph of the line.

- Is $(0, 45)$ a solution of the equation $d_{\text{Henri}} = 45 + t$? Explain.

- What would t be if $(t, 48)$ is a solution? Explain.

- What would d be if $(10, d)$ is a solution? Explain.

In this Problem, you will look at situations represented by an equation or a table.

Notes _____

_____

_____

Problem **2.3**

Ms. Chang's class decides to give T-shirts to each person who participates in the walkathon. They receive bids for the cost of the T-shirts from two different companies. Mighty Tee charges $49 plus $1 per T-shirt. No-Shrink Tee charges $4.50 per T-shirt. Ms. Chang writes the following equations to represent the relationships relating cost to the number of T-shirts:

$$C_{Mighty} = 49 + n$$

$$C_{No\text{-}Shrink} = 4.5n$$

The number of T-shirts is n. C_{Mighty} is the cost in dollars for Mighty Tee. $C_{No\text{-}Shrink}$ is the cost in dollars for No-Shrink Tee.

Ⓐ **1.** For each equation, explain what information the y-intercept and the coefficient of n represent. What is the independent variable? What is the dependent variable?

   2. For each company, what is the cost for 12 T-shirts? For 20 T-shirts?

   3. Lani calculates that the school has about $120 to spend on T-shirts. From which company will $120 buy the most T-shirts? Explain your answer.

   4. a. For what number of T-shirts is the cost of the two companies equal? What is that cost? Explain how you found the answers.

   b. How can this information be used to decide which plan to choose?

   5. a. Explain why the relationship between the cost and the number of T-shirts for each company is linear.

   b. In each equation, what is the pattern of change between the two variables? That is, by how much does C change for every 1 unit that n increases?

   c. How is this situation similar to the previous two Problems?

Notes

_____

_____

_____

Problem 2.3 continued

B The following table represents the costs from another company, The Big T.

T-Shirt Costs

n	C
0	34
3	41.5
5	46.5
8	54
10	59

1. Compare the costs for this company to the costs for the two companies in Question A.

2. Is the relationship between the two variables in this plan linear? If so, what is the pattern of change between the two variables?

3. **a.** Would the point (20, 84) lie on the graph of this cost plan? Explain.

   b. What information about the number of T-shirts and cost do the coordinates of the point (20, 84) represent?

   c. What equation relates C and n?

   d. Would (20, 80) be a solution of the equation? Would (14, 69) be a solution? Explain.

A C E Homework starts on page 38.

Notes

2.4 Connecting Tables, Graphs, and Equations

 Look again at Alana's pledge plan from Problem 1.3. Suppose A represents the amount raised in dollars and d represents the distance walked in kilometers. You can express this plan with the equation $A = 5 + 0.5d$.

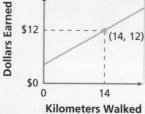

Alana's Pledge Plan

- Explain why the point (14, 12) is on the graph of Alana's pledge plan.
- Write a question you could answer by locating this point.
- How can you use the equation for Alana's pledge plan to check the answer to the question you made up?
- How can you use a graph to find the number of kilometers that Alana walks if a sponsor donates $17? How could you use an equation to answer this question?

In this Problem, you will investigate similar questions relating to pledge plans for a walkathon.

Problem 2.4

Consider the following pledge plans. In each equation, y is the amount pledged in dollars by each sponsor, and x is the distance walked in kilometers.

Plan 1	**Plan 2**	**Plan 3**
$y = 5x - 3$	$y = -x + 6$	$y = 2$

Notes

Problem 2.4 *continued*

A For each pledge plan:

1. What information does the equation give about the pledge plan? Does the plan make sense?

2. Make a table of values of x from -5 to 5.

3. Sketch a graph of the relationship. What part of each graph is relevant to the situation?

4. Do the y-values increase, decrease, or stay the same as the x-values increase? Explain how you can find the answer using a table, a graph, or an equation.

B 1. Which graph from Question A, part (3) contains the point (2, 4)?

2. How do the coordinates (2, 4) relate to the equation of the line? To the corresponding table of data?

3. Write a question you could answer by locating this point.

C 1. Which relationship has a graph you can use to find the value of x that makes $8 = 5x - 3$ a true statement?

2. How does finding the value of x in $8 = 5x - 3$ help you find the coordinates for a point on the graph of the relationship?

D The following three points all lie on the graph of the same plan:

$$(-7, 13) \qquad (1.2, \blacksquare) \qquad (\blacksquare, -4)$$

1. Two of the points have a missing coordinate. Find the missing coordinate. Explain how you found it.

2. Write a question you could answer by finding the missing coordinate.

E 1. Describe how a point on a graph is related to a table and an equation that represent the same relationship.

2. How can you use a table, a graph, or an equation that represents the relationship $y = 5x - 3$ to

a. find the value of y when $x = 7$?

b. find the value of x when $y = 23$?

A C E Homework starts on page 38.

Notes _____

_____

_____

 Applications

1. Grace and Allie are going to meet at the fountain near their houses. They both leave their houses at the same time. Allie passes Grace's house on her way to the fountain.

   - Allie's walking rate is 2 meters per second.

   - Grace's walking rate is 1.5 meters per second.

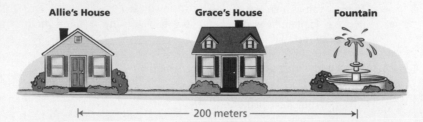

Allie's House **Grace's House** **Fountain**

|← ———————— 200 meters ———————— →|

   a. How many seconds will it take Allie to reach the fountain?

   b. Suppose Grace's house is 90 meters from the fountain. Who will reach the fountain first, Allie or Grace? Explain your reasoning.

2. In Problem 2.2, Emile's friend, Gilberto, joins the race. Gilberto has a head start of 20 meters and walks at 2 meters per second.

   a. Write an equation that gives the relationship between Gilberto's distance d from where Emile starts and the time t.

   b. How would Gilberto's graph compare to Emile's and Henri's graphs?

Notes

3. Ingrid stops at Tara's house on her way to school. Tara's mother says that Tara left 5 minutes ago. Ingrid leaves Tara's house, walking quickly to catch up with Tara. The graph below shows the distance each girl is from Tara's house, starting from the time Ingrid leaves Tara's house.

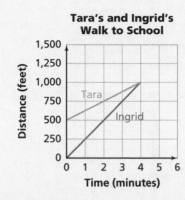

Tara's and Ingrid's Walk to School

a. In what way is this situation like the race between Henri and Emile? In what way is it different?

b. After how many minutes does Ingrid catch up with Tara?

c. How far from Tara's house does Ingrid catch up with Tara?

d. Each graph intersects the distance axis (the *y*-axis). What information do these points of intersection give about the situation?

e. Which line is steeper? How can you tell from the graph? How is the steepness of each line related to the rate at which the person travels?

f. What do you think the graphs would look like if we extended them to show distance and time after the girls meet?

Investigation 2   Exploring Linear Relationships With Graphs and Tables   39

Notes _____

In Exercises 4 and 5, the student council asks for cost estimates for a skating party to celebrate the end of the school year.

4. The following tables represent the costs from two skating companies.

Rollaway Skates

Number of People	Cost
0	$0
1	$5
2	$10
3	$15
4	$20
5	$25
6	$30
7	$35
8	$40

Wheelie's Skates and Stuff

Number of People	Cost
0	$100
1	$103
2	$106
3	$109
4	$112
5	$115
6	$118
7	$121
8	$124

a. For each company, is the relationship between the number of people and cost a linear relationship? Explain.

b. For each company, write an equation that represents the relationship between the cost and the number of people. What is the dependent variable? What is the independent variable?

c. Describe how you can use the table or a graph to find when the costs of the two plans are equal. How can this information help the student council decide which company to choose?

5. A third company, Wheels to Go, gives their quote in the form of the equation $C_W = 35 + 4n$, where C_W is the cost in dollars for n students.

a. What information do the numbers 35 and 4 represent in this situation?

b. For 60 students, which of the three companies is the cheapest? Explain how you could determine the answer using tables, graphs, or equations.

c. Suppose the student council wants to keep the cost of the skating party to $500. How many people can they invite under each of the three plans?

Notes _____

_____

_____

d. The points below lie on one or more of the graphs of the three cost plans. Decide to which plan(s) each point belongs.

   i. (20, 115)   **ii.** (65, 295)   **iii.** (50, 250)

e. Pick one of the points in part (d). Write a question that could be answered by locating this point.

6. A band decides to sell protein bars to raise money for an upcoming trip. The cost (the amount the band pays for the protein bars) and the income the band receives for the protein bars are represented on the graph.

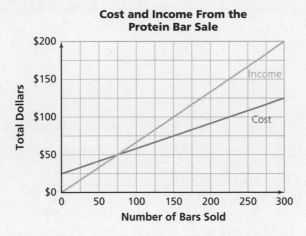

Cost and Income From the Protein Bar Sale

a. How many protein bars must be sold for the cost to equal the income?

b. What is the income from selling 50 protein bars? 125 bars?

c. Suppose the income is $200. How many protein bars were sold? How much of this income is profit?

Notes

7. Suppose each of the following patterns continues.

  • Which represent linear relationships? Explain your answer.

  • For those that are linear relationships, write an equation that expresses the relationship.

a.

x	y
−10	−29
0	1
10	31
20	61
30	91

b.

x	y
1	9
5	17
7	21
20	47
21	49

c.

x	y
1	1
2	4
3	9
4	16
5	25

d.

x	y
1	9
5	22
7	25
20	56
21	60

8. The organizers of a walkathon get cost estimates from two printing companies to print brochures to advertise the event. The costs are given by the equations below, where C is the cost in dollars and n is the number of brochures.

Company A	Company B
$C = 15 + 0.10n$	$C = 0.25n$

a. For what number of brochures are the costs the same for both companies? What method did you use to get your answer?

b. The organizers have $65 to spend on brochures. How many brochures can they have printed if they use Company A? If they use Company B?

c. What information does the y-intercept of the graph represent for each equation?

d. What information does the coefficient of n represent for each equation?

e. For each company, describe the change in the cost as the number of brochures increases by 1.

Notes

STUDENT PAGE

9. A school committee is assigned the task of selecting a DJ for the end-of-school-year party. Darius obtains several quotes for the cost of three DJs.

Compare DJs

$60 per hour

$100 set-up fee
plus
$40 per hour

$175 set-up fee
plus
$30 per hour

  a. For each DJ, write an equation that shows how the total cost *C* relates to the number of hours *x*.

  b. What information does the coefficient of *x* represent for each DJ?

  c. For each DJ, what information does the *y*-intercept of the graph represent?

  d. Suppose the DJ will need to work eight and one half hours. What is the cost of each DJ?

  e. Suppose the committee has only $450 dollars to spend on a DJ. For how many hours could each DJ play?

10. A local department store offers two installment plans for buying a $270 skateboard.

> **Plan 1** A fixed weekly payment of $10.80
>
> **Plan 2** A $120 initial payment plus $6.00 per week

  a. For each plan, how much money is owed after 12 weeks?

  b. Which plan requires the least number of weeks to pay for the skateboard? Explain.

  c. Write an equation for each plan. Explain what information the variables and numbers represent.

  d. Suppose the skateboard costs $355. How would the answers to parts (a)–(c) change?

Investigation 2   Exploring Linear Relationships With Graphs and Tables   43

Notes

For each equation in Exercises 11–14, answer parts (a)–(d).

    a. What is the rate of change?

    b. State whether the *y*-values are increasing, decreasing, or neither as *x* increases.

    c. Give the *y*-intercept.

    d. List the coordinates of two points that lie on the graph of the equation.

11. $y = 1.5x$ **12.** $y = -3x + 10$

13. $y = -2x + 6$ **14.** $y = 2x + 5$

15. Dani earns $7.50 per hour when she babysits.

    a. Draw a graph that relates the number of hours she babysits and the total amount of money she earns.

    b. Choose a point on the graph. Ask two questions that can be answered by finding the coordinates of this point.

16. Martel wants to use his calculator to find the value of *x* when $y = 22$ in the equation $y = 100 - 3x$. Explain how he can use each table or graph to find the value of *x* when $100 - 3x = 22$.

a.

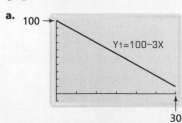

b.

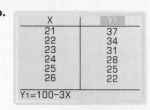

c.

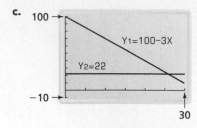

Notes

17. Match each equation to a graph.

a. $y = 3x + 5$ b. $y = x - 7$ c. $y = -x - 10$

Graph 1

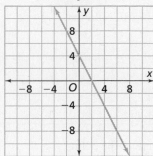

Graph 2

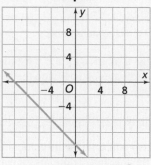

Graph 3

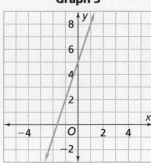

Graph 4

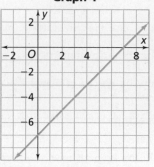

d. Write an equation for the graph that has no match.

For each equation in Exercises 18–21, give two values for x for which the value of y is negative.

18. $y = -2x - 5$ **19.** $y = -5$

20. $y = 2x - 5$ **21.** $y = \frac{3}{2}x - \frac{1}{4}$

Investigation 2   Exploring Linear Relationships With Graphs and Tables   **45**

Notes _____

For Exercises 22–28, consider the following equations:

i. $y = 2x$ ii. $y = -5x$ iii. $y = 2x - 6$

iv. $y = -2x + 1$ v. $y = 7$

22. Which equation has a graph you can use to find the value of x that makes $8 = 2x - 6$ a true statement?

23. How does finding a solution for x in the equation $8 = 2x - 6$ help you find the coordinates of a point on the line represented by the equation $y = 2x - 6$?

24. Which equation has a graph that contains the point $(7, -35)$?

25. The following two points lie on the graph that contains the point $(7, -35)$. Find the missing coordinate for each point.

$(-1.2, \blacksquare)$ $(\blacksquare, -15)$

26. Which equations have a positive rate of change?

27. Which equations have a negative rate of change?

28. Which equations have a rate of change equal to zero?

Connections

29. Use the Distributive Property to write an expression equivalent to each of the following:

a. $x(-2 + 3)$ b. $(-4x) + (2x)$ c. $(x) - (4x)$

30. Decide whether each statement is true or false. Explain your reasoning.

a. $15 - 3x = 15 + -3x$

b. $3.5x + 5 = 5(0.7x + 5)$

c. $3(2x + 1) = (2x + 1) + (2x + 1) + (2x + 1)$

Notes

31. The Ferry family decides to buy a new television that costs $215. The store has an installment plan that allows them to make a $35 down payment and then pay $15 a month. Use the graph to answer the questions below.

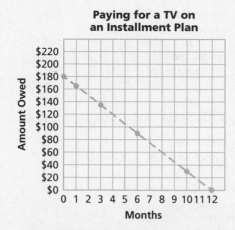

Paying for a TV on an Installment Plan

a. Write an equation that represents the relationship between the amount the Ferry family still owes and the number of months after the purchase. Explain what information the numbers and variables represent.

b. The point where the graph of an equation intersects the *x*-axis is called the **x-intercept**. What are the *x*- and *y*-intercepts of the graph for this payment plan? Explain what information each intercept represents.

32. Shallah Middle School is planning a school trip. The cost is $5 per person. The organizers know that three adults are going on the trip, but they do not yet know the number of students who will go. Write an expression that represents the total costs for *x* students and three adults.

Notes _____

_____

_____

33. Use the Distributive Property to write two expressions that show two different ways to compute the area of each rectangle.

a.
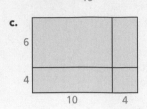

b.
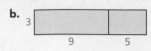

c.
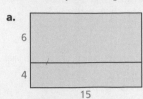

d.
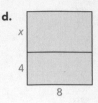

34. Harvest Foods has apples on sale at 12 for $3.

The Cost of Apples

Number of Apples	12	▪	1	48	10	▪
Cost	$3	$1.50	▪	▪	▪	$4.50

a. What is the cost per apple?

b. Complete the rate table to show the costs of different numbers of apples.

c. How many apples can you buy for $1?

d. Is the relationship between number of apples and cost linear? Explain.

35. Lamar bought some bagels for his friends. He paid $15 for 20 bagels.

a. How much did Lamar pay per bagel?

b. Write an equation relating the number of bagels, n, to the total cost, C.

c. Use your equation to find the cost of 150 bagels.

Notes

36. DeAndre says that $x = -1$ makes the equation $-8 = -3 + 5x$ true. Tamara checks this value for x in the equation. She says DeAndre is wrong because $-3 + 5 \times (-1)$ is -2, not -8. Why do you think these students disagree?

37. Determine whether the following mathematical sentences are true or false.

a. $5 + 3 \times 2 = 16$ **b.** $3 \times 2 + 5 = 16$

c. $5 + 3 \times 2 = 11$ **d.** $3 \times 2 + 5 = 11$

e. $\frac{3}{2} \div \frac{4}{3} - \frac{1}{8} = 1$ **f.** $\frac{1}{2} + \frac{3}{2} \div \frac{1}{2} = 2$

38. Jamal feeds his dog the same amount of dog food each day from a very large bag. The number of cups left on the 3rd day and the number of cups left on the 11th day are shown below.

a. How many cups of food does he feed his dog a day?

b. How many cups of food were in the bag when he started?

c. Write an equation for the total amount of dog food Jamal has left after feeding his dog for d days.

Notes _____

_____

_____

39. a. Match the following connecting paths for the last 5 minutes of Jalissa's race.

1. 　**2.** 　**3.** 　**4.** 　**5.**

    i. Jalissa finishes running at a constant rate.

    ii. Jalissa runs slowly at first and gradually increases her speed.

    iii. Jalissa runs quickly and then gradually decreases her speed.

    iv. Jalissa runs quickly and reaches the finish line early.

    v. After falling, Jalissa runs at a constant rate.

  b. Which of the situations in part (a) was most likely to represent Jalissa's running for the entire race? Explain your answer.

40. In *Stretching and Shrinking,* you plotted the points (8, 6), (8, 22), and (24, 14) on grid paper to form a triangle.

  a. Draw the triangle you get when you apply the rule (0.5x, 0.5y) to the three points.

  b. Draw the triangle you get when you apply the rule (0.25x, 0.25y) to the three points.

  c. How are the three triangles you have drawn related?

  d. What are the areas of the three triangles?

  e. Do you notice any linear relationships among the data of the three triangles, such as the area, scale factor, lengths of sides, and so on?

41. In *Covering and Surrounding,* you looked at perimeters of rectangles.

  a. Make a table of possible whole number values for the length and width of a rectangle with a perimeter of 20 meters.

  b. Write an equation that represents the data in this table. Make sure to define your variables.

  c. Is the relationship between length and width linear in this case? Explain.

  d. Find the area of each rectangle.

Notes

Extensions

42. For each equation below, decide whether it models a linear relationship. Explain how you decided.

   a. $y = 2x$
   b. $y = \frac{2}{x}$
   c. $y = x^2$

43. a. Write equations for three lines that intersect to form a triangle.

   b. Sketch the graphs and label the coordinates of the vertices of the triangle.

   c. Will any three lines intersect to form a triangle? Explain.

44. a. Which one of the following points is on the line $y = 3x - 7$: (3, 3), (3, 2), (3, 1), or (3, 0)? Describe where each of the other three points is in relation to the line.

   b. Find another point on the line $y = 3x - 7$ and three more points above the line.

   c. The equation $y = 3x - 7$ is true for (4, 5) and (7, 14). Use this information to find two points that make the inequality $y < 3x - 7$ true and two points that make the inequality $y > 3x - 7$ true.

45. Ms. Chang's class decides to order posters that advertise the walkathon. Ichiro obtains quotes from two different companies.

> **Clear Prints** charges $2 per poster.
>
> **Posters by Sue** charges $15 plus $.50 per poster.

   a. For each company, write an equation Ichiro could use to calculate the cost for any number of posters.

   b. For what number of posters is the cost the same for both companies? Explain.

   c. Which company do you think the class should buy posters from? Explain your reasoning.

   d. If Ms. Chang's class has an $18 budget for posters, which company do you think the class should buy posters from? If Ms. Chang donates an additional $10 for ordering posters, does it impact the decision made? What factors influenced your decision?

   e. Use the information from parts (a)-(c) to find an ordered pair that makes the inequality $C < 20$ true for Clear Prints. Find an ordered pair that makes the inequality $C > 20$ true for Posters by Sue.

Notes _____

Mathematical Reflections 2

In this Investigation, you continued to explore patterns of change between the independent and dependent variables in a linear relationship. You learned how to use tables, graphs, and equations to solve problems that involve linear relationships. The following questions will help you summarize what you have learned.

Think about these questions. Discuss your ideas with other students and your teacher. Then write a summary of your findings in your notebook.

1. a. **Explain** how the information about a linear relationship is represented in a table, a graph, or an equation.

   b. **Describe** several real-world situations that can be modeled by equations of the form $y = mx + b$ or $y = mx$. Explain how the latter equation represents a proportional relationship.

2. a. **Explain** how a table or a graph that represents a linear relationship can be used to solve a problem.

   b. **Explain** how you have used an equation that represents a linear relationship to solve a problem.

Notes _____

Common Core Mathematical Practices

As you worked on the Problems in this Investigation, you used prior knowledge to make sense of them. You also applied Mathematical Practices to solve the Problems. Think back over your work, the ways you thought about the Problems, and how you used Mathematical Practices.

Tori described her thoughts in the following way:

In Problem 2.1, we looked at how far apart the brothers were after t seconds. For example, at the start of the race, they are 45 meters apart. After 1 second, they are $45 - 1.5 = 43.5$ meters apart. After 2 seconds, they are 42 meters apart. After 10 seconds, they are 30 meters apart.

We made a table and found the time it took for Emile to catch up to Henri, or when the distance between them is 0, which is 30 seconds. We used this to choose the length of the race so that Henri wins the race.

Another group member made a graph of the data (time, distance apart), and we saw that it is a line that is decreasing. It started at the y-intercept of 45 meters and crossed the x-axis at 30 seconds.

Common Core Standards for Mathematical Practice
MP2 Reason abstractly and quantitatively.

 • What other Mathematical Practices can you identify in Tori's reasoning?

• Describe a Mathematical Practice that you and your classmates used to solve a different Problem in this Investigation.

Notes _____

_____

_____

▼ Investigation Overview

Investigation Description

Students continue to make the connection between points on a line, coordinate pairs in a table, and solutions to equations.

They represent pictorial situations symbolically and encounter equivalent expressions for a given situation. They use the Distributive Property to show that the two expressions are equivalent.

Students use the properties of equality for solving equations in pictorial form and then transition into solving equations in symbolic form. They add or subtract the same number or variable or multiply or divide by the same nonzero number or variable on both sides of an equation.

In Problem 3.5, students find the point of intersection of two lines (or the solution of a system of two linear equations) by setting the y-values equal and then solving for x. They also solve linear inequalities and use their solutions to answer questions about real-world contexts.

Investigation Vocabulary

- equivalent expressions
- inequality
- point of intersection
- properties of equality

Mathematics Background

- Finding the y-Intercept and Equation for a Linear Relationship
- Linear Equations
- Solving a Linear Equation
- Solving a System of Two Linear Equations
- Inequalities
- Equivalent Expressions

Planning Chart

Content	ACE	Pacing	Materials	Resources
Problem 3.1	1–4, 35, 37, 38, 49	1 day	**Labsheet 3ACE:** Exercise 1 (accessibility) • Blank Table and Graph	**Teaching Aid 3.1** Alana's Pledge Plan • Coordinate Grapher • Data and Graphs
Problem 3.2	5–8, 36, 39, 40, 48	1 day	**Labsheet 3.2** Pouch-and-Coin Situations poster paper	**Teaching Aid 3.2A** Pouches and Coins **Teaching Aid 3.2B** Pouch-and-Coin Strategies **Teaching Aid 3.2C** Nichole's Method **Teaching Aid 3.2D** Symbolic Representation Table
Problem 3.3	9–16, 42, 43, 51	1½ days	**Labsheet 3.3** Pouch-and-Coin Equations poster paper	
Problem 3.4	17–29, 41, 44–47, 50, 52, 53, 55–58	1 day	**Labsheet 3ACE:** Exercise 41 (accessibility) **Labsheet 3ACE:** Exercise 58 (accessibility) poster paper	
Problem 3.5	30–34, 54, 59	1 day	**Labsheet 3ACE:** Exercise 54 (accessibility) • Blank Table and Graph poster paper	**Teaching Aid 3.5A** Two T-Shirt Plans **Teaching Aid 3.5B** Fabian's Bakery • Climbing Monkeys
Mathematical Reflections		½ day		
Assessment: Check Up 2		½ day		• Check Up 2

▼ Goals and Standards

Goals

Linear Relationships Recognize problem situations in which two variables have a linear relationship

- Identify and describe the patterns of change between the independent and dependent variables for linear relationships represented by tables, graphs, equations, or contextual settings

- Construct tables, graphs, and symbolic equations that represent linear relationships

- Identify the rate of change between two variables and the x- and y-intercepts from graphs, tables, and equations that represent linear relationships

- Translate information about linear relationships given in a contextual setting, a table, a graph, or an equation to one of the other forms

- Write equations that represent linear relationships given specific pieces of information, and describe what information the variables and numbers represent

- Make a connection between slope as a ratio of vertical distance to horizontal distance between two points on a line and the rate of change between two variables that have a linear relationship

- Recognize that $y = mx$ represents a proportional relationship

- Solve problems and make decisions about linear relationships using information given in tables, graphs, and equations

Equivalence Understand that the equality sign indicates that two expressions are equivalent

- Recognize that the equation $y = mx + b$ represents a linear relationship and means that $mx + b$ is an expression equivalent to y

- Recognize that linear equations in one unknown, $k = mx + b$ or $y = m(t) + b$, where k, t, m, and b are constants, are special cases of the equation $y = mx + b$

- Recognize that finding the missing value of one of the variables in a linear relationship, $y = mx + b$, is the same as finding a missing coordinate of a point (x, y) that lies on the graph of the relationship

- Solve linear equations in one variable using symbolic methods, tables, and graphs

- Recognize that a linear inequality in one unknown is associated with a linear equation

- Solve linear inequalities using graphs or symbolic reasoning

- Show that two expressions are equivalent

- Write and interpret equivalent expressions

Mathematical Reflections

Look for evidence of student understanding of the goals for this Investigation in their responses to the questions in *Mathematical Reflections*. The goals addressed by each question are indicated below.

1. **a.** Suppose that, in an equation with two variables, you know the value of one of the variables. Describe a method for finding the value of the other variable using the properties of equality. Give an example to illustrate your method.

   b Compare the method you described in part (a) to the methods of using a table or a graph to solve linear equations.

   Goals

   - Construct tables, graphs, and symbolic equations that represent linear relationships

   - Translate information about linear relationships given in a contextual setting, a table, a graph, or an equation to one of the other forms

   - Write equations that represent linear relationships given specific pieces of information, and describe what information the variables and numbers represent

   - Solve problems and make decisions about linear relationships using information given in tables, graphs, and equations

   - Recognize that the equation $y = mx + b$ represents a linear relationship and means that $mx + b$ is an expression equivalent to y

   - Recognize that linear equations in one unknown, $k = mx + b$ or $y = m(t) + b$, where k, t, m, and b are constants, are special cases of the equation $y = mx + b$

   - Recognize that finding the missing value of one of the variables in a linear relationship, $y = mx + b$, is the same as finding a missing coordinate of a point (x, y) that lies on the graph of the relationship

   - Solve linear equations in one variable using symbolic methods, tables, and graphs

2. **a.** Explain how an inequality can be solved by methods similar to those used to solve linear equations.

   b. Describe a method for finding the solution to an inequality using graphs.

   Goals

   - Recognize that a linear inequality in one unknown is associated with a linear equation

   - Solve linear inequalities using graphs or symbolic reasoning

3. Give an example of two equivalent expressions that were used in this Investigation. Explain why they are equivalent.

   Goals

   - Show that two expressions are equivalent

   - Write and interpret equivalent expressions

Standards

Common Core Content Standards

7.EE.A.1 Apply properties of operations as strategies to add, subtract, factor, and expand linear expressions with rational coefficients. *Problems 2, 3, 4, and 5*

7.EE.A.2 Understand that rewriting an expression in different forms in a problem context can shed light on the problem and how the quantities in it are related. *Problems 1, 2, 3, 4, and 5*

7.EE.B.3 Solve multi-step real-life and mathematical problems posed with positive and negative rational numbers in any form (whole numbers, fractions, and decimals), using tools strategically. Apply properties of operations to calculate with numbers in any form; convert between forms as appropriate; and assess the reasonableness of answers using mental computation and estimation strategies. *Problems 1, 3, 4, and 5*

7.EE.B.4 Use variables to represent quantities in a real-world or mathematical problem, and construct simple equations and inequalities to solve problems by reasoning about the quantities. *Problems 3 and 5*

7.EE.B.4A Solve word problems leading to equations of the form $px + q = r$ and $p(x + q) = r$, where p, q, and r are specific rational numbers. Solve equations of these forms fluently. Compare an algebraic solution to an arithmetic solution, identifying the sequence of the operations used in each approach. *Problems 1, 2, 3, 4, and 5*

7.EE.B.4B Solve word problems leading to inequalities of the form $px + q > r$ or $px + q < r$, where p, q, and r are specific rational numbers. Graph the solution set of the inequality and interpret it in the context of the problem. *Problem 5*

Facilitating the Mathematical Practices

Students in *Connected Mathematics* classrooms display evidence of multiple Common Core Standards for Mathematical Practice every day. Here are just a few examples of when you might observe students demonstrating the Standards for Mathematical Practice during this Investigation.

Practice 1: **Make sense of problems and persevere in solving them.**

Students are engaged every day in solving problems and, over time, learn to persevere in solving them. To be effective, the problems embody critical concepts and skills and have the potential to engage students in making sense of mathematics. Students build understanding by reflecting, connecting, and communicating. These student-centered problem situations engage students in articulating the "knowns" in a problem situation and determining a logical solution pathway. The student-student and student-teacher dialogues help students not only to make sense of the problems, but also to persevere in finding appropriate strategies to solve them. The suggested questions in the Teacher Guides provide the metacognitive scaffolding to help students monitor and refine their problem-solving strategies.

Practice 3: **Construct viable arguments and critique the reasoning of others.**

Students construct arguments when they solve the pictorial equations in Problem 3.2. They justify the steps they took to their classmates, and they evaluate the processes of other students who used different methods.

Practice 5: **Use appropriate tools strategically.**

Students begin Investigation 3 by using methods familiar to them—tables and graphs—to solve equations. Some students may use paper and pencil to construct their tables and graphs, and others may use graphing calculators. By Problem 3.4, students have transitioned to using symbolic methods to solve equations, employing paper and pencil to record their steps and strategies.

Students identify and record their personal experiences with the Standards for Mathematical Practice during the Mathematical Reflections at the end of the Investigation.

Solving Equations Using Tables and Graphs

▼ Problem Overview

> *Focus Question* How are the coordinates of a point on a line or in a table related to the equation of the line?

Problem Description

Students make the connection among points on a line, pairs of values in a table, and solutions to equations. They also connect finding the value of one variable in an equation of the form $y = mx + b$ using a table or graph to finding a solution to an equation.

Problem Implementation

Students can work in groups of 2 to 3.

If you have some students who would benefit from making a table and a graph as they work through Question A, part (1a), you can give them a **Blank Table and Graph**.

Materials

- **Labsheet 3ACE:** Exercise 1 (accessibility)
- **Blank Table and Graph**
- **Teaching Aid 3.1:** Alana's Pledge Plan

Using Technology

If your students have access to computers, they can use **Coordinate Grapher** or **Data and Graphs** to plot points from a table on an interactive coordinate grid.

Vocabulary

There are no new glossary terms introduced in this Problem.

Mathematics Background

- Linear Equations

At a Glance and Lesson Plan

- At a Glance: Problem 3.1 Moving Straight Ahead
- Lesson Plan: Problem 3.1 Moving Straight Ahead

▼ Launch

Connecting to Prior Knowledge

Display **Teaching Aid 3.1: Alana's Pledge Plan**. Tell students that the graph and table are for Alana's pledge plan, which is represented by the equation $A = 5 + 0.5d$, where A is the amount of money Alana collects from each sponsor for walking d kilometers.

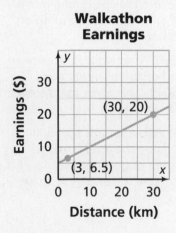

Walkathon Earnings

d	A
0	5
1	5.5
2	6
3	6.5
4	7
20	15
25	17.5
30	20

Suggested Questions

- How are the points (3, 6.5) and (30, 20) related to the equation $A = 5 + 0.5d$? (The point (3, 6.5) means that $d = 3$ and $A = 6.5$, so $6.5 = 5 + 0.5(3)$ is a true statement. Similarly, for (30, 20), $20 = 5 + 0.5(30)$ is also true.)

- We say that (3, 6.5) and (30, 20) are solutions to the equation $A = 5 + 0.5d$. Find another point on the line whose coordinates are a solution to the equation. (Be sure students explain why they are solutions—substitute the values into the equation and check if the resulting equation is true. Students can find other solutions by choosing a value for d or A and finding the corresponding value of the other variable.)

- Do you think every point on the line corresponds to a solution to the equation? (Yes, although some values may not be realistic. For example, (100, 55) is not realistic because 100 km is an unreasonable distance for a student to walk in a walkathon.)

Take one or two of the points suggested by students and ask:

- How can you locate this point on the line? (Draw in the vertical and horizontal lines corresponding to the coordinates of the point.)

- Find a pair of corresponding values in the table that are solutions to the equation. (Students may have to extend the table.)

- Write two questions about Alana's pledge plan that could be answered by the coordinates of the point (14, 12). (Students can say either "How far did Alana walk if a sponsor donates $12?" or "How much money would a sponsor donate if Alana walked 14 kilometers?")

- How can you use the equation for Alana's plan to check the answer to the question you made up? (You can substitute $d = 14$ and $A = 12$ into the equation $A = 5 + 0.5d$. If the resulting equation is true, then (14, 12) is a solution.)

- How can you use a graph to find the number of kilometers that Alana walked if a sponsor donated $17? (You go to 17 on the vertical axis and move straight across horizontally until you intersect the line. Then, move directly down until you intersect the horizontal axis. The value you hit on the horizontal axis is the number of kilometers walked.)

- How can you use a graph to solve $20 = 5 + 0.5d$? What would the answer mean? (Go to 20 on the vertical axis and move horizontally until you intersect the line. Read the "d" value at that point. This gives the distance Alana must walk in order to raise $20 from each sponsor.)

- What happens if you choose a point that is not visible on this section of the graph, such as (70, 40)? Does this point lie on the line? Explain. (Students might suggest extending the line. Some might suggest checking to see if the coordinates of the point make the equation a true statement.)

Presenting the Challenge

Tell students that, in this Investigation, they will explore strategies for finding solutions to equations using properties of operations and equality. This will be useful in finding solutions that are not obvious on a line or in a table.

▼ Explore

Providing for Individual Needs

Look for interesting solutions. Ask questions to check students' understanding of the connection between tables, graphs, and solutions to equations. Also, check students' understanding of using graphs and tables as viable methods for finding the solution to an equation.

Students may reason through Question B, part (2) numerically, following the thought process outlined below.

> "I have to undo the addition of 25, so I will subtract 25 from each side to get $45 = 2.5t$. Then, to undo multiplication by 2.5, I will divide each side by 2.5 to get $t = 18$."

Planning for the Summary

What evidence will you use in the summary to clarify and deepen understanding of the Focus Question?

What will you do if you do not have evidence?

▼ Summarize

Orchestrating the Discussion

Go over all parts of the Problem.

Suggested Questions

Question B is particularly important.

- How could you have used a graph (or a table) to find this information? (For Question B, part (1), you could use a graph to find the value of D by finding 7 on the horizontal axis. Then, move directly up until you intersect the line. Then, move horizontally until you intersect the vertical axis. The value at which you reach the vertical axis is the solution. You could use a table by finding 7 in the t column (you may have to extend the table). The value in the D column that corresponds to 7 is the solution to the equation.

  Students may give similar answers for part (2).)

- How could you use the equation? Explain. (For part (1), students may say that you can calculate the numeric expression on the right side of the equal sign to get 42.5 for D. For part (2), they may reason numerically as described in the Explore.)

- Write a question you could ask that could be answered by finding the value of the missing variable in each equation. (Answers will vary. Sample answers:

  For part (1): "In a walking race, suppose that you walk at a constant rate of 2.5 meters per second and that your opponent gives you a 25-meter head start. How far from the starting line are you after 7 seconds?" For part (2): "In the same race as in part (1), after how many seconds will you be 70 meters from the starting line?")

- Write a general equation that could represent the equations. What are the variables? ($D = 25 + 2.5t$; D represents distance, and t represents time.)

Check for Understanding

Troy is working with the equation $y = 100 - 3x$. He is trying to find a value of x that corresponds to $y = -8$. He writes the following question:

What is x if $100 - 3x = -8$?

- Explain how Troy can use a table or a graph to solve the equation $100 - 3x = -8$. (Troy can find -8 in the y column of a table. The corresponding x-value will be the solution to the equation.

  Troy can use a graph to find the solution by starting at -8 on the y-axis. He can move horizontally until he reaches the line and then vertically until he reaches the x-axis. The value he hits on the x-axis is the solution to the equation.)

Reflecting on Student Learning

Use the following questions to assess student understanding at the end of the lesson.

- What evidence do I have that students understand the Focus Question?
  - Where did my students get stuck?
  - What strategies did they use?
  - What breakthroughs did my students have today?
- How will I use this to plan for tomorrow? For the next time I teach this lesson?
- Where will I have the opportunity to reinforce these ideas as I continue through this Unit? The next Unit?

ACE Assignment Guide

- **Applications:** 1–4
- **Connections:** 35, 37, 38, 49
- **Labsheet 3ACE:** Exercise 1 (accessibility)

Note: This labsheet is an example of a way to provide students with additional support for an ACE Exercise.

Mystery Pouches in the Kingdom of Montarek

Exploring Equality

▼ Problem Overview

> *Focus Question* What does equality mean?

Problem Description

This Problem introduces students to symbolic ways of solving linear equations with one unknown. Equations are represented pictorially as coins (constant term) and pouches that hold an unknown number of coins (variables). Students explore the properties of equality pictorially as they find the number of coins in a pouch. This provides a transition into solving equations symbolically.

Students use the fact that the number of coins on both sides of the equation is equal to find the number of coins in a pouch. In the process, they find that there is more than one way to represent the number of coins on one side of the equation. This provides an opportunity to use equivalent expressions as part of a strategy for solving equations.

Problem Implementation

Students can work in pairs and share their work with another pair.

Labsheet 3.2: Pouch-and-Coin Situations contains the pictorial equations for all parts of Question A in the Student Edition. You can give this labsheet to students to help them organize their thinking as they work out their solutions.

You can ask groups to put their strategies on poster paper to display and discuss during the Summarize.

Materials

- **Labsheet 3.2:** Pouch-and-Coin Situations
- **Teaching Aid 3.2A:** Pouches and Coins
- **Teaching Aid 3.2B:** Pouch-and-Coin Strategies
- **Teaching Aid 3.2C:** Nichole's Method
- **Teaching Aid 3.2D:** Symbolic Representation Table

poster paper

Vocabulary

There are no new glossary terms introduced in this Problem.

Mathematics Background

- Solving a Linear Equation
- Equivalent Expressions

At a Glance and Lesson Plan

- At a Glance: Problem 3.2 Moving Straight Ahead
- Lesson Plan: Problem 3.2 Moving Straight Ahead

▼ Launch

Launch Video

This animation depicts a messenger bringing the King of Montarek eleven gold coins, in the form of 5 coins and 2 sealed pouches that each contain the same number of coins. You can show this animation after introducing the students to the context of the gold coins in the Student Edition. This animation can help spark a discussion about strategies for finding the number of gold coins in each pouch. Visit Teacher Place at mathdashboard.com/cmp3 to see the complete video.

Connecting to Prior Knowledge

Remind students that, in the last Problem, they found solutions to equations by using tables and graphs. They also substituted values for the independent variable to find the corresponding value of the dependent variable.

For example, in the equation $D = 25 + 2.5t$, students used the related equations $D = 25 + 2.5(7)$ and $70 = 25 + 2.5t$ to find the values of the unknown variables. It was relatively easy to find the value of D in the first equation. Finding the value of t in the second equation is a bit trickier when just using the equation. Tell students that, in this Problem, they will use money from the Kingdom of Montarek to explore equality.

Presenting the Challenge

Display **Teaching Aid 3.2A: Pouches and Coins** and tell the class about the pouches and gold coins used in the Kingdom of Montarek. You can also show the Launch Video at this point.

- The number of gold coins on each side of the equality sign is the same, but some coins are hidden in the pouches.

- In each situation, each pouch contains the same number of one-dollar gold coins.

- The challenge is to find the number of coins in each pouch.

As the students work on this Problem, you might want to record their work on the table in **Teaching Aid 3.2B: Pouch-and-Coin Strategies**.

▼ Explore

Providing for Individual Needs

Encourage students to record their strategies.

Suggested Questions

- What does *equality* mean? (It means that two quantities are equal.)

- How can we maintain equality? (A few students may be able to say that equality can be maintained by adding, subtracting, multiplying, or dividing each side of an equation by the same number (for multiplication and division, the number must be nonzero), but most will not be able to answer this question fully yet. At this time, you might look for students to describe adding or removing one coin from each of the equal quantities or dividing the coins and pouches on each side into two equal groups.)

- How do you know if your answer is correct? (You can substitute the value of the unknown into the equation and check that the resulting values on each side are equal.)

This is an opportunity to see how students handle parentheses. See the answers for some suggestions.

Look for interesting strategies to share during the Summarize.

Planning for the Summary

What evidence will you use in the summary to clarify and deepen understanding of the Focus Question?

What will you do if you do not have evidence?

▼ Summarize

Orchestrating the Discussion

If your students recorded their work on poster paper, display the posters and give the class time to examine the various strategies. The following are examples of how two groups of students solved Question A, part (1).

- First, we noted that there are 10 coins on the left and there are 4 coins and 3 bags on the right. So, the 3 bags must have a total of 6 coins in order to make the total number of coins on the right equal to 10. So, each bag must have 2 coins.

- We started by removing 4 coins from each side. Then we had 6 coins on the left and 3 pouches on the right. So, each pouch must have 2 coins. To check our answer, we found the total number of coins in the pouches, which is 6, and added it to the 4 coins to get a total of 10 coins on the right. This is equal to the 10 coins on the left.

Have students share all of the correct strategies they used (and some incorrect strategies if discussing them would be helpful in deepening students' understanding of equality). The strategies above are just two of the many informative ways that students might solve these problems. See the answers for more possible strategies.

After discussing each of the equations in Question A, ask if there were other strategies that students used. If there were, they are likely to already be on posters. However, during the discussion, some students may have thought of additional ways to solve each equation. Some students may have used the Distributive Property before Question B.

Display **Teaching Aid 3.2C: Nichole's Method** and make sure students understand how the Distributive Property is being used.

Suggested Questions

- Can you use the Distributive Property on any of the other equations? (Yes; in Question A, part (4), you can write the left side of the equation as three times 1 pouch and 1 coin and the right side of the equation as three sets of 10 coins. So, 1 pouch and 1 coin will equal 10 coins. By removing 1 coin from each side, you can see that 1 pouch equals 9 coins. A similar argument can be made for part (2). You can write the left side as two sets of 1 pouch and 2 coins and the right side as two sets of 6 coins.)

After all of the parts have been discussed, ask:

- Did each group use the same first step in each equation? (There is often more than one way to make the first step in solving an equation, so it is likely that different groups took different steps.)

- What are some common strategies that we can use to maintain equality? (As a student describes a strategy, ask him or her to refer to a step in the solution to an equation that illustrates the strategy.)

The conditions under which the equality relation is maintained are called the **properties of equality**. Note that this is not essential vocabulary, and that it is not introduced in the Student Edition until Problem 3.4. However, it might help in the discussion as students begin transitioning to symbolic methods of solving equations. You could display properties of equality on poster paper at this time.

Use the situation from Question A, part (4) to make the transition from pouches to variables. This could serve as a Launch to Problem 3.3.

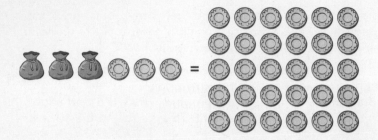

- Suppose we let x represent the number of coins in a pouch and 1 represent one coin. Rewrite the equality using x's and numbers. ($3x + 3 = 30$)

- Write the steps for solving this equation for x. (Some students may subtract 3 from both sides. Some may start by dividing both sides by 3. Some may use a fact-family idea and rewrite $3x + 3 = 30$ as $3x = 30 - 3$. Continue with each method to show that they are equivalent. Then have students check their solutions.)

- Find the number of coins in a pouch for the following situation.

(Each pouch contains one coin.)

Ask the class to solve the problem visually and then by using properties of equality. As you go along, record each step in a table like the one in **Teaching Aid 3.2D: Symbolic Representation Table**, which is filled in on the next page. You could add a fourth column and write in the property. Follow it through to the end. When you are done, ask if there was a different first step that could have been taken.

Pouch-and-Coin Problem

Original Equation	Steps for Finding the Number of Coins in a Pouch	Symbolic Representation
👝👝👝◯◯◯◯ = 👝👝◯◯◯◯		$3x + 3 = 2x + 4$
👝👝👝 = 👝👝◯	Subtract 3 coins from each side of the equality.	$3x = 2x + 1$
👝 = ◯	Subtract 2 pouches from each side of the equality. Each pouch contains 1 coin.	$x = 1$

Emphasize that, in a given equation, the value of x (or the number of coins in each pouch) is the same. Checking the answer provides an opportunity for students to practice work with parentheses and review the order of operations. In the preceding example, to check the answers, students could write $3(1) + 3 = 2(1) + 4$ or $6 = 6$. They could also write $1 + 1 + 1 + 3 = 1 + 1 + 4$. Review the use of parentheses if necessary.

An opportunity to revisit and apply the Distributive Property symbolically occurs in Question A, part (2). Students could reason as follows:

> In Question A, part (2), you could use the Distributive Property to write the left side as two groups of 1 pouch and 2 coins and the right side as two groups of 6 coins. Then, divide both sides by 2. The result is 1 pouch and 2 coins on the left and 6 coins on the right. Symbolically, $2x + 4 = 12$ becomes $2(x + 2) = 2(6)$, which in turn becomes $x + 2 = 6$.
>
> Next, you could remove 2 coins from each side, leaving 1 pouch on the left side and 4 coins on the right side. So, there are 4 coins in each pouch. Symbolically, $x + 2 = 6$ becomes $x = 4$.
>
> To check your work, you can substitute 4 into the equation for x: $2(4) + 4 = 12$ or $2(4 + 2) = 12$ or $(4 + 2) + (4 + 2) = 12$. All of these equations give the same result: $12 = 12$.

An opportunity to discuss a common misunderstanding arises with this context. Ask students to consider the equality $3x = 12$. Suppose a student proposes that subtracting 3 from both sides will produce $x = 9$. Ask students to use the idea of gold coins in pouches to investigate this strategy. Moving back to the visual makes it clear that dividing, not subtracting, is the logical operation.

Reflecting on Student Learning

Use the following questions to assess student understanding at the end of the lesson.

- What evidence do I have that students understand the Focus Question??
  - Where did my students get stuck?
  - What strategies did they use?
  - What breakthroughs did my students have today?
- How will I use this to plan for tomorrow? For the next time I teach this lesson?
- Where will I have the opportunity to reinforce these ideas as I continue through this Unit? The next Unit?

ACE Assignment Guide

- **Applications:** 5–8
- **Connections:** 36, 39, 40, 48

PROBLEM
3.3

From Pouches to Variables
Writing Equations

▼ Problem Overview

Focus Question   How can the properties of equality be used to solve linear equations?

Problem Description

Students translate the pictorial form of linear equations into symbolic linear equations in one variable. They begin to use the properties of equality to solve the equations symbolically. They explore equivalent expressions that can represent a given situation involving pouches and coins.

Problem Implementation

Let the class work in pairs.

You can ask pairs to put their solutions on poster paper to display and discuss during the Summarize.

Labsheet 3.3: Pouch-and-Coin Equations contains a larger version of the table in the Student Edition. You can give this labsheet to students to help them organize their solutions. This can allow students to remain focused on the mathematics of Question A while saving time.

Materials

• **Labsheet 3.3:** Pouch-and-Coin Equations

poster paper

Vocabulary

• equivalent expressions

Mathematics Background

• Solving a Linear Equation
• Equivalent Expressions

At a Glance and Lesson Plan

- At a Glance: Problem 3.3 Moving Straight Ahead
- Lesson Plan: Problem 3.3 Moving Straight Ahead

▼ Launch

Connecting to Prior Knowledge

Start by presenting the example at the beginning of the introduction. Write the equation $85 = 70 + 15$ on the board. Then, pose each of the questions one at a time, always using the original equation. For example, for the first question, you could record the following:

$$
\begin{array}{ll}
85 = 70 + 15 & \\
\underline{-15 \qquad -15} & \text{or} \\
70 = 70 &
\end{array}
\qquad
\begin{array}{l}
85 = 70 + 15 \\
\underline{85 - 15 = 70 + 15 - 15} \\
70 = 70
\end{array}
$$

Suggested Questions

After subtracting 15 from the left side of the equation, you could ask:

- What should you do to keep the two sides equal? (Subtract 15 from the right side.)

Repeat this method for each of the questions in the introduction. Then, have students try their methods on another example of equality.

- What should you do to keep the two sides equal? (Equality is maintained by adding, subtracting, multiplying, or dividing each side by the same number. For multiplication and division, the number must be nonzero.)

Presenting the Challenge

If you did not make the transition from pouches and coins to variables and numbers at the end of the Summarize for Problem 3.2, do so now. Be sure students have a general idea of the procedures. You might want to work through Question A, part (1) as a class or use one of the situations from Problem 3.2.

Explore

Providing for Individual Needs

Be sure students are recording their methods and checking their answers. See how students are translating the situation in Question A, part (2). Students can write the left side as $(x + 2) + (x + 2) + (x + 2)$ or as $3(x + 2)$ and the right side as 18. Return to this in the summary and ask if the two expressions are equivalent and why. This will review the Distributive Property, which was developed in earlier Units.

Some students may struggle with writing the solutions to the equations.

Suggested Questions

For Question A, part (1), ask:

- What is your equation? ($4x + 2 = 18$ or $2(2x + 1) = 18$)

- What was the first thing you did with the pictorial equation to begin solving it? (Using the first method above, the first step would be to take away 2 coins from each side.)

- How can you show this with your equation? (Subtract 2 from each side. This results in $4x + 2 - 2 = 18 - 2$ or $4x = 16$.)

- What did you do next? (Split the coins into four equal sets.)

- How can you show this with your equation? ($4x = 4(4)$)

- What was your next step? (Set each of the 4 pouches equal to one of the 4 sets of coins.)

- How can you show this with your equation? (Divide by 4 on each side. So, $x = 4$.)

- How can you check your answer? (Using the coins and pouches, you can add up all the coins inside and outside the pouches on the left side and then check to make sure your result equals the number of coins on the right side. On the left side, there are 4 pouches, each of which we think contains 4 coins. If we are correct, there are 16 coins in the pouches. If you add those 16 coins to the 2 coins outside the pouches, the result is 18 coins on the left side. There are also 18 coins on the right side, so the answer is correct.

    Or, you can substitute 4 into the equation for x. The result shows that 4 is correct.

    $$4(4) + 2 = 18$$
    $$16 + 2 = 18$$
    $$18 = 18)$$

Planning for the Summary

What evidence will you use in the summary to clarify and deepen understanding of the Focus Question?

What will you do if you do not have evidence?

▼ Summarize

Orchestrating the Discussion

Post the solutions around the room. Call on different students to describe how they solved the equations. Make sure you highlight equations in which students may have done something different for the first step. Some may begin by combining pouches (like terms), while others may start by removing coins.

Suggested Questions

- What did you do at each step to maintain equality? (Answers will vary. Some may divide first, some may add first, etc.)

- Is there another way to make the first step in the solution? Explain. (In Question B, part (3), some students may start by subtracting either 2 or 12 from both sides of the equation. Others may start by subtracting either 5 pouches or 7 pouches ($5x$ or $7x$) from both sides. Note that some of these strategies will have students working with negative numbers. This is an opportunity to check on their understanding and use of integers.)

- Are there other equations in which a different first step could be taken? (Answers will vary. Most equations can be solved in many different ways.)

- What is different about the solution to the equation in Question B, part (2)? (Its solution, 2.5, is not a whole number.)

- Does this have any meaning in the Kingdom of Montarek? (A solution of 2.5 could mean that each pouch contains 2.5 dollars or 2 gold $1 coins and 1 fifty-cent piece.)

- Look back over your work for each equation. What general rules were you using to solve the equations? (Students should say something about maintaining equality by removing the same quantity from each side of the equation.)

- Describe a general method for solving equations. (Generally, you want to isolate the variable (pouch) on one side of the equation and a number (coins) on the other side. To do this, you can use properties of equality or undo the operations until you have the variable alone on one side of the equality and a number on the other side. You use the number that the variable equals to check your solution. You substitute the number for the value of the variable in the original equation to see if you have a true statement.)

To move from pouches and coins to solving equations symbolically, you can write $5x + 8 = 23$ on the board and ask:

- What situation with pouches and coins does this represent? (There are 5 pouches and 8 coins on the left side of the equality and 23 coins on the right side.)

- Use your methods from Problem 3.2 to find the value of *x*. (The first step is to take away 8 coins from each side. That leaves 5 pouches on the left side and 15 coins on the right side. The second step is to divide the 15 coins into 5 equal parts of 3 coins. So, the number of coins in each pouch is 3.)

- Next to your work, write down a similar method using the equation that represents this situation. (Step 1: Subtract 8 from each side of the equation:

$$5x + 8 - 8 = 23 - 8$$
$$5x = 15$$

Step 2: Divide by 5 on each side:

$$5x = 15$$
$$x = 3)$$

As students move away from pouches and toward symbolic statements, they may find that their experience with pouches and coins is useful for recalling strategies.

Students should be able to generalize that adding, subtracting, multiplying, and dividing by the same number maintains equality. Be sure to stress that they cannot multiply or divide by 0. Dividing by 0 has no meaning, and multiplying by 0 would make any statement always true, so it is not a helpful strategy in finding a specific solution. For example, suppose we start with $3b = 27$, which we know is true only when $b = 9$. Multiplying each side by 0 gives $3b \times 0 = 9 \times 0$, or 0×0. This statement is true for all values of the variable, not just 9. So, multiplying both sides by 0 gives an equality that is not equivalent to the original equation because it has different solutions.

If you have not already addressed the common error of subtracting when dividing is needed, do so now. See the Summarize of Problem 3.2 for further discussion of this common student mistake.

Problem 3.3 Summarize   179

Reflecting on Student Learning

Use the following questions to assess student understanding at the end of the lesson.

- What evidence do I have that students understand the Focus Question?
  - Where did my students get stuck?
  - What strategies did they use?
  - What breakthroughs did my students have today?
- How will I use this to plan for tomorrow? For the next time I teach this lesson?
- Where will I have the opportunity to reinforce these ideas as I continue through this Unit? The next Unit?

ACE Assignment Guide

- **Applications:** 9–16
- **Connections:** 42, 43
- **Extensions:** 51

PROBLEM

3.4   Solving Linear Equations

▼ Problem Overview

> *Focus Question*   What are some strategies for solving linear equations?

Problem Description

In this Problem, students develop symbolic strategies for solving linear equations with rational-number solutions. Students find the solutions to linear equations using the properties of equality. Student solutions for three different linear equations are given as an opportunity for students to analyze typical errors or strategies that can occur in solving a linear equation.

Students then compare this method with other methods they have used for solving equations. Students may mention tabular methods. They may also describe graphical methods that involve associating a linear equation in one variable (such as $20 = 5x + 10$) with a specific point on the graph of a linear equation in two variables (such as $y = 5x + 10$).

Problem Implementation

Students can work on the Problem in pairs and then move into groups of 4 to discuss their work.

You may want to summarize after Question A and then assign Questions B and C. For Question A, you may choose to do only a few of the equations from part (2). You could assign different equations to different groups: one of a, b, or c and one of d or e.

You can ask pairs to put their solutions on poster paper to display and discuss during the Summarize.

Materials

- **Labsheet 3ACE:** Exercise 41 (accessibility)
- **Labsheet 3ACE:** Exercise 58 (accessibility)

poster paper

Vocabulary

- properties of equality

Mathematics Background

- Solving a Linear Equation
- Equivalent Expressions

At a Glance and Lesson Plan

- At a Glance: Problem 3.4 Moving Straight Ahead
- Lesson Plan: Problem 3.4 Moving Straight Ahead

▼ Launch

Connecting to Prior Knowledge

Suggested Questions

- Compare these two equations: $2x + 10 = 16$ and $2x - 10 = 16$ (They are the same except that 10 is added to the left side of the first equation and 10 is subtracted from the left side of the second equation.)

- What property of equality would you use to begin solving these two equations? (In the first equation, you would subtract 10 from each side, since we want to "undo" the "+10." In the second equation, you would add 10 to each side, since we want to "undo" the "−10." Some students may note that you could divide by 2 first.)

The following is a quotation from a teacher:

"At this point, students have discovered and accepted the algorithm of 'undoing' the order of operations. The pouch-and-coin model just reveals the algorithm, and then they go from there."

- In the first equation, instead of subtracting 10 from each side, could we add −10 to each side? (Yes, because subtracting 10 is the same as adding −10.)

Refer back to *Accentuate the Negative* if students need more help with this.

- How can you solve the second equation? (One student responded that it is like you owe 10 coins. Add 10 coins to each side. Since $2x = 26$, $x = 13$. Some students have commented that this is similar to the red chips in *Accentuate the Negative*.)

To help students focus on individual parts of the equations, ask:

- In Question A, part (1), how are the equations alike and how are they different? (All of the equations have the same numbers. The only differences are the signs of those numbers.)

Presenting the Challenge

Ask the class to solve the equations, show their work, and check their answers.

▼ Explore

Providing for Individual Needs

Ask students to look at the six equations in Question A, part (1).

Suggested Questions

- What do these equations have in common? (They all involve the same three quantities, but in different arrangements or with different operations.)

Be sure students are making a record of their methods and checking their answers. Encourage students to look for commonalities and differences in each set of equations. This should help them make the shift from equations that had all positive numbers to those that also include negative numbers.

If students are puzzled as to how to proceed, ask:

- What operations on x have been used to create the expressions on each side? (Addition and subtraction are used on the terms $5x$ and 10. Multiplication is used on 5 and x.)

- Look at the equation. What is a good starting step? (Answers will vary. Some students may divide each side of the equation by 5. Others may add or subtract 10 or $5x$ to each side.)

- How can you get rid of, or "undo," each operation, but still maintain equality? (You can use the opposite, or inverse, operation. To "undo" subtraction, you add.)

Planning for the Summary

What evidence will you use in the summary to clarify and deepen understanding of the Focus Question?

What will you do if you do not have evidence?

▼ Summarize

Orchestrating the Discussion

Go over each part of the Problem. Call on different students to discuss their methods.

After a group has presented their solutions, ask the class if they have any questions they want to ask the group. For example, encourage them to ask questions like the following:

- Why did you do this at step 2?

- Why did you not consider starting with a different step?

- Was there a shorter way of getting to the answer?

In Question A, the same set of numbers is used; only the plus and minus signs change. This is a good opportunity to observe if students are making sense of the operations.

Suggested Questions

- What do the equations in Question A, parts (1a) and (1c) have in common? (They can be associated with the same two-variable equation, $5x + 10 = y$. In the first equation, $y = 20$, and we are trying to find the corresponding value of x. In the second equation, $y = -20$, and we are trying to find the corresponding value of x.)

- How else could you find the corresponding values for x? (You could use a table or a graph.)

Note: The question above is posed in Question C.

- What about the equations in Question A, parts (1b) and (1d)? What do they have in common? (They can be associated with the same two-variable equation, $5x - 10 = y$. In the first equation, $y = 20$, and we are trying to find the corresponding value of x. In the second equation, $y = -20$, and we are trying to find the corresponding value of x.)

In Question A, part (3a), students may apply the Distributive Property to the left-hand side of the equation, but this is not necessary. They could also begin by dividing each side by 3. Students will likely choose whichever method they find easier to solve.

Note: Students may have some confusion about applying the Distributive Property. It is not necessary to apply the Distributive Property to both sides of an equation. It is used to replace one expression with an equivalent expression that makes the equation easier to solve.

Write the following equation on the board: $3.2x + 5 = 16$

- How is this equation different from the equations in this Problem? (The coefficient of x is not a whole number.)

- How can we solve this equation? (The principles of equality work for all real numbers, so we can apply the principles of equality:

$$3.2x + 5 = 16$$
$$3.2x = 11$$
$$x = \frac{11}{3.2} \text{ or } 3.4375)$$

Put the following equation on the board and repeat the questions: $3.2x + 5 = 14.6$

Then, repeat the questions for $3.2x + 15 = 6.5x + 10$. These questions will lead into the work on finding points of intersection in the next Problem.

Check for Understanding

- Consider the equation $y = 5x + -11$. Use a symbolic method to find x if $y = 30$.

$$(y = 5x + -11$$
$$30 = 5x + -11$$
$$41 = 5x$$
$$8.2 = x)$$

- Use a symbolic method to find x if $y = 23.5$.

$$(y = 5x + -11$$
$$23.5 = 5x + -11$$
$$34.5 = 5x$$
$$6.9 = x)$$

- Describe how you could use a graph or a table to find the solutions. (To use a graph, you could find the given y-value on the vertical axis. Move horizontally until you reach the line, and then move vertically until you reach the horizontal axis. The value you hit on the horizontal axis will be the value of x.

To use a table, find the given y-value in the column for the dependent variable. Then find the corresponding value in the independent variable column. This value will be the value of x.)

- Consider the equations $y_1 = 5x + 11$ and $y_2 = 2x$. Use a symbolic method to find x when $y_1 = y_2$.

$$(y_1 = y_2$$
$$5x + 11 = 2x$$
$$11 = -3x$$
$$-3.6 = x)$$

Reflecting on Student Learning

Use the following questions to assess student understanding at the end of the lesson.

- What evidence do I have that students understand the Focus Question?
  - Where did my students get stuck?
  - What strategies did they use?
  - What breakthroughs did my students have today?
- How will I use this to plan for tomorrow? For the next time I teach this lesson?
- Where will I have the opportunity to reinforce these ideas as I continue through this Unit? The next Unit?

ACE Assignment Guide

- **Applications:** 17–29
- **Connections:** 41, 44–47, 50
- **Extensions:** 52, 53, 55–58
- **Labsheet 3ACE:** Exercise 41 (accessibility)
- **Labsheet 3ACE:** Exercise 58 (accessibility)

Note: These two labsheets contain larger versions of the tables in the Student Edition. You can give these labsheets to students to help them organize their answers. This can allow students to remain focused on the mathematics of Exercises 41 and 58 while saving time.

PROBLEM

3.5

Finding the Point of Intersection
Equations and Inequalities

▼ Problem Overview

> *Focus Question* How can you find when two expressions are equal, or when one expression is greater or less than the other?

Problem Description

In this Problem, students explore a symbolic method for finding the point of intersection of two lines. Students connect this method to other methods of finding the point of intersection, such as using a graph or table of data that represents each relationship.

Students find the point of intersection of two lines by setting the expressions for y equal to each other and then solving for x. They use the x-value to find the y-value for the coordinates of the intersection point. If the two relationships are represented by $y_1 = mx + b$ and $y_2 = kx + c$, then the point of intersection of the lines representing each equation occurs when $y_1 = y_2$, or $mx + b = kx + c$.

Students find the values of x that satisfy the inequalities $y_1 < y_2$ and $y_1 > y_2$. They also write and interpret equivalent expressions and solve inequalities using graphs.

Problem Implementation

Students can work in pairs.

You may want to summarize after Question B to be sure that students are comfortable finding the profit numerically and recognizing how this solution is represented on a graph. This will set the scene for representing the answers to the inequalities on graphs in Question E.

You can encourage students to make a table, a graph, or an explanation of a symbolic method on poster paper. These can be used during the Summarize to make connections among the representations—verbal description, table, graph, and equation.

Blank Table and Graph contains a table and a graph that students can use as they work through Question E, part (4).

Materials

- **Labsheet 3ACE:** Exercise 54 (accessibility)
- **Blank Table and Graph**
- **Teaching Aid 3.5A:** Two T-Shirt Plans
- **Teaching Aid 3.5B:** Fabian's Bakery
- **Check Up 2**

poster paper

Using Technology

If your students have access to computers, they can use **Climbing Monkeys** to identify the point of intersection of two lines on an interactive graph.

Vocabulary

- inequality
- point of intersection

Mathematics Background

- Finding the y-Intercept and Equation for a Linear Relationship
- Solving a System of Two Linear Equations
- Inequalities
- Equivalent Expressions

At a Glance and Lesson Plan

- At a Glance: Problem 3.5 Moving Straight Ahead
- Lesson Plan: Problem 3.5 Moving Straight Ahead

▼ Launch

Launch Video

This animation gives students an insight into the context of the Problem: the expenses and income of a bakery. The characters, two bakers, discuss a strategy for helping the bakery become more profitable, and they determine that they need to bake more cakes. You can use this video to help students understand why, even though the cakes cost money to make, spending the money to make more of them is necessary for the bakers to increase their income enough to make a profit. This video can also give students an idea of what the bakery spends its fixed expense of $825 on each month. Visit Teacher Place at mathdashboard.com/cmp3 to see the complete video.

Connecting to Prior Knowledge

Display **Teaching Aid 3.5A: Two T-Shirt Plans** and use it to review how to interpret the information that the point of intersection provides in this situation. Explain that the point of intersection lies on both lines, so its coordinates must be a solution to the equation of each line.

Choose a point, such as (10, 45).

Suggested Questions

- Does it lie on both lines? (No, it only lies on the line representing $C_n = 4.5n$.)

- What information does it represent? (10 T-shirts cost $45. Because the point lies below the line representing $C_m = 49 + n$, the cost of 10 T-shirts from No-Shrink is cheaper than the cost of 10 T-shirts from Mighty Tee.)

Choose a point that does not lie on either line, such as (6, 40).

- Does this point lie on either line? (No, it falls below the line for C_m and above the line for C_n.)

Draw students' attention to the point of intersection on the graph.

- What information do the coordinates of the point of intersection of the two lines give you about this situation? (They tell you the number of T-shirts required for the cost of the two plans to be equal.)

- Show how you could use the two equations to find the coordinates of the point of intersection of the two lines. That is, for what number of T-shirts n is $C_m = C_n$? (You can solve the equation $4.5n = 49 + n$. $n = 14$. You substitute this value into one of the equations to find the value of C, which is 63.)

- For what number(s) of T-shirts is plan C_m less than plan C_n? That is, when is $C_m < C_n$? (Once you know for what value of n the two plans are equal, you can choose a value either greater or less than this value of n. You can substitute this value into the equality to determine which cost is greater for that value of n.

  For example, you know that the plans are equal when $n = 14$. Suppose you choose a value of n that is greater than 14, such as 20. When $n = 20$, $C_m = 69$ and $C_n = 90$. So, $C_m < C_n$. This means that 20 is a solution of the inequality $C_m < C_n$.

Another way to find solutions to the inequality $C_m < C_n$ is to look at the graph. Students will see that when $n = 20$, the graph of C_m is below the graph of C_n. This should make sense to them because they have just shown algebraically that the value of C_m is less than the value of C_n. In fact, for all values of n that are greater than 14, the graph of C_m is below the graph of C_n. This means that all numbers greater than 14 are solutions to the inequality $C_m < C_n$. Be sure students are comfortable using the graph to answer these questions.

You may want to review inequality statements that were explored in earlier Units, such as $x < 6$, $x > 5$, or $-3 < x$. Ask students to show the solution to each on a number line.

Presenting the Challenge

Tell the story of the bakery, or show the Launch Video. Explain or ask students what the "break-even point" means. If needed, review the concepts of income, expense, and profit with the students.

Suggested Questions

- In the equations for income and expenses, what information do the y-intercepts give? (In the equation for income, the y-intercept tells you the income the bakery makes for selling 0 cakes in a month. In the equation for expenses, the y-intercept tells you the expenses the bakery has each month before it sells any cakes.)

- What information do the coefficients of n represent? (In the equation for income, the coefficient of n represents the income the bakery earns for each cake sold. In the equation for expenses, the coefficient of n represents the cost to make each cake.)

▼ Explore

Providing for Individual Needs

As you move around, make a note of how students are solving the problems. Some may use tables, some may use graphs, and some may use symbolic methods. Make sure that each of these strategies comes out in the Summarize.

In Question B, when students determine whether there is a profit for making and selling 100 cakes, they can just compute the expenses and income and then subtract the expenses from the income. Be sure students see the connection between this numerical strategy and how it is represented on the graph. The profit is the vertical distance between the two points (100, I) and (100, E) on the graphs. Point out that, in this case, the expenses are greater than the income, so the vertical distance actually represents a loss.

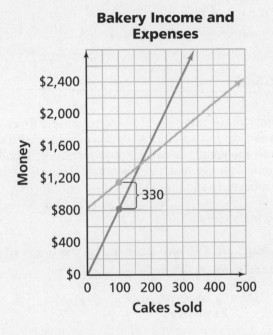

Bakery Income and Expenses

In Question E, this is the first time students have been asked to record their solution to an inequality on a graph. If students are struggling, you can suggest that they find when the two expressions are equal and then adjust their answer.

The situation in Question E, part (1) can be represented by the inequality $E < 2,400$. To solve this inequality, students can find the value of n for which E equals 2,400 and then adjust n:

Since $E = 825 + 3.25n$, then

$$825 + 3.25n = 2,400$$

$$3.25n = 1,575$$

$$n = 484.6, \text{ or about } 485$$

So, the solution is $n < 485$. Students can check this by choosing a value less than 485 for n and substituting it into the equation they solved. For example, if $n = 100$, then $E = 825 + 3.25(100) = 1,150$. This value of E satisfies the inequality $E < 2,400$ because $1,150 < 2,400$.

Students can graph their solution on a number line or on a graph in the coordinate plane. See the answers for samples.

Encourage students to check their answers.

Planning for the Summary

What evidence will you use in the summary to clarify and deepen understanding of the Focus Question?

What will you do if you do not have evidence?

▼ Summarize

Orchestrating the Discussion

Use Question B to check on students' understanding of linear equations. They should make the connection between solving equations symbolically and with a graph (or table). Ask students to tell you what the symbols and numbers mean in the equation and where this information is displayed in the graph. This will help them interpret the questions about equality and inequality.

Discuss all the methods for finding the solutions.

For Question B, display **Teaching Aid 3.5B: Fabian's Bakery**. Use the graph of the two equations to determine whether Fabian made a profit.

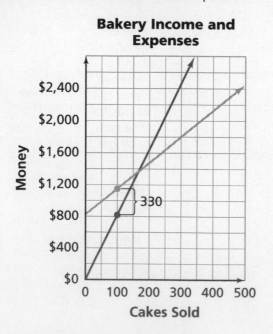

Bakery Income and Expenses

Profit occurs when expenses are less than income, or when income is greater than expenses. Use the graph to show that the expenses exceed the income if Fabian makes and sells 100 cakes. Mark the difference with a vertical line segment between the point (100, 1,150) on the graph of *E* and the point (100, 820) on the graph of *I*. Some students may be ready to interpret the vertical distance symbolically.

Suggested Questions

- How can the vertical distance be interpreted as a symbolic expression? What would this expression mean? (Instead of thinking of $825 + 3.25x = 8.2x$, we think of Income − Expenses, or $8.2x − (825 + 3.25x)$, and note when this expression is positive. When it is positive, Income is greater than Expenses, and there is a profit.)

In Question B, students used their knowledge of the context and their understanding of graphical representations of linear relationships to determine when there is a profit by using the graph. In Question E, students use symbolic methods to solve inequalities that represent income, expenses, and profit.

Repeat this discussion for Question E, part (4c). Again, show graphically how the profit is illustrated. Note that most students may just find the intersection point and then find the location on the graph where the distance between the expense line and income line is 800. They will then find the corresponding value for *n*. Some students may write and graph the equation for Profit, $P = 4.95n − 825$. Then, they will look for 800 on the *y*-axis, locate the point on the graph of the profit line with this *y*-coordinate, and find the *x*-value of this point, which represents the value of *n* that corresponds to a profit of $800.

In Question D, students use the properties of equality to find the coordinates of the point of intersection.

- How is this similar to the equations in Problem 3.4? (You are setting the expressions for income and expenses equal to each other and then solving this equation to find the number of cakes.)

- How is this Problem similar to the walking rate between the two brothers in Problem 2.1? (Both Problems involve finding the point of intersection of two lines. In Problem 2.1, students used tables and graphs to find the intersection point. In this Problem, students have learned a new strategy: solving an equation symbolically. Also, both Problems can be solved using inequalities. In the walking race situation, the goal was for Henri's distance to be slightly greater than Emile's distance when the race ended. In the bakery situation, Fabian's goal is for his income to be greater than his expenses, so that he makes a profit.)

Tell students that this Problem is an example of finding the point of intersection of two lines by applying the principles of equality to an equation.

If it is needed for your program, you can introduce the language of "systems of linear equations." In a later Unit, *It's In the System*, students will develop other strategies for finding the solution to a 2-by-2 system of equations.

Check for Understanding

End by giving two more equations. Ask students to find the point of intersection and solve an inequality.

- Is the point (10, 40) the point of intersection of the lines of the following equations: $y_1 = 70 - 3x$ and $y_2 = 44 + 10x$? (No. The point lies on the line that represents y_1 because $40 = 70 - 3(10)$, but it does not lie on the line that represents y_2 because $40 \neq 44 + 10(10)$.)

- Find the point of intersection symbolically. (If $70 - 3x = 44 + 10x$, then $x = 2$ and $y_1 = y_2 = 64$.)

- When is $y_1 > 60$? Explain your method. ($y_1 > 60$ when $x = 3.\overline{3}$. If you test out a value for x that is less than $3.\overline{3}$, the value of y_1 will be greater than 60. So, $y_1 > 60$ when $x < 3.\overline{3}$.)

- When is $y_1 < y_2$? Explain your method. ($y_1 = y_2$ when $x = 2$. If you test out a value for x that is greater than 2, the value of y_1 will be less than the value of y_2. So, $y_1 < y_2$ when $x > 2$.)

Reflecting on Student Learning

Use the following questions to assess student understanding at the end of the lesson.

- What evidence do I have that students understand the Focus Question?
  - Where did my students get stuck?
  - What strategies did they use?
  - What breakthroughs did my students have today?
- How will I use this to plan for tomorrow? For the next time I teach this lesson?
- Where will I have the opportunity to reinforce these ideas as I continue through this Unit? The next Unit?

ACE Assignment Guide

- **Applications:** 30–34
- **Extensions:** 54, 59
- **Labsheet 3ACE:** Exercise 54 (accessibility)

Note: This labsheet contains a larger version of the table in the Student Edition as well as a blank first-quadrant grid. You can give this labsheet to students to help them organize their answers. This can allow students to remain focused on the mathematics of Exercise 55 while saving time.

▼ Mathematical Reflections

Possible Answers to Mathematical Reflections

1. **a.** If you have an equation of the form $y = mx + b$ and you know the value of x or y, you can substitute the value of the variable into the equation. Then, use the properties of equality to solve for the other variable. For example, if $y = 3x + 4$ and you want to find x when $y = 10$, then you substitute 10 in place of y: $10 = 3x + 4$. Next, you can subtract 4 from both sides to get $6 = 3x$. Now, divide both sides by 3 to get $x = 2$.

   b For the equation $y = 3x + 4$, to find the value of x when $y = 10$, you can graph the equation. Trace along the line to find the point whose y-coordinate is 10 and then read the corresponding x-value, which is 2. To use a table, construct a table of values for the equation either by hand or with a graphing calculator. Next, locate the pair of values in which $y = 10$ and find the corresponding x-value, which is 2.

2. **a.** To find the values that satisfy an inequality such as $3x + 4 < 10$, you can solve the corresponding equation $3x + 4 = 10$. The solution of this equation is $x = 2$. Then, test values less than and greater than 2 to determine the solution. In this case, x-values less than 2 make the inequality $3x + 4 < 10$ true, so the solution is $x < 2$.

   b. To find the values that satisfy an inequality such as $3x + 4 < 10$, you can graph the corresponding linear relationship $y = 3x + 4$. Then, find the points on the line whose y-values are less than 10. You can also locate the x-values of these points on the x-axis or on a number line.

3. In Problem 3.3, Question A, part (1), two equivalent expressions for the number of pouches on the left side of the equation are $4x + 2$ and $2(2x + 1)$. You can use the properties of operations to show that they are equivalent. Applying the Distributive Property to one of the expressions yields the other: $4x + 2 = 2(2x + 1)$. You can also argue that both of the expressions represent the number of pouches and coins in the picture.

   In Problem 3.4, Question A, part (3a), two equivalent ways of writing the expression on the left side of the equation are $3(x + 1)$ and $3x + 3$. You can tell they are equivalent because the equations $3(x + 1) = 21$ and $3x + 3 = 21$ have the same solution, even though you would take different steps when solving them. (To solve the first equation, you would divide each side by 3 and then subtract 1 from each side. To solve the second equation, you would subtract 3 from each side and then divide each side by 3. The solution for both equations is $x = 6$.)

Possible Answers to Mathematical Practices Reflections

Students may have demonstrated all of the eight Common Core Standards for Mathematical Practice during this Investigation. During the class discussion, have students provide additional Practices that the Problem cited involved and identify the use of other Mathematical Practices in the Investigation.

One student observation is provided in the Student Edition. Here is another sample student response.

In Problem 3.4, Question A, Sally wrote $5x - 10 = 20$ as $5(x - 2) = 20$. She noted that 5 times the number in the parentheses must equal 20. She knew that $5 \times 4 = 20$. So, $x - 2 = 4$. Then she added 2 to both sides of the equation to get $x = 6$. I also used a symbolic method to solve this equation, but I followed different steps. I started by adding 10 to both sides to get $5x = 30$. Then I divided both sides by 5 to get $x = 6$. Sally and I compared our methods. Both are correct. We also checked the solution. Pete was listening to our conversation, and he commented that these strategies were similar to those we used in solving the pouch-and-coin problems. He also reminded us that we could use tables or graphs to solve the equations.

MP5: Use appropriate tools strategically.

Notes

3

Solving Equations

In the last Investigation, you examined the patterns in the table and graph for the relationship relating Alana's distance d and money earned A in the walkathon.

The equation $A = 5 + 0.5d$ is another way to represent that relationship. The graph of the relationship is a line that contains infinitely many points. The coordinates of each point can be substituted into the equation to make a true statement. The coordinates of these points are solutions to the equation.

Common Core State Standards

7.EE.A.1 Apply properties of operations as strategies to add, subtract, factor, and expand linear expressions with rational coefficients.

7.EE.A.2 Understand that rewriting an expression in different forms in a problem context can shed light on the problem and how the quantities in it are related.

7.EE.B.4a Solve word problems leading to equations of the form $px + q = r$ and $p(x + q) = r$, where p, q, and r are specific rational numbers. Solve equations of these forms fluently. Compare an algebraic solution to an arithmetic solution, identifying the sequence of the operations used in each approach.

7.EE.B.4b Solve word problems leading to inequalities of the form $px + q > r$ or $px + q < r$, where p, q, and r are specific rational numbers. Graph the solution set of the inequality and interpret it in the context of the problem.

Also 7.EE.B.4

Notes _____

_____

_____

_____

For example, the point (3, 6.5) lies on the line of $A = 5 + 0.5d$. This means that $d = 3$, $A = 6.5$, and $6.5 = 5 + 0.5(3)$ is a true statement. So, the coordinate pair (3, 6.5) is a solution to the equation.

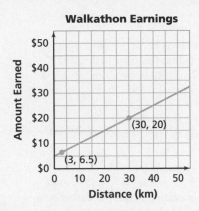

Walkathon Earnings

- Does the point (30, 20) lie on the line? Is it a solution to the equation? Explain.

- Does the point (20, 20) lie on the line? Is it a solution to the equation? Explain.

- What happens if you choose a point that is not visible on this section of the graph, such as (70, 40)? Is it on the line? Explain.

The corresponding entries in a table are the coordinates of points on the line representing the equation $A = 5 + 0.5d$. So, we can also find a solution to an equation by using a table.

- How could you find the value of d that corresponds to $A = 30$ in the table?

d	A
0	5
1	5.5
2	6
3	6.5
4	7
20	15
25	17.5
30	20

Notes _____

3.1 Solving Equations Using Tables and Graphs

In a relationship between two variables, if you know the value of one variable, you can use a table or a graph to find the value of the other variable. For example, suppose Alana raises $10 from a sponsor in the walkathon from Problem 1.3. Then you can ask: How many kilometers does Alana walk?

In the equation $A = 5 + 0.5d$, this means that $A = 10$. The equation is now $10 = 5 + 0.5d$.

- What value of d will make this a true statement?

Finding the value of d that will make this a true statement is called *solving the equation* for d. You can use tables or graphs to find the missing value. In this Investigation, you will develop strategies for solving equations symbolically, using properties of operations and equality.

Problem 3.1

A Use the equation $A = 5 + 0.5d$.

1. a. Suppose Alana walks 23 kilometers. Show how you can use a table and a graph to find the amount of money each sponsor donates.

b. Write an equation that represents the amount of money Alana collects if she walks 23 kilometers. Can you use the equation to find the amount? Explain.

2. Suppose Alana writes the equation $30 = 5 + 0.5d$.

a. What question is she trying to ask?

b. Show how you can answer Alana's question by reasoning with a table of values, a graph of the relationship $A = 5 + 0.5d$, or with the equation $30 = 5 + 0.5d$ itself.

Notes

continued

B The equation $D = 25 + 2.5t$ is related to situations that you have explored. In parts (1) and (2) below, the value of one variable in the equation is known. Find the solution (the value of the unknown variable) in each part. Then, describe another way you can find the solution.

1. $D = 25 + 2.5(7)$ **2.** $70 = 25 + 2.5t$

 Homework starts on page 69.

3.2 Mystery Pouches in the Kingdom of Montarek
Exploring Equality

In the Kingdom of Montarek, money takes the form of $1 gold coins called rubas. Messengers carry money between the king's castles in sealed pouches that always hold equal numbers of coins.

$1 gold coin   sealed pouch

One day a messenger arrived at one of the castles with a box containing two sealed pouches and five loose $1 coins. The ruler thanked the messenger for the money, which equaled $11.

- Can you figure out the number of coins in each pouch?

- Does the following visual equation help in finding the number of coins in each pouch?

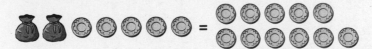

In this Problem, you will solve more problems involving mystery pouches.

Notes _____

_____

_____

Problem 3.2

A In parts (1)–(6) below, each pouch contains the same number of $1 gold coins. Also, the total number of coins on each side of the equation is the same.

- Find the number of gold coins in each pouch. Write down your steps so that someone else could follow your steps to find the number of coins in a pouch.

- Describe how you can check your answer. That is, how do you know you have found the correct number of gold coins in each pouch?

1.

2.

3.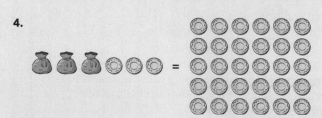

4.

5.

6.

Notes

Problem 3.2 *continued*

B In Question A, part (2), Nichole thought of the left-hand side of the situation as having two groups. Each group contained one pouch and two coins. She visualized the following steps to help her find the number of coins in a pouch.

1. Is Nichole correct? Explain.

2. Noah looked at Nichole's strategy and claimed that she was applying the Distributive Property. Is Noah's claim correct? Explain.

3. Are there other situations in which Nichole's method might work? Explain.

A C E Homework starts on page 69.

Investigation 3 **Solving Equations**   **59**

Notes _____
_____
_____

3.3 From Pouches to Variables
Writing Equations

In the last Problem, you used pictures of pouches and gold coins to solve equations. Your solutions maintained the equality of the coins on both sides of the equal sign. For example, you might have removed (or subtracted) the same number of coins or pouches from each side of the equation. To better understand how to maintain equality, let's look first at numerical statements.

The equation $85 = 70 + 15$ states that the quantities 85 and $70 + 15$ are equal.

What do you have to do to maintain equality if you:

- subtract 15 from the left-hand side of the original equation?

- add 10 to the right-hand side of the original equation?

- divide the left-hand side of the original equation by 5?

- multiply the right-hand side of the original equation by 4?

Try your methods on another example of equality. Summarize what you know about maintaining equality between two quantities.

Throughout this Unit, you have been solving equations with two variables. Sometimes the value of one variable is known, and you want to find the value of the other variable. In this Problem, you will continue to find the value of a variable without using a table or a graph. You will learn to use *symbolic* methods to solve a linear equation.

Notes

_____

_____

_____

The picture below shows a situation from Problem 3.2.

Because the number of gold coins in each pouch is unknown, you can let x represent the number of coins in one pouch. You can let 1 represent the value of one gold coin.

You can write the following equation to represent the situation:

$$2x + 4 = 12$$

Or, you can use Nichole's method from Problem 3.2 to write this equation:

$$2(x + 2) = 12$$

The expressions $2x + 4$ and $2(x + 2)$ are **equivalent expressions.** Two or more expressions are equivalent if they have the same value, regardless of what number is substituted for the variable. These two expressions are an example of the Distributive Property for numbers.

$$2(x + 2) = 2x + 4$$

In this Problem, you will revisit situations with pouches and coins, but you will use symbolic equations to represent your solution process.

Notes _____

_____

_____

STUDENT PAGE

Problem 3.3

A For each situation, find the number of coins in each pouch. Record your answers in a table like the one shown.

Picture	Steps for Finding the Coins in Each Pouch	Solution Using Equations

- In the second column, use your method from Problem 3.2 to find the number of gold coins in each pouch. Record your steps.

- In the third column, write an equation that represents the situation. Use *x* to represent the number of gold coins in each pouch. Use the number 1 to represent each coin. Then, use your equation to find the number of gold coins in each pouch.

- Check your answers.

1.

2.

3.

Notes

_____

_____

_____

Problem **3.3** continued

4.

5. Describe two situations in Question A for which you could write more than one equation to represent the situation.

B For each equation:

- Use your strategies from Question A to solve the equation.
- Check your answer.

    1. $30 = 6 + 4x$

    2. $7x = 5 + 5x$

    3. $7x + 2 = 12 + 5x$

    4. $2(x + 4) = 16$

C Describe a general method for solving equations using what you know about equality.

A C E Homework starts on page 69.

STUDENT PAGE

Notes _____

_____

_____

3.4 Solving Linear Equations

To maintain the equality of two expressions, you can add, subtract, multiply, or divide each side of the equality by the same number. These are called the **properties of equality**. In the last Problem, you applied properties of equality and numbers to find a solution to an equation.

So far in this Investigation, all of the situations have involved positive whole numbers.

- Does it make sense to think about negative numbers in a coin situation?

- Does it make sense to think about fractions in a coin situation?

 What strategies do you have for solving an equation like $-2x + 10 = 15$?

You have used the properties of equality to solve equations involving pouches and coins. These properties are also useful in solving all linear equations.

 Problem 3.4

A For parts 1–3:

- Record each step you take to find your solution.

- Then, check your answer.

1.   **a.** $5x + 10 = 20$ **b.** $5x - 10 = 20$ **c.** $5x + 10 = -20$

     d. $5x - 10 = -20$ **e.** $10 - 5x = 20$ **f.** $10 - 5x = -20$

2.   **a.** $\frac{1}{4}x + 6 = 12$ **b.** $1\frac{1}{2} + 2x = 6\frac{1}{2}$ **c.** $\frac{3}{5} = -x + 1$

     d. $3.5x = 130 + 10x$ **e.** $15 - 4x = 10x + 45$

3.   **a.** $3(x + 1) = 21$ **b.** $2 + 3(x + 1) = 6x$ **c.** $-2(2x - 3) = -2$

Notes _____

_____

_____

Problem 3.4 *continued*

B Below are examples of students' solutions the equations from Question A, part (3) above. Is each solution correct? If not, explain what the error is.

$$3(x + 1) = 21$$

Corry's Solution

3 times something in the parentheses must be 21.
So 3( ) = 21.
The something is 7.
So x + 1 = 7, and
x = 6.

$$2 + 3(x + 1) = 6x$$

Hadden's Solution

2 + 3(x + 1) is equivalent to 5(x + 1).
So I can rewrite the original equation as 5(x + 1) = 6x.
Using the Distributive Property, this is the same as
   5x + 5 = 6x.
Subtracting 5x from each side, I get 5 = 1x.
So x = 5.

$$-2(2x - 3) = -2$$

Jackie's Solution

By using the Distributive Property on the left-hand
   side of the equality, I get −4x − 6 = −2.
By adding 6 to each side, I get −4x = 4.
By dividing both sides by −4, I get x = −1.

C Describe the strategies you have used for solving linear equations. When might you use one over another?

 **Homework starts on page 69.**

Notes _____

_____

_____

3.5 Finding the Point of Intersection
Equations and Inequalities

In Problem 2.3, you used graphs and tables to find when the costs of two different plans for buying T-shirts were equal. The graphs of the two cost plans are shown below. C_n represents the costs of the No-Shrink Tee. C_m represents the costs of the Mighty Tee. The **point of intersection** of the two lines tells us when the costs for the two T-shirt plans are equal.

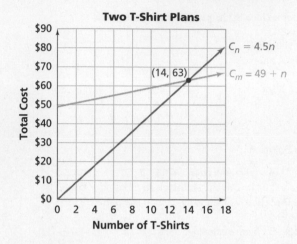

Two T-Shirt Plans

$C_n = 4.5n$

$C_m = 49 + n$

(14, 63)

- What information do the coordinates of the point of intersection of the two lines give you about this situation?

- Show how you could use the two equations to find the coordinates of the point of intersection of the two lines. That is, for what number of T-shirts n is $C_m = C_n$?

- For what number(s) of T-shirts is plan C_m less than plan C_n? That is, when is $C_m < C_n$?

Statements like $C_m = C_n$ are called equality statements or equations. You learned how to solve these equations symbolically in this Investigation.

Statements like $C_m < C_n$, $x < 5$, and $x > -5$ are called **inequality statements** or inequalities.

Notes _____

_____

_____

In this Problem, you will answer questions about points of intersection and about when the cost of one plan is less than or greater than that of another plan.

Problem 3.5

At Fabulous Fabian's Bakery, the expenses E to make n cakes per month is given by the equation $E = 825 + 3.25n$. The income I for selling n cakes is given by the equation $I = 8.20n$.

A 1. In the equations for I and E, what information do the y-intercepts give you?

2. What do the coefficients of n represent?

B Fabian sells 100 cakes in January.

1. What are his expenses and his income?

2. What is his profit? Describe how you found your answer.

3. Kevin drew the graph below. Explain how he could use his graph to determine Fabian's profit.

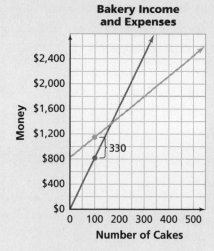

C 1. Write an equation that represents the profit, P, for selling n cakes. Describe how you can use this equation to find the profit.

2. Fabian uses the equation $P = 4.95n - 825$ to predict the profit. Does this equation make sense? Explain.

continued on the next page >

Notes

Problem **3.5** *continued*

D The *break-even* point is when expenses equal income ($E = I$). Fabian thinks that this information is useful.

   1. Write an equation to find the number of cakes n needed to break even. How many cakes does Fabian need to make in order to break even?

   2. Describe how you could use a table or graph to find the break-even point.

E **1.** How many cakes can Fabian make if he wants his expenses to be less than $2,400 a month?

   2. How many cakes can he make if he wants to his income to be greater than $2,400 a month?

   3. Fabian's sister Mariah wrote the following inequality statements to answer parts (1) and (2) above.

$$825 + 3.25n < 2,400 \quad \text{and} \quad 8.20n > 2,400$$

   Do these statements make sense? Why?

   4. For each of the following inequalities

     • find the number of cakes Fabian needs to make in a month.

     • record the solution on a graph.

     • explain how you found your answers.

      a. $E < 1,475$

      b. $I > 1,640$

      c. $P > 800$

 Homework starts on page 69.

Notes _____

_____

_____

Applications

1. Ms. Chang's class decides to use the *Cool Tee's* company to make their T-shirts. The following equation represents the relationship between the cost C and the number of T-shirts n.

$$C = 2n + 20$$

   a. The class wants to buy 25 T-shirts from *Cool Tee's*. Describe how you can use a table and a graph to find the cost for 25 T-shirts.

   b. Suppose the class has $80 to spend on T-shirts. Describe how you can use a table and a graph to find the number of T-shirts the class can buy.

   c. Taleah writes the following equation in her notebook:

$$C = 2(15) + 20$$

   What information is Sophia looking for?

   d. Keisha uses the coordinates (30, 80) to find information about the cost of the T-shirts. What information is she looking for?

2. Mary uses the following equations to find some information about three walkathon pledge plans.

Plan 1	Plan 2	Plan 3
$14 = 2x$	$y = 3.5(10) + 10$	$100 = 1.5x + 55$

   In each equation, y is the amount donated in dollars, and x is the number of kilometers walked. For each equation:

   a. What information is Mary trying to find?

   b. Describe how you could find the information.

3. Find the solution (the value of the variable) for each equation.

   a. $y = 3(10) + 15$ **b.** $24 = x + 2$ **c.** $10 = 2x + 4$

4. Consider the equation $y = 5x - 15$.

   a. Find y if $x = 1$.   **b.** Find x if $y = 50$.

   c. Describe how you can use a table or a graph to answer parts (a) and (b).

Notes _____

_____

_____

For each situation in Exercises 5–8, find the number of coins in each pouch. Each pouch contains the same number of $1 gold coins, and the total number of coins on each side of the equation is the same.

5.
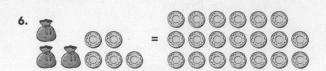

6.
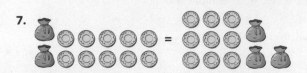

7.
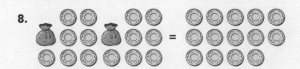

8.

9. For each equation, sketch a picture using pouches and coins. Then, determine how many coins are in a pouch.

   a. $3x = 12$

   b. $2x + 5 = 19$

   c. $4x + 5 = 2x + 19$

   d. $x + 12 = 2x + 6$

   e. $3(x + 4) = 18$

Notes _____

_____

_____

10. Gilberto's grandfather gives him $5 for his birthday and then 50¢ for each math question he answers correctly on his math exams for the year.

   a. Write an equation that represents the amount of money that Gilberto receives during a school year. Explain what the variables and numbers mean.

   b. Use the equation to find the number of correct answers Gilberto needs to buy a new shirt that costs $25. Show your work.

   c. Gilberto answered all 12 problems correctly on his first math exam. How much money is he assured of receiving for the year? Show your work.

11. For parts (a) and (b), find the mystery number and explain your reasoning.

   a. If you add 15 to 3 times the mystery number, you get 78. What is the mystery number?

   b. If you subtract 27 from 5 times the mystery number, you get 83. What is the mystery number?

   c. Make up clues for a riddle whose mystery number is 9.

12. Use properties of equality and numbers to solve each equation for x. Check your answers.

   a. $7 + 3x = 5x + 13$

   b. $3x - 7 = 5x + 13$

   c. $7 - 3x = 5x + 13$

   d. $3x + 7 = 5x - 13$

13. **Multiple Choice** Which of the following is a solution to the equation $11 = -3x - 10$?

   A. 1.3   B. $-\frac{1}{3}$ C. -7 D. 24

14. Solve each equation for x. Check your answers.

   a. $3x + 5 = 20$

   b. $3x - 5 = 20$

   c. $3x + 5 = -20$

   d. $-3x + 5 = 20$

   e. $-3x - 5 = -20$

15. Determine whether each expression is *always, sometimes,* or *never* equal to $-2(x - 3)$.

   a. $-2x + 6$

   b. $-2x - 6$

   c. $2x + 6$

   d. $-2x - 3$

   e. $-2(x + 3)$

   f. $2(3 - x)$

Notes

16. For each equation in Group 1, find a matching equation in Group 2 that has the same solution. Write down any strategies you used.

Group 1

A: $3x + 6 = 12$
B: $3x - 6 = 12$
C: $-3x + 6 = 12$
D: $3x + 6 = -12$
E: $6x - 3 = 12$

Group 2

F: $x = 6$
G: $3(2 - x) = 12$
H: $3x = 6$
J: $x - \frac{1}{2} = 2$
K: $x + 2 = -4$

17. Solve each equation. Check your answers.

a. $3(x + 2) = 12$
b. $3(x + 2) = x - 18$
c. $3(x + 2) = 2x$
d. $3(x + 2) = -15$

18. Solve each equation for x.

a. $5 - 2(x - 1) = 12$
b. $5 + 2(x - 1) = 12$
c. $5 - 2(x + 2) = 12$
d. $5 - 2x + 2 = 12$

19. Solve each equation for x.

a. $2x + 6 = 6x + 2$
b. $2x + 6 = 6x - 2$
c. $2x - 6 = -6x + 2$
d. $-2x - 6 = -6x - 2$

For Exercises 20 and 21, use the equation $y = 4 - 3x$.

20. Find y when:

a. $x = 4$
b. $x = -3$
c. $x = 2$
d. $x = -\frac{4}{3}$
e. $x = 0$

21. Find x when:

a. $y = 0$
b. $y = 21$
c. $y = -15$
d. $y = 3.5$

22. Explain how the information you found for Exercises 20 and 21 relates to locating points on a line representing $y = 4 - 3x$.

Notes

23. In each part below, identify the equations that have the same solution.

a. A: $x = 8$
B: $-x = 8$
C: $x + 3x = 8$
D: $1x = 8$
E: $8 = 4x$
F: $8 = -1x$

b. G: $x - 1 = 6$
H: $x - 1 = -6$
J: $-x + 1 = -6$
K: $-x + 1 = 6$
L: $6 = 1 - x$
M: $-1 + x = 6$

c. N: $x - \frac{1}{2} = 4$
O: $\frac{1}{2}x = -4$
P: $x = 4 + \frac{1}{2}$
Q: $-\frac{1}{2}x = 4$
R: $\frac{1}{2} - x = 4$
S: $-x + \frac{1}{2} = 4$

24. Two students' solutions to the equation $6(x + 4) = 3x - 2$ are shown below. Both students made an error. Find the errors and give a correct solution.

Student 1

$6(x + 4) = 3x - 2$
$x + 4 = 3x - 2 - 6$
$x + 4 = 3x - 8$
$x + 4 + 8 = 3x - 8 + 8$
$x + 12 = 3x$
$12 = 2x$
$x = 6$ ✗

Student 2

$6(x + 4) = 3x - 2$
$6x + 4 = 3x - 2$
$3x + 4 = -2$
$3x + 4 - 4 = -2 - 4$
$3x = -6$
$x = -2$ ✗

25. Two students' solutions to the equation $58.5 = 3.5x - 6$ are shown below. Both students made an error. Find the errors and give a correct solution.

Student 1

$58.5 = 3.5x - 6$
$58.5 - 6 = 3.5x$
$52.5 = 3.5x$
$\dfrac{52.5}{3.5} = x$
so, $x = 15$ ✗

Student 2

$58.5 = 3.5x - 6$
$58.5 + 6 = 3.5x - 6 + 6$
$64.5 = 3.5x$
$\dfrac{64.5}{3.5} = \dfrac{3.5}{3.5}x$
so, $x \approx 1.84$ ✗

Notes _____

_____

_____

26. Describe how you could use a graph or a table to solve each equation.

    a. $5x + 10 = -20$

    b. $4x - 9 = -7x + 13$

27. Use the equation $P = 10 - 2.5c$.

    a. Find P when $c = 3.2$.

    b. Find c when $P = 85$.

    c. Describe how you can use a table or a graph to answer parts (a) and (b).

28. Use the equation $m = 15.75 + 3.2d$.

    a. Find m when:

       i. $d = 20$

       ii. $d = 0$

       iii. $d = 3.2$

    b. Find d when:

       i. $m = 54.15$

       ii. $m = 0$

       iii. $m = 100$

29. Khong thinks he has a different way to solve equations, by first factoring out both sides of the equation by the greatest common factor. This is how he solved the first equation in Problem 3.4.

    > $5x + 10 = 20$ is the same as $5(x + 2) = 5(4)$.
    > So, If I divide both sides by 5, I get $x + 2 = 4$.
    > This means that $x = 2$.

    a. Is Khong correct, that this method works for this problem? Explain.

    b. Use Khong's method to solve the equation $40x + 20 = 120$.

    c. Khong says his method won't work to solve $7x + 3 = 31$. Why is that?

    d. Write an equation that can be solved using Khong's method. Then solve your equation.

Notes _____

_____

_____

30. The expenses E and income I for making and selling T-shirts with a school logo are given by the equations $E = 535 + 4.50n$ and $I = 12n$, where n is the number of T-shirts.

   a. How many T-shirts must be made and sold to break even? Explain.

   b. Suppose only 50 shirts are sold. Is there a profit or a loss? Explain.

   c. Suppose the income is $1,200. Is there a profit or a loss? Explain.

   d. i. For each equation, find the coordinates of a point that lies on the graph of the equation.

      ii. What information does this point give you?

      iii. Describe how to use the equation to show that the point lies on the graph.

31. The International Links long-distance phone company charges no monthly fee but charges 18 cents per minute for long-distance calls. The World Connections' long-distance company charges $50 per month plus 10 cents per minute for long-distance calls. Compare the World Connections long-distance plan to that of International Links.

   a. Under what circumstances is it cheaper to use International Links? Explain your reasoning.

   b. Write an inequality that describes when each company is cheaper. Represent the solution to the inequality on a graph.

32. Two cell-phone providers have different charges per month for text-messaging plans. Driftless Region Telephone has a plan charging $1\frac{1}{2}$ cents per text, with a monthly rate of $10. Walby Communications charges $16 per month for unlimited texting.

   a. If you were paying for a plan, which one would you purchase? Explain.

   b. Would you make the same recommendation for anyone else?

   c. Write an inequality that would help someone decide which plan to purchase. Then, represent the solution on a graph.

Notes

33. Students at Hammond Middle School are raising money for the end-of-year school party. They decide to sell roses for Valentine's Day. The students can buy the roses for 50 cents each from a wholesaler. They also need $60 to buy ribbon and paper to protect the roses as well as materials for advertising the sale. They sell each rose for $1.30.

   a. How many roses must they sell to break even? Explain.

   b. What is the students' profit if they sell 50 roses? 100 roses? 200 roses?

34. Ruth considers buying a cell phone from two different companies. Company A has a cost plan given by the equation $C_A = 32n$, where n is the number of months she has the phone and C_A is the total cost. Company B has a cost plan represented by the equation $C_B = 36 + 26n$, where n is the number of months she is on the plan and C_B is the total cost.

   a. Graph both equations on the same set of axes.

   b. What is the point of intersection of the two graphs? What information does this give you?

Connections

35. Describe what operations are indicated in each expression. Then, write each expression as a single number.

   a. $-8(4)$ **b.** $-2 \cdot 4$

   c. $6(-5) - 10$ **d.** $2(-2) + 3(5)$

36. Find each quotient.

   a. $\frac{12}{-3}$ **b.** $\frac{-12}{3}$ **c.** $\frac{-12}{-3}$ **d.** $\frac{0}{-10}$

   e. $\frac{-5}{5}$ **f.** $\frac{5}{-5}$ **g.** $\frac{-5}{-5}$

37. Decide whether each pair of quantities is equal. Explain your reasoning.

   a. $6(5) + 2$ and $6(5 + 2)$ **b.** $8 - 3x$ and $3x - 8$ **c.** $4 + 5$ and $5 + 4$

   d. $-2(3)$ and $3(-2)$ **e.** $3 - 5$ and $5 - 3$ **f.** 2 quarters and 5 dimes

   g. 1.5 liters and 15 milliliters

   h. 2 out of 5 students prefer wearing sneakers to school and 50% of the students prefer wearing sneakers to school

Notes

38. a. Use fact families to write a related sentence for $n - (-3) = 30$. Does this related sentence make it easier to find the value for n? Why or why not?

b. Use fact families to write a related sentence for $5 + n = -36$. Does this related sentence make it easier to find the value for n? Why or why not?

c. Solve the equations in parts (a) and (b) using properties of equality. How does this method compare to using the fact families?

39. Write two different expressions to represent the area of each rectangle.

a.

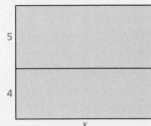

b.

40. Find the value of x that makes each equation true.

a. $3\frac{1}{2}x = \frac{3}{4}$

b. $3\frac{1}{2} = \frac{3}{4}x$

c. $\frac{7}{8}x = \frac{1}{8}$

d. $\frac{5}{6} = \frac{3}{4}x$

41. Fill in the missing representation for each inequality.

	In Symbols	On a Number Line	In Words
a.	$x > -4$	number line with open circle at -4; marks at $-8, -6, -4, -2, 0, 2$	▪
b.	$x \leq 2$	▪	all numbers less than or equal to 2
c.	$3 < x$	▪	▪
d.	▪	number line with closed circle at 3; marks at $-3, 0, 3, 6$	▪
e.	▪	▪	all numbers greater than negative 3

Notes _____

_____

_____

42. The number of times a cricket chirps in a minute is related to the temperature. You can use the formula

$$n = 4t - 160$$

to determine the number of chirps n a cricket makes in a minute when the temperature is t degrees Fahrenheit. If you want to estimate the temperature by counting cricket chirps, you can use the following form of the equation:

$$t = \tfrac{1}{4}n + 40$$

   a. At 60°F, how many times does a cricket chirp in a minute?

   b. What is the temperature if a cricket chirps 150 times in a minute?

   c. At what temperature does a cricket stop chirping?

   d. Sketch a graph of the equation with number of chirps on the x-axis and temperature on the y-axis. What information do the y-intercept of the graph and the coefficient of n give you?

43. The higher the altitude, the colder the temperature. The formula $T = t - \frac{d}{150}$ is used to estimate the temperature T at different altitudes, where t is the ground temperature in degrees Celsius and d is the altitude in meters.

   a. Suppose the ground temperature is 0 degrees Celsius. What is the temperature at an altitude of 1,500 meters?

   b. Suppose the temperature at 300 meters is 26 degrees Celsius. What is the ground temperature?

44. The sum S of the angles of a polygon with n sides is $S = 180(n - 2)$. Find the angle sum of each polygon.

   a. triangle   **b.** quadrilateral   **c.** hexagon

   d. decagon (10-sided polygon)

   e. icosagon (20-sided polygon)

45. Suppose the polygons in Exercise 44 are regular polygons. Find the measure of an interior angle of each polygon.

46. How many sides does a polygon have if its angle sum is

   a. 540 degrees?   **b.** 1,080 degrees?

Notes

47. The perimeter of each shape is 24 cm. Find the value of *x*.

a.

b.

c.

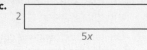

d. Find the area of the triangle in part (a) and the rectangle in part (c).

48. World Connections long-distance phone company charges $50 per month plus 10 cents per minute for each call.

a. Write an equation for the total monthly cost *C* for *t* minutes of long-distance calls.

b. Dwayne makes $10\frac{1}{2}$ hours of long-distance calls in a month. How much is his bill for that month?

c. If Andrea receives a $75 long-distance bill for last month's calls, how many minutes of long-distance calls did she make?

d. Should the solution to part (c) be written as an equality or inequality? Is it possible that the total number of minutes Andrea was charged was not equal to the amount of time she actually talked on the phone? Explain.

49. As a person ages beyond 30, his or her height can start to decrease by approximately 0.06 centimeter per year.

a. Write an equation that represents a person's height *h* after the age of 30. Let *t* be the number of years beyond 30 and *H* be the height at age 30.

b. A 60-year-old female is 160 centimeters tall. About how tall was she at age 30? Explain how you found your answer.

c. Suppose a basketball player is 6 feet, 6 inches tall on his thirtieth birthday. About how tall will he be at age 80? Explain. (Remember, 1 inch ≈ 2.54 centimeters.)

d. Jena says that in part (a), the equation should actually be written as an inequality. Why might Jena use an inequality to represent this relationship? What inequality do you think Jena has in mind?

STUDENT PAGE

Notes _____

_____

_____

50. Forensic scientists can estimate a person's height by measuring the
length of certain bones, including the femur, the tibia, the humerus,
and the radius.

The table below gives equations for the relationships between the
length of each bone and the estimated height of males and females.
These relationships were found by scientists after much study and
data collection. In the table, F represents the length of the femur,
T the length of the tibia, H the length of the humerus, R the length
of the radius, and h the person's height. All measurements are
in centimeters.

Bone	Male	Female
Femur	$h = 69.089 + 2.238F$	$h = 61.412 + 2.317F$
Tibia	$h = 81.688 + 2.392T$	$h = 72.572 + 2.533T$
Humerus	$h = 73.570 + 2.970H$	$h = 64.977 + 3.144H$
Radius	$h = 80.405 + 3.650R$	$h = 73.502 + 3.876R$

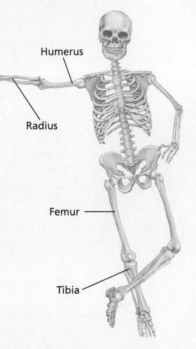

Humerus

Radius

Femur

Tibia

a. About how tall is a female if her femur is
46.2 centimeters long?

b. About how tall is a male if his tibia is
50.1 centimeters long?

c. Suppose a woman is 152 centimeters tall.
About how long is her femur? Her tibia? Her
humerus? Her radius?

d. Suppose a man is 183 centimeters tall.
About how long is his femur? His tibia? His
humerus? His radius?

e. Describe generally what the graph would
look like for each equation without drawing
the specific graph. What do the x- and
y-intercepts represent in this problem? Does
this make sense? Why?

Notes _____

_____

_____

Extensions

51. The maximum weight allowed in an elevator is 1,500 pounds.

    a. The average weight per adult is 150 pounds, and the average weight per child is 40 pounds. Write an equation for the number of adults A and the number of children C the elevator can hold.

    b. Suppose ten children are in the elevator. How many adults can get in?

    c. Suppose six adults are in the elevator. How many children can get in?

52. Solve each equation. Explain what your answers might mean.

    a. $2(x + 3) = 3x + 3$ **b.** $2(x + 3) = 2x + 6$ **c.** $2(x + 3) = 2x + 3$

53. Frank thinks he can solve inequalities the same way he can solve equations. He uses the method shown below.

> $2x + 6 < 16$
> First, I subtract 6 from both sides. Then I divide by 2.
> This simplifies the inequality to $x < 5$.
>
> My last step is to check my answer.
> $x = 4$ $2(4) + 6 = 14$ $14 < 16$
> $x = 6$ $2(6) + 6 = 18$ $18 \not< 16$

    a. Does Frank's method work in general for other inequalities?

    b. Frank runs into some difficulties trying to solve the following problem:

$$-2x + 1 > 5$$
$$-2x > 4$$

He thinks the answer is $x > -2$. He knows that if this is true, then $x = 0$ should be a solution, because $0 > -2$. But when he checks his work, he notices that $-2(0) + 1 \not> 5$. What numbers should be solutions for the original inequality?

Notes _____

_____

_____

54. Wind can affect the speed of an airplane. Suppose a plane is flying round-trip from New York City to San Francisco. The plane has a cruising speed of 300 miles per hour. The wind is blowing from west to east at 30 miles per hour. When the plane flies into (in the opposite direction of) the wind, its speed decreases by 30 miles per hour. When the plane flies with (in the same direction as) the wind, its speed increases by 30 miles per hour.

a. Make a table that shows the total time the plane has traveled after each 200-mile interval on its trip from New York City to San Francisco and back.

Airplane Flight Times

Distance (mi)	NYC to SF Time (h)	SF to NYC Time (h)
0	■	■
200	■	■
400	■	■
600	■	■
■	■	■

b. For each direction, write an equation for the distance d traveled in t hours.

c. On the same set of axes, sketch graphs of the time and distance data for travel in each direction.

d. How long does it take a plane to fly 5,000 miles against a 30-mile-per-hour wind? With a 30-mile-per-hour wind? Explain how you found your answers.

Notes _____

_____

_____

55. Students in Mr. Rickman's class are asked to solve the equation $\frac{2}{3}(6x - 9) + \frac{1}{3}(6x - 9) = 3$. Look at the three solutions below. Are they correct? Explain which method makes the most sense to you.

Jess's Solution

I began by distributing the numbers outside the parentheses on the left side.

$$\frac{2}{3}(6x - 9) + \frac{1}{3}(6x - 9) = 3$$
$$4x - 6 + 2x - 3 = 3$$
$$6x - 9 = 3$$
$$6x = 12$$
$$x = 2$$

Terri's Solution

I began by multiplying each side of the equation by 3.

$$3\left[\frac{2}{3}(6x - 9) + \frac{1}{3}(6x - 9)\right] = 3(3)$$
$$2(6x - 9) + 1(6x - 9) = 9$$
$$12x - 18 + 6x - 9 = 9$$
$$18x - 27 = 9$$
$$18x = 36$$
$$x = 2$$

Brian's Solution

I knew that $\frac{2}{3} + \frac{1}{3} = 1$, so I simplified the right side to $6x - 9$.

$$\frac{2}{3}(6x - 9) + \frac{1}{3}(6x - 9) = 3$$
$$1(6x - 9) = 3$$
$$6x - 9 = 3$$
$$6x = 12$$
$$x = 2$$

56. Multiple Choice Dorine solves the equation $3x + 3 = 3x + 9$ and is trying to make sense of her answer.

$$3x + 3 = 3x + 9$$
$$\underline{-3x - 3 \quad -3x - 3}$$
$$0 = 6$$

Which of the following should Dorine say is the correct solution?

A. $x = 6$, because 6 is the final number in the equation.

B. $x = 6$ or $x = 0$, because both of these numbers are in the last equation.

C. There is no solution, because each value of x will lead to $0 = 6$, which is not true.

D. The solution is all numbers, because x will satisfy the equation.

Notes

57. Multiple Choice Flora solves an equation similar to Dorine's:

$$3(x + 1) = 3x + 3$$

Flora uses the following method.

$$3(x + 1) = 3x + 3$$
$$3x + 3 = 3x + 3$$
$$\underline{-3x - 3 \quad -3x - 3}$$
$$0 = 0$$

Which of the following should Flora say is the correct solution?

A. $x = 0$, since $0 = 0$ is the last line of the equation.

B. No solution, because x does not show up in the equation $0 = 0$.

C. Any number x will work.

58. Fill in the missing representation for each inequality.

	In Symbols	On a Number Line	In Words
a.	■	←———+———+———+———+———→ −4 −2 0 2 4	all positive numbers
b.	$x^2 < 9$	■	all numbers whose squares are less than 9
c.	■	■	all numbers whose absolute values are greater than or equal to 2
d.	$x^3 > x$	■	all numbers for which the cube of the number is greater than the number itself
e.	$x + \frac{1}{x} > 1$	■	all numbers for which the sum of the number and its reciprocal is greater than 1

59. The Small World long-distance phone company charges 55¢ for the first minute of a long-distance call and 23¢ for each additional minute.

a. Write an equation for the total cost C of an m-minute long-distance call. Explain what your variables and numbers mean.

b. How much does a 10-minute long-distance call cost?

c. Suppose a call costs $4.92. How long does the call last?

Notes _____

_____

_____

Mathematical Reflections 3

In this Investigation, you learned how to solve equations by operating on the symbols. The following questions will help you summarize what you have learned.

Think about these questions. Discuss your ideas with other students and your teacher. Then write a summary of your findings in your notebook.

1. **a.** Suppose that, in an equation with two variables, you know the value of one of the variables. **Describe** a method for finding the value of the other variable using the properties of equality. Give an example to illustrate your method.

   b. **Compare** the method you described in part (a) to the methods of using a table or a graph to solve linear equations.

2. **a.** **Explain** how an inequality can be solved by methods similar to those used to solve linear equations.

   b. **Describe** a method for finding the solution to an inequality using graphs.

3. Give an example of two equivalent expressions that were used in this Investigation. **Explain** why they are equivalent.

Notes _____

_____

_____

Common Core Mathematical Practices

As you worked on the Problems in this Investigation, you used prior knowledge to make sense of them. You also applied Mathematical Practices to solve the Problems. Think back over your work, the ways you thought about the Problems, and how you used Mathematical Practices.

Nick described his thoughts in the following way:

> In Problem 3.2, Question A, part (1), we first noted that there are 10 coins on the left and there are 4 coins and 3 bags on the right. So, the three bags must contain a total of 6 coins so that the total number of coins on the right is 10. We figured out that each bag must have 2 coins in it.
>
> But then another group showed us their method. They took four coins off of each side. Now they had 6 coins on the left and 3 bags on the right. They also found that each bag must have 2 coins. Both methods are correct.

Common Core Standards for Mathematical Practice

MP3 Construct viable arguments and critique the reasoning of others.

 • What other Mathematical Practices can you identify in Nick's reasoning?

• Describe a Mathematical Practice that you and your classmates used to solve a different Problem in this Investigation.

Notes _____

_____

_____

Exploring Slope: Connecting Rates and Ratios

▼ Investigation Overview

Investigation Description

Students find the ratio of vertical change to horizontal change between two points on a line. The connection between this ratio and constant rate of change is made explicit. Students find the slope of a line given two points on the line and then find the y-intercept using either a table or a graph. They write an equation of the form $y = mx + b$, in which m is the slope and b is the y-intercept.

Students then explore the idea that lines with the same slope are parallel lines, and that two lines whose slopes are the negative reciprocals of each other are perpendicular lines. Graphing calculators help students explore the slopes of many lines before they make their conjectures.

Investigation Vocabulary

• slope

Mathematics Background

• Rate of Change, Ratio, and Slope of a Line
• Finding the Rate of Change, or Slope, of a Linear Relationship
• Finding the y-Intercept and Equation for a Linear Relationship
• Equivalent Expressions

Planning Chart

Content	ACE	Pacing	Materials	Resources
Problem 4.1	1, 43–45, 49	1½ days	**Labsheet 4.1** Stair Measurement Table • Coordinate Grid measuring tape in inches, large sheets of graph paper or poster paper	
Problem 4.2	2–15, 46, 50, 52	1 day	**Labsheet 4.2** Linear Relationships **Labsheet 4ACE:** Exercise 7 (accessibility) • Coordinate Grid	**Teaching Aid 4.2A** A Set of Stairs **Teaching Aid 4.2B** Two Graphs and a Table **Teaching Aid 4.2C** Rate of Change Table **Teaching Aid 4.2D** Mary's Method • Climbing Monkeys
Problem 4.3	16–34, 47, 51	1½ days	• Coordinate Grid graphing calculators	**Teaching Aid 4.3** Pairs of Lines • Climbing Monkeys
Problem 4.4	35–42, 48, 53, 54	1 day	**Labsheet 4.4:** Linear Logic Activity (accessibility) poster paper	
Mathematical Reflections		½ day		
Looking Back		½ day		
Unit Project		optional		**Labsheet** Wasted Water Experiment **Labsheet** Ball Bounce Experiment
Self-Assessment		Take-home		• Notebook Checklist • Self-Assessment
Assessment: Unit Test		1 day		• Unit Test

▼ Goals and Standards

Goals

Linear Relationships Recognize problem situations in which two variables have a linear relationship

- Identify and describe the patterns of change between the independent and dependent variables for linear relationships represented by tables, graphs, equations, or contextual settings

- Construct tables, graphs, and symbolic equations that represent linear relationships

- Identify the rate of change between two variables and the x- and y-intercepts from graphs, tables, and equations that represent linear relationships

- Translate information about linear relationships given in a contextual setting, a table, a graph, or an equation to one of the other forms

- Write equations that represent linear relationships given specific pieces of information, and describe what information the variables and numbers represent

- Make a connection between slope as a ratio of vertical distance to horizontal distance between two points on a line and the rate of change between two variables that have a linear relationship

- Recognize that $y = mx$ represents a proportional relationship

- Solve problems and make decisions about linear relationships using information given in tables, graphs, and equations

Equivalence Understand that the equality sign indicates that two expressions are equivalent

- Recognize that the equation $y = mx + b$ represents a linear relationship and means that $mx + b$ is an expression equivalent to y

- Recognize that linear equations in one unknown, $k = mx + b$ or $y = m(t) + b$, where k, t, m, and b are constants, are special cases of the equation $y = mx + b$

- Recognize that finding the missing value of one of the variables in a linear relationship, $y = mx + b$, is the same as finding a missing coordinate of a point (x, y) that lies on the graph of the relationship

- Solve linear equations in one variable using symbolic methods, tables, and graphs

- Recognize that a linear inequality in one unknown is associated with a linear equation

- Solve linear inequalities using graphs or symbolic reasoning

- Show that two expressions are equivalent

- Write and interpret equivalent expressions

Mathematical Reflections

Look for evidence of student understanding of the goals for this Investigation in their responses to the questions in *Mathematical Reflections*. The goals addressed by each question are indicated below.

1. Explain what the slope of a line is. How does finding the slope compare to finding the rate of change between two variables in a linear relationship?

   Goals

   • Make a connection between slope as a ratio of vertical distance to horizontal distance between two points on a line and the rate of change between two variables that have a linear relationship

2. How can you find the slope of a line from

   a. an equation?

   b. a graph?

   c. a table of values of the line?

   d. the coordinates of two points on the line?

   Goals

   • Identify the rate of change between two variables and the *x*- and *y*-intercepts from graphs, tables, and equations that represent linear relationships

3. For parts (a) and (b), explain how you can write an equation of a line from the information. Use examples to illustrate your thinking.

   a. the slope and the *y*-intercept of the line

   b. two points on the line

   Goals

   • Write equations that represent linear relationships given specific pieces of information, and describe what information the variables and numbers represent

   • Translate information about linear relationships given in a verbal description, a table, a graph, or an equation to one of the other forms

   • Solve problems and make decisions about linear relationships using information given in tables, graphs, and equations

   • Recognize that the equation $y = mx + b$ represents a linear relationship and means that $mx + b$ is an expression equivalent to y

   • Solve linear equations in one variable using symbolic methods, tables, and graphs

Standards

Common Core Content Standards

7.RP.A.2d Explain what a point (x, y) on the graph of a proportional relationship means in terms of the situation, with special attention to the points $(0, 0)$ and $(1, r)$ where r is the unit rate. *Problem 2*

7.EE.A.1 Apply properties of operations as strategies to add, subtract, factor, and expand linear expressions with rational coefficients. *Problems 3 and 4*

7.EE.A.2 Understand that rewriting an expression in different forms in a problem context can shed light on the problem and how the quantities in it are related. *Problems 1, 3, and 4*

7.EE.B.4 Use variables to represent quantities in a real-world or mathematical problem, and construct simple equations and inequalities to solve problems by reasoning about the quantities. *Problems 1, 2, 3, and 4*

7.EE.B.4A Solve word problems leading to equations of the form $px + q = r$ and $p(x + q) = r$, where p, q, and r are specific rational numbers. Solve equations of these forms fluently. Compare an algebraic solution to an arithmetic solution, identifying the sequence of the operations used in each approach. *Problems 1 and 4*

Facilitating the Mathematical Practices

Students in *Connected Mathematics* classrooms display evidence of multiple Common Core Standards for Mathematical Practice every day. Here are just a few examples of when you might observe students demonstrating the Standards for Mathematical Practice during this Investigation.

Practice 1: **Make sense of problems and persevere in solving them.**

Students are engaged every day in solving problems and, over time, learn to persevere in solving them. To be effective, the problems embody critical concepts and skills and have the potential to engage students in making sense of mathematics. Students build understanding by reflecting, connecting, and communicating. These student-centered problem situations engage students in articulating the "knowns" in a problem situation and determining a logical solution pathway. The student-student and student-teacher dialogues help students not only to make sense of the problems, but also to persevere in finding appropriate strategies to solve them. The suggested questions in the Teacher Guides provide the metacognitive scaffolding to help students monitor and refine their problem-solving strategies.

Practice 4: **Model with mathematics.**

Students model with mathematics when they use a linear equation to find the amount of water dripping from a faucet in the Unit Project. They will see that, while the linear model is a good approximation for this situation, factors such as measurement error have an impact on the accuracy of the model.

Practice 7: **Look for and make use of structure.**

In Problem 4.3, students analyze the structure of equations of groups of lines. They also look for patterns in the graphs of these groups of lines. They will conclude that lines whose slopes are equal are parallel and that lines whose slopes are opposite reciprocals are perpendicular.

Students identify and record their personal experiences with the Standards for Mathematical Practice during the Mathematical Reflections at the end of the Investigation.

PROBLEM
4.1

Climbing Stairs
Using Rise and Run

▼ Problem Overview

> 𝓕𝓸𝓬𝓾𝓼 𝓠𝓾𝓮𝓼𝓽𝓲𝓸𝓷 How is the steepness of a set of stairs related to a straight-line graph?

Problem Description

Students investigate the "steepness" of a set of stairs by measuring the rise and run of the stairs and comparing their data to carpenters' guidelines. The ratio of "rise-to-run" informally introduces the concept of slope of a line.

Problem Implementation

Let students work in groups of 3 to 4.

You can give **Labsheet 4.1: Stair Measurement Table** to students to help them organize their data in Question A. It provides students with a table on which they can record all of the measurements they will need in order to compare their stairs with the carpenters' guidelines.

You can also hand out **Coordinate Grid**. This will allow students to remain focused on the mathematics of Question B while saving time.

Materials

• **Labsheet 4.1:** Stair Measurement Table

• **Coordinate Grid**

measuring tape in inches

large sheets of graph paper or poster paper

Vocabulary

There are no new glossary terms introduced in this Problem.

At a Glance and Lesson Plan

- At a Glance: Problem 4.1 Moving Straight Ahead
- Lesson Plan: Problem 4.1 Moving Straight Ahead

▼ Launch

Launch Video

This video shows a tourist climbing a large set of of stairs leading up to a monument. There are many different types of stairs at this monument. They have varying heights and lengths, and some are steeper than others. This video can illustrate for students the ways in which changing one or more of the dimensions of a stair can affect its steepness. It can give students ideas about how to measure the steepness of stairs, which can lead into a discussion of how to measure the steepness of a line. Visit Teacher Place at mathdashboard.com/cmp3 to see the complete video.

Connecting to Prior Knowledge

Remind students that they have explored many patterns of change that involve constant rates. They have explored the ways that the rate affects the steepness of the graph, the coefficient of x in a linear equation, and the rate of change between the variables. Tell students that, in this Investigation, they will explore another way to express a constant rate.

Presenting the Challenge

Discuss why stair climbing is a popular aerobic exercise, or show the Launch Video.

Suggested Questions

- Does the steepness of a set of stairs affect the exercise? (Yes; the steeper the stairs, the more difficult they are to climb, and the more exercise you get while climbing them.)

- Do all stairs have the same steepness? How can we determine the steepness? (No; some stairs are steeper than others. We can determine the steepness by measuring the stairs.)

You might have students examine the stairs in their house, apartment, or school for homework.

Pose the questions in the Introduction to the Problem. These questions ask students to think about how to describe steepness.

- How can you describe the steepness of the stairs?(The steepness of stairs depends on how tall each step is (the height) and on the distance from the edge of the step to the next step (the width). So really tall steps where the flat part you step on isn't very wide will make for a really steep set of stairs.)

- Is the steepness the same between any two consecutive steps?(Yes; it seems like the steepness would be the same because you would want all the steps to be consistent. So, the steepness between the consecutive steps should be the same.)

For the experiment in Question A, let students go out in groups to measure the rise and the run and then find the ratio of the rise to the run. Tell the groups that they need to measure more than one step in each set of stairs and compare the ratios. Use different sets of stairs for each group if possible.

Note: There are builders' codes that limit the variability of the rise and run, so new buildings may have stairs for which the "rise-to-run" ratio is consistent. Sometimes steps outside or in stadium bleachers will have a different steepness than stair steps inside houses.

Alternative Presentation

Pose this Problem a day or so before you intend to have the class work on it. This will allow students to do some physical experimentation. They should find several sets of stairs that have different-sized steps. Physically climbing several different sets of steps allows students to "feel" steepness. Challenge them to think about what makes one set of steps feel steeper than another.

Suggested Questions

- How could you use a mathematical measure to give an indication of steepness? (Have students make measurements on at least a couple of different sets of steps that they think might help in indicating steepness. When you are ready to launch the in-school part of this Problem, ask for suggestions on what factors seem to influence the steepness. What measures can give us a mathematical way to compare steepness? If no one mentions the rise and the run, make this suggestion as a possible measure. Draw a picture of a set of stairs and demonstrate the rise and run. You can either give the carpenters' guidelines for the ratio now or wait until after they have collected their data and then have them compare their ratios to the official guidelines.)

▼ Explore

Providing for Individual Needs

For Question A, when the groups have recorded their measures of a staircase in the building, have them organize what they have found out about the ratio of rise to run between several of the steps in the staircase. Also, have them look at the ratios of the rise to the run on the staircases they measured. Have the groups organize their information about steps and steepness.

For Question B, some students may need help in drawing the line that matches the ratio of changes. Grid paper may help. Suggest that students use the ratio 3 : 5 and the limit of 17 inches to sketch a couple of stairs on the grid paper. Then they can use the same grid paper to make a graph of a line through the origin with slope $\frac{3}{5}$ and compare the graph and the sketch of the stairs. They should see that the stairs align with the slope of the graph.

Suggested Questions

- What are the measurements for the rise and run that have the ratio of 3 to 5? Explain your reasoning. (Students need to use the guidelines for the length of the rise and run. For example, for a ratio of 3 to 5, the rise could be approximately 6.4 in. The run would be about 10.6 in. Students will most likely guess and check, but some might set up the ratio $\frac{3}{5} = \frac{x}{17 - x}$ and solve it for x, where x is the length of the rise.)

Planning for the Summary

What evidence will you use in the summary to clarify and deepen understanding of the Focus Question?

What will you do if you do not have evidence?

▼ Summarize

Orchestrating the Discussion

For Question A, let each group report on stairs they have investigated. Make a class record of the stairs and measures of the stairs that are reported. Compare the ratios for various sets of stairs.

Suggested Questions

- Are some stairs steeper than others? If so, how can you tell? (Yes. When climbing stairs, you can tell that some sets are steeper than others because some are easier to climb than others. Mathematically, you can tell that some stairs are steeper than others if their rise-to-run ratios are different.)

- What is the steepest set of stairs in our list? The least steep set of stairs? How do you know? (Answers will vary based on student measurements. Students should be able to justify their answers, though, by comparing the ratios of rise to run. The stairs with the greatest ratio would be the steepest, and the stairs with the least ratio would be the least steep.)

- Can you order the entire list of stairs from least to greatest in terms of steepness? (Yes; you can do this by ordering their ratios from least to greatest.)

These questions focus attention on uses of the ratio as a way of characterizing steepness in a mathematical sense. Steer the discussion to measures of rise and run. Make the connection to the Unit *Comparing and Scaling*, in which the students learned to form ratios as a way to compare situations.

If you have not done so already, talk about the carpenters' guidelines with your students. Then ask questions such as the following:

- How do the ratios of the stairs we measured compare to the carpenters' guidelines? Which ones meet the standards and which ones do not? (Answers will vary, but they should be reasonably close. If not, discuss possible reasons for large deviations.)

- What do you think influences a builder's decision on the run of a set of steps? (Answers will vary. Students may suggest that handicap requirements, wider run to accommodate items such as planters, and aesthetics may influence a builder's design.)

- What do you think influences a builder's decision on the rise of a set of steps? (A builder may consider how high a person of average height can comfortably step when deciding on the rise of a set of stairs. In these questions, students should be making comparisons using the ratio of the rise to the run.)

- Now let's think about another common object that you have climbed—a ladder. How can you use what you have learned so far to help make sense of steepness as it applies to ladders? What would make a ladder feel steep and what would make the same ladder feel less steep? (The angle of the ladder against the house will affect the rise, so it will affect how easy or difficult the ladder is to climb.)

Collect several equations from Question B. You may want to display several of their graphs for the class.

- What do you notice about these lines? (They are the same line.)

Discuss the strategies that students used to answer Question B.

- How is finding points on this line related to sketching a staircase with a rise to run ratio of 3 to 5? (Going from one point to another on the line is similar to moving 3 units vertically and then moving 5 units horizontally.)

- Sketch a line that does not meet the carpenters' guidelines. (Finding a line that does not meet the carpenters' guidelines is an opportunity for students to test their understanding of the ratio of rise to run.)

Problem 4.1 Summarize   241

Use this summary to define slope and to launch the next Problem. Use an illustration of stairs when you define the slope. Help students to make visual connections between these things that they have physically experienced and the lines on a graph representing linear relationships. Slope is the ratio of the change in the vertical distance to the change in the horizontal distance between two points on a line, or slope $= \frac{\text{vertical change}}{\text{horizontal change}}$.

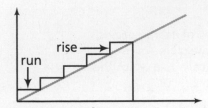
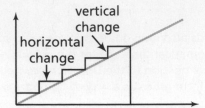

Reflecting on Student Learning

Use the following questions to assess student understanding at the end of the lesson.

- What evidence do I have that students understand the Focus Question?
  - Where did my students get stuck?
  - What strategies did they use?
  - What breakthroughs did my students have today?
  - How will I use this to plan for tomorrow? For the next time I teach this lesson?
- Where will I have the opportunity to reinforce these ideas as I continue through this Unit? The next Unit?

ACE Assignment Guide

- **Applications:** 1
- **Connections:** 43–45, 49

PROBLEM
4.2   Finding the Slope of a Line

▼ Problem Overview

> *Focus Question* How can you find the y-intercept and the slope of a line from data in a table, graph, or equation?

Problem Description

In this Problem, students find the slope of a line from a graph, a table, an equation, or two points on the line. They compare slope of a line to the constant rate of change between the two variables in the relationship represented by $y = mx + b$.

The slope of a line is the ratio of vertical change to horizontal change between two points on a line. The connection between this ratio and constant rate of change between the two variables in a linear relationship is made explicit.

To find the equation of a line through two points, students use the points to find the slope of the line through the given points. They then find the y-intercept using either a table or graph. Finally, they write an equation of the form $y = mx + b$, where m is the slope and b is the y-intercept.

Problem Implementation

Students can work on the problems in pairs. You can assign different groups to do one table, one graph, and one equation.

You can give **Labsheet 4.2: Linear Relationships** to students to help them organize their answers to Question A. It provides students with a table on which they can record the slope, y-intercept, and equation for each linear relationship.

If you have some students who would benefit from plotting the points in Question B on a graph, you can give them a **Coordinate Grid**. This can allow students to remain focused on the mathematics of the Question while saving time.

Materials

- **Labsheet 4.2:** Linear Relationships
- **Labsheet 4ACE:** Exercise 7 (accessibility)
- **Coordinate Grid**
- **Teaching Aid 4.2A:** A Set of Stairs
- **Teaching Aid 4.2B:** Two Graphs and a Table
- **Teaching Aid 4.2C:** Rate of Change Table
- **Teaching Aid 4.2D:** Mary's Method

Using Technology

If your students have access to computers, they can use **Climbing Monkeys** to find the slopes of lines on an interactive graph.

Vocabulary

- slope

Mathematics Background

- Rate of Change, Ratio, and Slope of a Line
- Finding the Rate of Change, or Slope, of a Linear Relationship
- Finding the *y*-Intercept and Equation for a Linear Relationship

At a Glance and Lesson Plan

- At a Glance: Problem 4.2 Moving Straight Ahead
- Lesson Plan: Problem 4.2 Moving Straight Ahead

▼ Launch

Launch Video

This video shows a dynamic definition of slope. A set of footprints walks up a staircase on a coordinate grid. The staircase aligns with the graph of the line $y = 2x + 3$, and the footprints illustrate how to locate the rise and run on the graph. You can show this video to start a discussion about slope and about whether or not the slope of a line is the same for any two points on the line. Visit Teacher Place at mathdashboard.com/cmp3 to see the complete video.

Connecting to Prior Knowledge

Use the introduction to launch the Problem. Display **Teaching Aid 4.2A: A Set of Stairs**.

Tell students that the steepness of the line is the ratio of rise to run, or vertical change to horizontal change, for each step. Tell students that this ratio is called the **slope** of the line.

$$\text{slope} = \frac{\text{verticalchange}}{\text{horizontalchange}} = \frac{\text{rise}}{\text{run}}$$

This is also a good time to show the Launch Video.

Suggested Questions

- Does the slope change if we take two stairs at a time? Explain. (No, because you just create an equivalent ratio. For example, suppose the rise to run between two stairs is 3 to 5. Then, if you take two stairs at a time, the rise- to-run ratio is 6 to 10, which is equivalent to the ratio of 3 to 5.)

- Is the slope the same between any two stairs? Explain. (Yes; see previous answer.)

These two questions represent important aspects of determining the slope of a line given two points.

Presenting the Challenge

Pose the challenge of finding the slope of a line from a table, graph, or equation. If needed, you can use some of the questions from the Alternative Presentation below during the Explore.

Alternative Presentation

If you think your class needs more structure, you can ask the following questions from the Introduction. Display **Teaching Aid 4.2B: Two Graphs and a Table**.

Suggested Questions

- What is the slope of each line? Explain how you can find it. (The slope of the first graph is $\frac{2}{3}$. The slope of the second graph is $-\frac{2}{3}$. The slope of the line represented by the table is $\frac{3}{1}$. You can find the slope of the line in each graph by figuring out the vertical change (rise) between the two points and the horizontal change (run) between the two points. You can find the slope of the line represented by the table by calculating the change in y-values for a one-unit change in the x-values.)

- How do we indicate the change in direction? That is, how do we indicate if the steepness of a line is decreasing or increasing from left to right? (The slope is negative if the line decreases from left to right and positive if it increases from left to right. It is 0 if the line is horizontal.)

You might want to use the metaphor of "going up" a hill vs. "going down" the same hill. The steepness is the same, but the direction changes. Use student responses to model how to find the vertical change and horizontal change. We can think of the run as an increment in *x*, the independent variable, so we usually read the graph from left to right, the same way we would usually set up a table. If the vertical change goes down as we move from one point to the next, *reading from left to right*, then the change is negative, and the slope is negative. Similarly, if the vertical change goes up as we move from one point to the next, the change is positive and the slope is positive.

- Does it make any difference which two points we pick? (For each line, pick 2 or 3 different pairs of points and use them to find the slope of the line. Show that the ratios are equal.)

Repeat the preceding questions for the second graph.

- Describe the graph of the data. (It has a slope of 3 and a *y*-intercept of 3. It is rising from left to right. For each unit change in *x* (horizontal change) there is a 3-unit change in *y* (vertical change).

▼ Explore

Providing for Individual Needs

As you move around the room, check to see if students are finding the vertical and horizontal changes correctly. Have students show you on the graph where the changes are. For the most part, finding the *y*-intercept should be a review for students. For the tables, students may work backward in the table to find the *y*-intercept.

Suggested Questions

Look for ways that students will find two more points given two points on a line. (See the answers for ways students might do Question B.) Refer to these in the Summarize.

- Start at the point where *x* is 3. What is the corresponding value for *y*? (5)

- Now look at the point where *x* is −2. What is the corresponding value for *y*? (10)

- What is the change in the horizontal and the vertical directions between these two points? How do you know? (In order to move from 3 to −2 on the *x*-axis, you move 5 units to the left. So, the change in the horizontal direction is −5. In order to move from 5 to 10 on the *y*-axis, you move up 5 units. So, the change in the vertical direction is 5.)

- What does this tell you about the slope of the line representing the equation? (This tells you that the slope is $\frac{5}{-5}$, or −1.)

- If you looked at the ratio of the horizontal change to the vertical change between two different points on the graph of the line, what would the ratio be? How do you know? (The line has the same steepness throughout the graph, so the ratio would still be −1.)

For some students, the most difficult part of finding the slope from two points on a line is finding the vertical and horizontal distances between two points, particularly if the point does not lie on the intersection of two grid lines. If you see students struggling with this, you might suggest that they display the two points in a table. Some students find the table easier to use for determining the rate or ratio. In any case, the connection between rate and ratio needs to be highlighted. Suggest that students make a table such as the one on **Teaching Aid 4.2C: Rate of Change Table.** Ask them to fill in the coordinates of the points in the table in order to help connnect rate and ratio.

x	−2	−1	0	1	2	3	Change in $x = 1$
y	10					5	Change in $y = ?$

For Question C, ask:

- How is the coefficient of x in a linear equation related to the ratio of vertical change to horizontal change on a graph? (The coefficient of x in a linear equation is equal to the ratio of vertical change to horizontal change on a graph.)

Planning for the Summary

What evidence will you use in the summary to clarify and deepen understanding of the Focus Question?

What will you do if you do not have evidence?

▼ Summarize

Orchestrating the Discussion

Discuss all of the Questions. Be sure to make the connections among the various representations of slope—as the constant rate of change between two variables, the ratio of vertical change to horizontal change between two points of the graph of a linear relationship, and the coefficient m in the equation $y = mx + b$. The following questions can help students develop understanding of the connection between slope and rate of change, using slope to find points on a line, and methods for finding the y-intercept.

Suggested Questions

Connecting Slope and Rate of Change

Making the connection between the geometric interpretation of slope and the coefficient may be the most difficult. Use the equation $y = 2x$ to make a table.

- What patterns do you see in the table? (As x increases by 1 unit, y increases by 2 units.)

Be more directive, if necessary.

- As *x* increases by 1 unit, how does *y* increase? (by 2 units)

- How will this pattern of change appear on the graph of this line? (We would expect to see the line "stepping up" 2 units vertically for every 1 unit horizontally.)

Draw the graph of $y = 2x$, using the coordinate pairs from the table to mark points on the graph.

- What is the ratio of the change in vertical distance to the horizontal distance? ($\frac{2}{1}$)

- What happens to the ratio of vertical change to horizontal change when two different, not necessarily consecutive, points, such as $(-2, -4)$ and $(1, 2)$, are measured? (This is a very important point that will need to be discussed several times. The ratio between any horizontal change to its corresponding vertical change is constant for a given linear relationship.)

Demonstrate that this ratio of change is the same no matter which two points are picked.

For the points $(0, 0)$ and $(1, 2)$, the ratio is $\frac{2}{1}$, or 2.

For the points $(3, 6)$ and $(5, 10)$, the ratio is or $\frac{4}{2}$, or 2.

Draw a picture to help the students find the vertical distance and the horizontal distance.

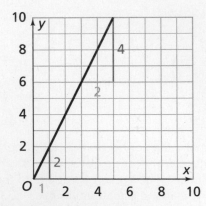

- What is the slope of this line? ($\frac{2}{1}$)

- How could we tell this from the equation? (It is the coefficient of *x* if the equation is of the form $y = mx + b$.)

Two vertical number lines can be used as another representation of the change in *y* related to the change in *x*. The picture below is helpful to some students. It shows that as *x* is changing in a regular way, *y* is also changing in a regular way, but that the two changes may be different. A change of one unit in *x* is accompanied by a change of two units in *y*.

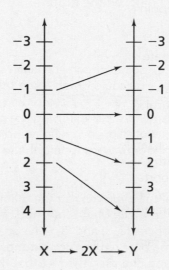

$$X \longrightarrow 2X \longrightarrow Y$$

Using Slope to Find Other Points on the Line

- If you know one point on the graph of a line and you know the slope of the line, how can you use the slope to create a set of points that all lie on the line? (For example, suppose the slope is $\frac{2}{1}$ and the point on the graph of the line is (1, 2). Then the point (2, ■) can be found by moving one unit to the right and two units up on the graph:)

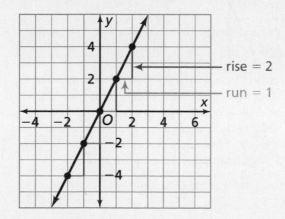

Be more directive, if necessary.

An important observation is to note that no matter what two points you choose to find the vertical change and horizontal change, the ratio is always the same. To go from (1, 2) to (3, ■), move two units to the right and four units up. This point is (3, 6). A similar method can be used to find other points. In later math courses, students will use another name for this ratio—it is the tangent of the angle formed by the graph of the equation and the *x*-axis. The angle is called the angle of inclination.

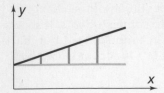

Vertical change
to horizontal change
is always the same
between any two
points on the graph.

Finding the y-Intercept

- How can you find the *y*-intercept given 2 points on the line, such as
  (3, 3) and (5, 9)? (To find the *y*-intercept, you could graph a line that
  goes through the points (3, 3) and (5, 9) and see if you could read the
  y-intercept off the graph. You could also find the slope using the points
  (3, 3) and (5, 9). Since this is a linear relationship, you could complete a
  table, using the slope to count backward or forward to find the value for *y*
  when *x* is 0.

To help students find the *y*-intercept symbolically, you can use the following
situation, which also appears on **Teaching Aid 4.2D: Mary's Method**. Mary was
trying to find the slope of the line that the points (3, 3) and (5, 9) lie on. Mary used
her understanding of slope as the ratio of rise over run to find that the slope is
equal to 3. She needed to find the *y*-intercept. She used the fact that the point
(5, 9) lies on the line to find the *y*-intercept. She explained her method to the class:

$y = 3x + b$	The slope of the line is the coefficient of *x*. The *y*-intercept is *b*.
$9 = 3(5) + b$	The point (5, 9) lies on the line. The coordinates of the point make this a true statement.
$b = -6$	Solve the equation for *b*.
$y = 3x - 6$	Write the equation of a line with slope 3 and *y*-intercept equal to -6.

- Is Mary's method correct? Explain how you might check that the linear
  equation she found is the correct one for this situation. (Students might
  try *both* points in the equation. There is only one line that would pass
  through both points, so she has the right equation if both points are
  solutions. Or they might draw a graph, which is not as accurate. Or they
  might make a table and check that both points are in the table.)

- Is there another way to find the *y*-intercept? (You can use a table or
  a graph.)

Check for Understanding

- What is the equation of the line that goes through the points (2, 6) and
  (0, 4)? (We need the slope and *y*-intercept. There is a change of +2 in
  the vertical direction for a change of +2 in the horizontal direction. This
  gives a slope of $\frac{2}{2}$, or 1. Since we have the point (0, 4), we know that the
  y-intercept is 4. This gives the equation $y = x + 4$.)

- Is there another way to find the *y*-intercept? (You can use a table or
  a graph.)

You may have to help students find the vertical and horizontal changes. A picture helps.

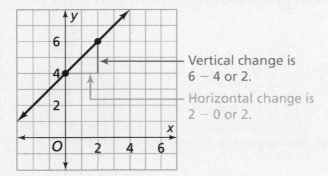

Vertical change is 6 − 4 or 2.

Horizontal change is 2 − 0 or 2.

- If you have the two points (1, 6) and (5, 4), how can you find the slope of the line through these two points? (Sketch a graph of the line. Let students describe how to find the slope. It is the same method as in the previous two problems.)

Reflecting on Student Learning

Use the following questions to assess student understanding at the end of the lesson.

- What evidence do I have that students understand the Focus Question?
  - Where did my students get stuck?
  - What strategies did they use?
  - What breakthroughs did my students have today?
- How will I use this to plan for tomorrow? For the next time I teach this lesson?
- Where will I have the opportunity to reinforce these ideas as I continue through this Unit? The next Unit? Check for Understanding

ACE Assignment Guide

- **Applications:** 2–15
- **Connections:** 46, 50, 52
- **Labsheet 4ACE:** Exercise 7 (accessibility)

Note: This Labsheet is an example of a way to provide students with additional support for an ACE Exercise.

Exploring Patterns With Lines

▼ Problem Overview

> *Focus Question* How can you predict if two lines are parallel or perpendicular from their equations?

Problem Description

Students apply their knowledge of slope and lines to explore patterns among sets of lines—those with the same slope (parallel lines) and those whose slopes are opposite reciprocals of each other (perpendicular lines). Graphing calculators help students explore many lines before they make their conjectures.

Problem Implementation

Students can work in pairs or groups of 3 to 4.

You can ask groups to put their solutions on large sheets of graph paper to display and discuss during the Summarize.

Hand out three copies of **Coordinate Grid** to each student. You can also give students extra copies of **Coordinate Grid** to use for ACE Exercises 16–19 and 24–26.

Materials

- **Teaching Aid 4.3:** Pairs of Lines
- **Coordinate Grid**

graphing calculators

large sheets of graph paper

Using Technology

If your students have access to computers, they can use **Climbing Monkeys** to compare the slopes of lines on an interactive graph. Students can compare the graphs of monkeys who climb at the same rate but begin at different heights. Students can then make conjectures about similarities and differences in the equations representing the monkeys' heights.

Vocabulary

There are no new glossary terms introduced in this Problem.

At a Glance and Lesson Plan

- At a Glance: Problem 4.3 Moving Straight Ahead
- Lesson Plan: Problem 4.3 Moving Straight Ahead

▼ Launch

Connecting to Prior Knowledge

Suppose a line has slope 3. Provide students with a **Coordinate Grid**.

Suggested Questions

- Sketch a line with this slope. Is your line the same as those of your classmates? What patterns do you notice? (Students should notice that they can sketch many lines with a slope of 3 that are parallel to their first line.)

- How can we predict this outcome from the equations of the lines? (The lines will all have the same slope, 3. The slope, 3, is also the coefficient of x in the equation $y = b + mx$.)

Presenting the Challenge

Tell students that, in this Problem, they will use slope to explore some patterns among linear relationships. Ask the class to briefly look at each set of lines in Question A. Ask them for any observations that they may have. Tell them they can use their calculators, but that they should keep a sketch of each graph for reference.

▼ Explore

Providing for Individual Needs

As you walk around, encourage the students to look for patterns and make conjectures. Then, encourage them to think about why their conjectures might work. You can use large sheets of graph paper for groups to record their work. Suggest that they try a different coefficient (slope) for Question A to test their conjectures.

Suggested Questions

- What do the graphs of the lines $y = 2x + 5$ and $y = 4x + 10$ look like? Do they fit the patterns in Question A? (No; the slopes of the lines in each group in Question A are the same.)

Going Further

Have students explore other families of lines, such as:

$y = a$ (horizontal lines)

$x = a$ (vertical lines)

Planning for the Summary

What evidence will you use in the summary to clarify and deepen understanding of the Focus Question?

What will you do if you do not have evidence?

▼ Summarize

Orchestrating the Discussion

Have groups share their conjectures and reasoning. You can refer to the student posters and/or use the overhead or interactive whiteboard display of the graphing calculator to show examples from various groups.

After you have summarized the Problem, you could ask questions that help summarize the ideas in the Unit.

Suggested Questions

- Is the line that passes through the points (0, 6) and (2, 12) parallel to the line $y = 3x + b$? Why or why not? (Students need to find the slope of the line that passes through the given points, which is 3. So it is parallel to the line $y = 3x + b$ as long as the two lines have different y-intercepts. If the intercepts are the same, the lines are identical.)

- Are the lines $y = 5x + 2$ and $y = -0.2x$ perpendicular to each other? Why or why not? (Yes; the slope of the second line, -0.2, is equal to $-\frac{1}{5}$, which is the negative reciprocal of the slope of the first line, 5.)

- Which of the following lines are parallel to each other? Which are perpendicular to each other?

    $y = 6 - 4x$

    $y = 8 + 2.5x$

    $2y = -8x$

    $y = 0.25x - 1$

    $y = 6 - 0.4x$

    The lines $y = 6 - 0.4x$ and $2y = -8x$ are parallel. The lines $y = 6 - 4x$ and $y = 0.25x - 1$ are perpendicular.

Display **Teaching Aid 4.3: Pairs of Lines** and ask:

- Decide whether each pair of linear relationships represents parallel lines, perpendicular lines, or neither. Explain your reasoning.

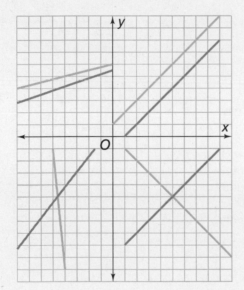

The two lines in the first quadrant are parallel, because they both have a slope of 1. You can find the slopes of these lines by choosing points on the lines and measuring the rise and run between the points. The two lines in the fourth quadrant are perpendicular. You can find the slopes of these lines by choosing points on the lines and measuring the rise and run between the points. The slope of one of the lines is 1, and the slope of the other is −1, so their slopes are opposite reciprocals. The pairs of lines in the second and third quadrants are neither parallel nor perpendicular. The slopes of the lines in the second quadrant are $\frac{1}{4}$ and $\frac{1}{8}$. The slopes of the lines in the third quadrant are −10 and approximately 1.3.

Reflecting on Student Learning

Use the following questions to assess student understanding at the end of the lesson.

- What evidence do I have that students understand the Focus Question?
  - Where did my students get stuck?
  - What strategies did they use?
  - What breakthroughs did my students have today?
- How will I use this to plan for tomorrow? For the next time I teach this lesson?
- Where will I have the opportunity to reinforce these ideas as I continue through this Unit? The next Unit?

ACE Assignment Guide

- **Applications:** 16–34
- **Connections:** 47, 51

PROBLEM

4.4

Pulling It All Together
Writing Equations for Linear Relationships

▼ Problem Overview

Focus Question What information do you need to write an equation for a
linear relationship? Is the expression for the dependent
variable always the same?

Problem Description

This Problem provides three situations. The first situation gives information about
the coordinates of two points on the line of a linear relationship. The context helps
students find the needed information in a variety of ways.

In the second situation, students find an equation that represents a relationship
between Celsius and Fahrenheit temperatures. Again, two points of the
relationship are given, one being the y-intercept. Students will most likely find the
slope of the line using the coordinates of the two points and then use the slope
and y-intercept to write an equation.

The third situation involves a sequence of square tiles. Students are asked to
find equations that represent the perimeter and area of the nth figure and to
determine if either the perimeter or area patterns represent linear relationships.

This Problem pulls together the main ideas in the Unit. Students find the slope and
y-intercept from contextual cues and write equations for linear relationships. They
separate linear from nonlinear situations. Students deepen their understanding of
what it means for a relationship to be linear, and they see the connection between
a constant rate of change and the slope of a line.

Students also see that there are different ways to indicate relationships between
quantities by writing equivalent expressions for the dependent variable. As they
answer specific questions about the value of one of the variables, they are also
solving linear equations.

Problem Implementation

Let students work in pairs and then move to larger groups to discuss their solutions.

You can ask different groups to solve the problem in either Question A or B. Discuss these and then ask all students to complete Questions C and D. Question C leads to equivalent expressions and to a pattern that is not linear.

Students could put their work on poster paper or a display sheet to use in the Summarize.

As a summary activity, you can give extra vocabulary support to students by having them make an idea web, such as the **Labsheet 4.4: Linear Logic Activity** that comes at the end of this Investigation. Linking vocabulary words together provides another way to help students remember important words.

After students have finished the activity, have them complete a vocabulary chart using the words from the Unit. On the board, draw a large version of the idea web. As a class, have students use their charts to come up with additional concepts and descriptions of relationships between concepts. Students should also record these words in their vocabulary list.

Materials

- **Labsheet 4.4:** Linear Logic Activity (accessibility)
- **Notebook Checklist**
- **Self-Assessment**
- **Unit Test**

poster paper

Vocabulary

There are no new glossary terms introduced in this Problem.

Mathematics Background

- Equivalent Expressions

At a Glance and Lesson Plan

- At a Glance: Problem 4.4 Moving Straight Ahead
- Lesson Plan: Problem 4.4 Moving Straight Ahead

▼ Launch

Connecting to Prior Knowledge

Suggested Questions

- Describe some situations from this Unit that we have explored. (Answers will vary. Students may mention walking rates, money raised for charity during a walkathon, the income and expenses of Fabulous Fabian's Bakery, etc.)

- Are there any clues in the situation that might help us determine that it is linear? If so, what clues indicate the slope or y-intercept? (Again, answers will vary, but students should mention that the constant rate of change (walking rate in meters per second, money raised in dollars per kilometer, income earned in dollars per cake sold, etc.) tells you the slope. They should also be able to say that the y-intercept is the value of the independent variable at the beginning of the situation (a head start of 40 meters in a walking race, a donor who pledges $5 even if you walk 0 kilometers, an income of $0 for selling 0 cakes, etc.).)

Presenting the Challenge

Tell the class that they are to explore several situations and decide whether or not they are linear. If they are linear, students will write an equation that represents the relationship.

If students need more assistance, you can ask the following questions.

Suggested Questions

For Question A, tell the story of Chantal. Challenge the class to solve the puzzle.

- Do you think this situation will be represented by a linear equation? What cues help you recognize that this is a linear relationship? (Yes; Chantal is saving a constant amount each week, so the relationship will have a constant rate of change.)

For Question B, present the following scenario about temperature.

- If you have traveled in Europe or Canada where the temperature is in Celsius and you hear a temperature report on TV that says it is 20° Celsius, how would you interpret how hot or cold it is? (Answers will vary. Students may suggest paying attention to the weather forecast for several days and comparing each temperature to what it felt like outside.)

After students have shared what they know from their experiences, read Question B with them. It gives two points of reference between the two temperature scales: the temperatures at which water boils and freezes.

- What information do we have? How is this similar to previous problems? (You have the coordinates of two points that lie on the line that represents this linear relationship: (0, 32) and (100, 212).)

- What are the variables? (the temperatures given by each of the scales: degrees Celsius and degrees Fahrenheit)

Have a conversation with the students about the variables. You may want to decide as a class which variable will be the dependent variable (the variable on the *x*-axis) and independent variable (the variable on the *y*-axis). In this case, there is no truly dependent variable. The relationship makes sense either way. You can predict Celsius from Fahrenheit or predict Fahrenheit from Celsius.

▼ Explore

Providing for Individual Needs

You can ask some of the questions raised in the Launch if needed.

Suggested Questions

Circulate and ask questions such as:

- **Why does that make sense?**

- **Can you tell me how this relationship would look as a graph?**

- **Where would the line cross the *y*-axis? How do you know?**

In Question B, if students treat Celsius as the independent variable (the variable on the horizontal axis) and Fahrenheit as the dependent variable (the variable on the vertical axis), the slope comes out to be $\frac{9}{5}$. **Note:** In this situation, it does not matter which is the independent variable and which is the dependent variable; so there are two correct equations. If students use Fahrenheit as the independent variable and Celsuis as the dependent variable, the slope comes out to be $\frac{5}{9}$.

You may need to help or give some hints to the groups. Suggest that they make a sketch. This may help them find the vertical and horizontal changes. *Slope is best remembered if it is attached to a picture.* Some students will find the differences between the freezing and boiling points of water for Fahrenheit and Celsius. This gives

$$F - 180° \qquad\qquad C - 100°$$

Then they write the ratio $\frac{180}{100}$ and get 1.8 without drawing a sketch. This is good reasoning.

For Question C, many students may use the pictures to find a relationship between the perimeter and the figure number. Some may make a table. The table suggests that the pattern is linear. They can use this to write an equation. Note that we do not know for sure that the pattern in the table will continue, but if we assume it does, then we claim it is linear. This is an important concept to point out to the class.

Look for equivalent expressions. Be sure to ask students to show that the expressions are or are not equivalent.

These comments also apply to Question C, part (4).

Planning for the Summary

What evidence will you use in the summary to clarify and deepen understanding of the Focus Question?

What will you do if you do not have evidence?

▼ Summarize

Orchestrating the Discussion

Ask students how much money Chantal saved from her allowance each week and how much her grandfather gave her for her birthday. Have students explain how they found these amounts.

Look for different ways of solving the problem.

Some students may notice that in three weeks Chantal has saved $15. If she puts in the same amount every week, then she is putting in $5 a week. This is the slope or the rate at which Chantal is saving her money. Some students might find the y-intercept by using the idea of rate. By working backward, they see that, in the first five weeks, she has saved $5 a week, for a total of $25. This means she must have started with $150, since $175 - 25 = 150$. The y-intercept is 150.

Suggested Questions

- What is the slope? What is the y-intercept? How did you find them? (Sample methods students may use are listed below.

  - Making a table and working out the missing steps to find the rate or using the ratio of $\frac{\text{vertical change}}{\text{horizontal change}}$. (The y-intercept is found by using the rate to go backward to find the point (0, b) in the table.)

  -

Week	Amount
5	175
6	
7	
8	190

    Using a graph and reading the rise and run from point to point. (The line is extended to give an approximate value for the y-intercept.)

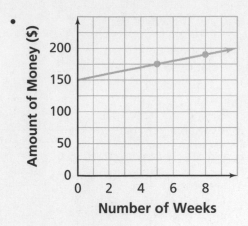

Reasoning verbally, which is most common with the students. (If Chantal saved $15 in 3 weeks, then she must be saving $5 a week. So, she must have saved $25 since her birthday. Thus, she started with $150.))

Discuss Question B and ask how students found the equations. Check the answers to the questions.

Ask students to find a third point on the line. Check a few possibilities for the third point that lies on the line—there should be several different ones.

- How many points are on the line? Could we list them all? (No; the equation describes the relationship for the infinite number of points that lie on the line, and the graph is a picture of this relationship.)

- Did you use a graphing calculator or the equation to find answers? (Answers will vary based on how students solved the problem.)

- What is the *x*-intercept? What information does it represent? (If students used degrees Celsius as the independent variable and degrees Fahrenheit as the dependent variable, the *x*-intercept is $-17.\overline{7}$. This represents the temperature, in degrees Celsius, that corresponds to a temperature of 0 °F.

  If students used degrees Fahrenheit as the independent variable and degrees Celsius as the dependent variable, the *x*-intercept is 32. This represents the temperature, in degrees Fahrenheit, that corresponds to a temperature of 0 °C.)

Once you have the equation, test it by using different temperatures. Graph the equation on a calculator. You can use the following rule of thumb for conversion: "Double the Celsius and add 30." Tell the students that the relationship is linear. It is easy to find an equation for the rule of thumb. Now put the graphs of both the actual equation and the rule of thumb equation on the graphing calculator.

- For what temperatures is the rule of thumb fairly close to the actual temperatures? (For temperatures around 10 °C, the results given by the rule of thumb are fairly close to the actual temperatures in degrees Fahrenheit.)

Note: This might be a good time to probe student understanding of dependent and independent variables. You might ask whether the relationship $F = \frac{9}{5}C + 32$ (which many students write as $F = 1.8C + 32$) shows a relationship in which one variable is dependent on the other.

- If you rewrite the equation as $C = \frac{5}{9}F - \frac{160}{9}$ (or $C = \frac{5}{9}F - \frac{160}{9}$), does the dependent variable change? (Yes; the dependent variable is now degrees Celsius rather than degrees Fahrenheit. Either temperature scale can be used as the independent or dependent variable.)

- How is this relationship different from the cricket-chirp rule $t = \frac{n}{4} + 40$ from ACE Exercise 42 in Investigation 3? (This rule also can be rewritten as $n = 4t - 160$. One variable is clearly dependent on the other. What makes a difference in form is which variable you are likely to have a value for and from which you want to predict the other variable.)

Solicit strategies for identifying and representing the patterns in Question C or D. See the answers for possible strategies that might emerge.

Reflecting on Student Learning

Use the following questions to assess student understanding at the end of the lesson.

- What evidence do I have that students understand the Focus Question?
  - Where did my students get stuck?
  - What strategies did they use?
  - What breakthroughs did my students have today?
- How will I use this to plan for tomorrow? For the next time I teach this lesson?
- Where will I have the opportunity to reinforce these ideas as I continue through this Unit? The next Unit?

ACE Assignment Guide

- **Applications:** 35–42
- **Connections:** 48
- **Extensions:** 53, 54

▼ Mathematical Reflections

Possible Answers to Mathematical Reflections

1. Slope describes the steepness of a line. It is the ratio of vertical change to horizontal change. If it is positive, then the line is increasing from left to right. If it is negative, then it is decreasing from left to right. If the slope is zero, the line is horizontal. This is like walking on a flat surface as opposed to up or down a hill.

   Finding the slope is the same as finding the rate of change between two variables in a linear relationship. The horizontal distance change between two points is the same as the difference between two corresponding x-values of points in a table. The vertical change in distance is the same as the difference between two corresponding y-values of points in a table.

2. **a.** If the equation of a line is in the form $y = mx + b$, then m is the slope.

   b. In a graph, find two points on the graph and then find the difference between the y-coordinates (the vertical change) and the difference between the x-coordinates (the horizontal change). Then, find the ratio of vertical change to horizontal change.

   c. In a table for a linear relationship, the slope can be found by finding the change in two x-values and the change in two corresponding y-values. The slope is the ratio of the change in the y-values to the change in the x-values.

   d. If you know the coordinates of two points on the line, you can find the slope by figuring out what the change in the y-value is for a change of 1 in the x-value. For example, for the points (0, 4) and (2, 6), the slope is 1. This is because the y-value change is 2 for an x-value change of 2, and $\frac{2}{2} = 1$.

3. **a.** If you have the slope and the y-intercept, you can substitute them into the equation $y = mx + b$. For example, if the slope is 2 and the y-intercept is 3, the equation of the line is $y = 2x + 3$.

   b. If you know two points on the line, you can first find the slope by figuring out what the change in the y-value is for a change of 1 in the x-value.

   Then, you need to find the y-intercept. If one of the points has an x-value of 0, then the y-value of that point is the y-intercept. Otherwise, you will have to find the y-intercept in a different way. You could graph the given points and see where the line crosses the y-axis. Or you could figure out what the y-value would be for an x-value of 0 by seeing how the y-values change in relation to the x-values.

   For example, for the points (0, 4) and (2, 6), the slope is 1 because the y-value change is 2 for an x-value change of 2 and the y-intercept is 4, so the equation is $y = x + 4$. Also, once you find the slope, you can substitute it for m in the equation $y = mx + b$. Then, you can substitute the coordinates of one of the points for x and y in the equation and solve for b.

Possible Answers to Mathematical Practices Reflections

Students may have demonstrated all of the eight Common Core Standards for Mathematical Practice during this Investigation. During the class discussion, have students provide additional Practices that the Problem cited involved and identify the use of other Mathematical Practices in the Investigation.

One student observation is provided in the Student Edition. Here is another sample student response.

> The data points in the Wasted Water Experiment from the Unit Project are very close to lying on the same line. Data collected in an experiment like this are subject to measurement error and to other circumstances that may cause the points not to fit exactly on a straight line. However, the points should be very close to fitting on a line. It is interesting and helpful to use a linear equation to model a dripping faucet when you are trying to determine how much water is wasted.
>
> **MP4: Model with mathematics.**

Notes

Exploring Slope: Connecting Rates and Ratios

All of the patterns of change you have explored in this Unit involved constant rates. For example, you worked with walking rates expressed in meters per second and pledge rates expressed in dollars per kilometer. In these situations, you found that the rate affects the following things:

- the steepness of the graph

- the coefficient, m, of x in the equation $y = mx + b$

- how the y-values in the table change for each unit change in the x-values

In this Investigation, you will explore another way to express the constant rate.

....

Common Core State Standards

7.RP.A.2d Explain what a point (x, y) on the graph of a proportional relationship means in terms of the situation, with special attention to the points $(0, 0)$ and $(1, r)$, where r is the unit rate.

7.EE.A.2 Understand that rewriting an expression in different forms in a problem context can shed light on the problem and how the quantities in it are related.

Also 7.EE.A.1, 7.EE.B.4, 7.EE.B.4a

Notes _____

_____

_____

_____

4.1 Climbing Stairs
Using Rise and Run

Climbing stairs is good exercise, so some athletes run up and down stairs as part of their training. The steepness of stairs determines how difficult they are to climb. By investigating the steepness of stairs, you can find another important way to describe the steepness of a line.

Consider these questions about the stairs you use at home, in your school, and in other buildings.

- How can you describe the steepness of the stairs?

- Is the steepness the same between any two consecutive steps?

Carpenters have developed the guidelines below to ensure that the stairs they build are relatively easy for a person to climb. Steps are measured in inches.

- The ratio of rise to run for each step should be between 0.45 and 0.60.

- The rise plus the run for each step should be between 17 and $17\frac{1}{2}$ inches.

The steepness of stairs is determined by the ratio of the rise to the run for each step. The rise and run are labeled in the diagram below.

Notes

Problem 4.1

A **1.** Determine the steepness of a set of stairs in your school or home. To calculate the steepness you will need to

- measure the rise and run of at least two steps in the set of stairs.

- make a sketch of the stairs, and label the sketch with the measurements you found.

- find the ratio of rise to run.

2. How do the stairs you measured compare to the carpenters' guidelines on the previous page?

B A set of stairs is being built for the front of the new Arch Middle School. The ratio of rise to run is 3 to 5.

1. Is this ratio within the carpenters' guidelines?

2. Make a sketch of a set of stairs that meet this ratio. Label the lengths of the rise and run of a step.

3. Sketch the graph of a line that passes through the origin and whose y-values change by 3 units for each 5-unit change in the x-values.

4. **a.** Write an equation for the line in part (3).

b. What is the coefficient of x in the equation?

c. How is the coefficient related to the steepness of the line represented by the equation?

d. How is the coefficient related to the steepness of a set of stairs with this ratio?

ACE Homework starts on page 98.

Notes

4.2 Finding the Slope of a Line

 The method for finding the steepness of stairs suggests a way to find the steepness of a line. A line drawn from the bottom step of a set of stairs to the top step touches each step at one point. The rise and the run of a step are the vertical and the horizontal changes, respectively, between two points on the line.

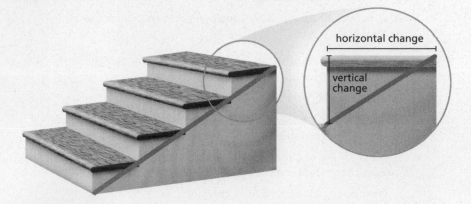

The steepness of the line is the ratio of rise to run, or vertical change to horizontal change, for this step. We call this ratio the **slope** of the line.

$$\text{slope} = \frac{\text{vertical change}}{\text{horizontal change}} = \frac{\text{rise}}{\text{run}}$$

- Does the slope change if we take two stairs at a time?
- Is the slope the same between any two stairs?

Unlike the steepness of stairs, the slope of a line can be negative. To determine the slope of a line, you need to consider the direction, or sign, of the vertical and horizontal changes from one point to another. If vertical change is negative for positive horizontal change, the slope will be negative. Lines that slant *upward* from left to right have *positive slope*. Lines that slant *downward* from left to right have *negative slope*.

90   Moving Straight Ahead

Notes _____

The following situations all represent linear relationships.

- For each graph, describe how you can find the slope of the line.

Line With Positive Slope

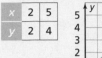

Line With Negative Slope

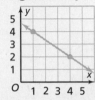

- Describe how you can find the slope of the line that represents the data in the table below.

x	−1	0	1	2	3	4
y	0	3	6	9	12	15

Information about a linear relationship can be given in several different representations, such as a table, a graph, an equation, or a contextual situation. These representations are useful in answering questions about linear situations.

Investigation 4   Exploring Slope: Connecting Rates and Ratios   91

Notes _____

_____

Problem 4.2

A The graphs, tables, and equations all represent linear relationships.

Graph 1   **Graph 2**

Table 1

x	−6	−4	−2	0	2	4
y	−10	−7	−4	−1	2	5

Table 2

x	1	2	3	4	5	6
y	4.5	4.0	3.5	3.0	2.5	2.0

Equation 1   **Equation 2**

$y = 2.5x + 5$ $y = 20 − 3x$

1. Find the slope and y-intercept of the line associated with each of these representations.

2. Write an equation for each graph and table.

Notes

Problem 4.2 continued

B The points (3, 5) and (–2, 10) lie on a line.

1. What is the slope of the line?

2. Find two more points that lie on this line. Explain your method.

3. Eun Mi observed that any two points on a line can be used to find the slope. How is Eun Mi's observation related to the idea of "linearity?"

C **1.** John noticed that for lines represented by equations of the form $y = mx$, the points (0, 0) and (1, m) are always on the line. Is he correct? Explain.

2. What is the slope of a horizontal line? A vertical line? Explain your reasoning.

D **1.** Compare your methods for finding the slope of a line from a graph, a table, and an equation.

2. In previous Investigations, you learned that linear relationships have a constant rate of change. As the independent variable changes by a constant amount, the dependent variable also changes by a constant amount. How is the constant rate of change of a linear relationship related to the slope of the line that represents that relationship?

 Homework starts on page 98.

4.3 Exploring Patterns With Lines

Your understanding of linear relationships can be used to explore some ideas about groups of lines.

For example, suppose the slope of a line is 3.

- Sketch a line with this slope.

- Can you sketch a different line with this slope? Explain.

In this Problem, you will use slope to explore some patterns among linear relationships.

Notes _____

_____

_____

Problem 4.3

A Consider the two groups of lines shown below.

Group 1 $y = 3x$ $\qquad y = 5 + 3x$ $\qquad y = 10 + 3x$ $\qquad y = -5 + 3x$

Group 2 $y = -2x$ $\qquad y = 4 - 2x$ $\qquad y = 8 - 2x$ $\qquad y = -4 - 2x$

1. What features do the equations in each group have in common?

2. For each group, graph the equations on the same coordinate axes. What patterns do you observe in the graphs?

3. Describe another group of lines that have the same pattern.

B Consider the three pairs of lines shown below.

Pair 1	Pair 2	Pair 3
$y = 2x$	$y = 4x$	$y = -3x + 5$
$y = -\frac{1}{2}x$	$y = -0.25x$	$y = \frac{1}{3}x - 1$

1. What features do the equations in each pair have in common?

2. For each pair, graph both equations on the same coordinate axes. What patterns do you observe in the graphs?

3. Describe another pair of lines that have the same pattern.

C Consider the three pairs of lines shown below.

Pair 1	Pair 2	Pair 3
$y = 2x + 1$	$y = 5 - 2x$	$y = 2(x - 1)$
$y = 2(x + 1) - 1$	$y = 3 - 2(x - 1)$	$y = 4x - 2x - 2$

1. For each pair, graph both equations on the same coordinate axes.

2. What do you notice about the graphs of each pair of equations? How might you have predicted this from the equations?

ACE Homework starts on page 98.

Notes

4.4 Pulling It All Together
Writing Equations for Linear Relationships

Throughout this Unit, you have learned several ways to model linear relationships. You have also learned ways to move back and forth between tables, graphs, and equations to solve problems. The next Problem pulls some of these ideas together.

Problem 4.4

A Today is Chantal's birthday. Her grandfather gave her some money as a birthday gift. Chantal plans to put her birthday money in a safe place and add part of her allowance to it each week. Her sister, Chanice, wants to know how much their grandfather gave her and how much of her allowance she is planning to save each week. As usual, Chantal does not answer her sister directly. Instead, she wants her to figure out the answer for herself. She gives her these clues:

> After five weeks, I will have saved a total of $175
>
> After eight weeks, I will have saved $190.

1. How much of her allowance is Chantal planning to save each week?

2. How much birthday money did Chantal's grandfather give her?

3. Write an equation for the total amount of money A Chantal will have saved after n weeks. What information do the y-intercept and coefficient of n represent in this context?

continued on the next page >

STUDENT PAGE

Notes _____

_____

_____

Problem 4.4 *continued*

B In the United States, temperature is measured using the Fahrenheit scale. Some countries, such as Canada, use the Celsius temperature scale. In cities near the border of these two countries, weather forecasts present the temperature using both scales.

The relationship between degrees Fahrenheit and degrees Celsius is linear. Two important reference points for this relationship are:

- Water freezes at 0°C, which is 32°F.
- Water boils at 100°C, which is 212°F.

1. Use this information to write an equation relating degrees Fahrenheit and degrees Celsius.

2. How did you find the *y*-intercept? What does the *y*-intercept tell you about this situation?

3. A news Web site uses the image below to display the weather forecast. However, some of the temperatures are missing. Use your equation from part (1) to find the missing temperatures.

? °F	**?** °F	63° F	70° F	58° F
13° C	14° C	**?** °C	**?** °C	**?** °C
Mon	**Tues**	**Wed**	**Thurs**	**Fri**

Notes _____

_____

_____

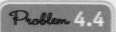

Problem 4.4 *continued*

C Square tiles were used to make the pattern below:

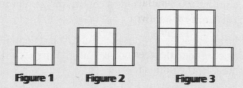

Figure 1   Figure 2   Figure 3

1. Write an equation that gives the perimeter P of the mth figure.

2. Compare your equation with that of your classmates. Are the expressions for perimeter equivalent? Explain.

3. Is the relationship linear? Explain.

4. Hachi observed that there was an interesting pattern for the number of square tiles needed to build each figure.

   a. What pattern might she have observed?

   b. Write an equation that gives the number of square tiles T in the mth figure.

   c. Is this relationship linear?

D 1. Look back to the equations you wrote in Question A, part (3); Question B, part (1); and Question C, part (1). Without graphing any of the equations, describe what the graph of each would look like. Which variable would be on the x-axis? Which variable would be on the y-axis? Would the line have a positive slope or a negative slope?

2. When it is helpful to represent a relationship as an equation? A table? A graph?

A C E Homework starts on page 98.

Notes

Applications

1. Plans for a set of stairs for the front of a new community center use the ratio of rise to run of 2 units to 5 units.

   a. Recall that the carpenters' guidelines state that the ratio of rise to run should be between 0.45 and 0.60. Are these stairs within the carpenters' guidelines?

   b. Sketch a set of stairs that meets the rise-to-run ratio of 2 units to 5 units.

   c. Sketch the graph of a line where the y-values change by 2 units for each 5-unit change in the x-values.

   d. Write an equation for your line in part (c).

2. a. Find the horizontal distance and the vertical distance between the two labeled points on the graph below.

   b. What is the slope of the line?

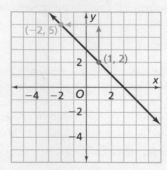

For Exercises 3–6, find the slope and the y-intercept of the line associated with the equation.

3. $y = 10 + 3x$

4. $y = 0.5x$

5. $y = -3x$

6. $y = -5x + 2$

7. Seven possible descriptions of lines are listed below.

  i. positive slope   **ii.** negative slope

  iii. y-intercept equals 0   **iv.** passes through the point $(1, 2)$

  v. slope of zero   **vi.** positive y-intercept

  vii. negative y-intercept

For each equation, list *all* of the descriptions i–vii that describe the graph of that equation.

  a. $y = 2x$ **b.** $y = 3 - 3x$

  c. $y = 2x + 3$ **d.** $y = 5x - 3$

  e. $y = 2$

In Exercises 8–12, the tables represent linear relationships. Give the slope and the y-intercept of the graph of each relationship. Then match each of the following equations with the appropriate table.

$$y = 5 - 2x \qquad\qquad y = 2x \qquad\qquad y = -3x - 5$$

$$y = 2x - 1 \qquad\qquad y = x + 3.5$$

8.

x	0	1	2	3	4
y	0	2	4	6	8

9.

x	0	1	2	3	4
y	3.5	4.5	5.5	6.5	7.5

10.

x	1	2	3	4	5
y	1	3	5	7	9

11.

x	0	1	2	3	4
y	5	3	1	−1	−3

12.

x	2	3	4	5	6
y	−11	−14	−17	−20	−23

STUDENT PAGE

Notes _____

_____

_____

13. a. Find the slope of the line represented by the equation $y = x - 1$.

b. Make a table of x- and y-values for the equation $y = x - 1$. How is the slope related to the table entries?

14. a. Find the slope of the line represented by the equation $y = -2x + 3$.

b. Make a table of x- and y-values for the equation $y = -2x + 3$. How is the slope related to the table entries?

15. In parts (a) and (b), the equations represent linear relationships. Use the given information to find the value of b.

a. The point $(1, 5)$ lies on the line representing $y = b - 3.5x$.

b. The point $(0, -2)$ lies on the line representing $y = 5x - b$.

c. What are the y-intercepts in parts (a) and (b)? What are the patterns of change in parts (a) and (b)?

d. Find the x-intercepts for the linear relationships in parts (a) and (b). (The x-intercept is the point where the graph intersects the x-axis.)

For each pair of points in Exercises 16–19, answer parts (a)–(e).

a. Plot the points on a coordinate grid and draw a line through them.

b. Find the slope of the line.

c. Find the y-intercept of the line. Explain how you found the y-intercept.

d. Use your answers from parts (b) and (c) to write an equation for the line.

e. Find one more point that lies on the line.

16. $(0, 0)$ and $(3, 3)$

17. $(-1, 1)$ and $(3, -3)$

18. $(0, -5)$ and $(-2, -3)$

19. $(3, 6)$ and $(5, 6)$

Notes

For Exercises 20–22, determine which of the linear relationships A–K
fit the description given.

A.
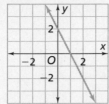

B.
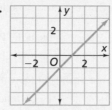

C.
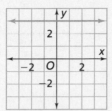

D.
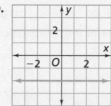

E.
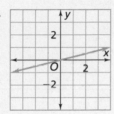

F.

x	−3	−2	−1	0
y	7	5	3	1

G.

x	−4	−2	−1	0
y	2	2	2	2

H. $y = 1.5$ **J.** $y = -5 + 3x$ **K.** $y = 4 + -2x$

20. The line corresponding to this relationship has positive slope.

21. The line corresponding to this relationship has a slope of −2.

22. The line corresponding to this relationship has a slope of 0.

23. Decide which graph from Exercises 20–22 matches each equation.

  a. $y = x - 1$ **b.** $y = -2$ **c.** $y = \frac{1}{4}x$

STUDENT PAGE

Notes

For each equation in Exercises 24–26, answer parts (a)–(d).

24. $y = x$

25. $y = 2x - 2$

26. $y = -0.5x + 2$

   a. Make a table of x- and y-values for the equation.

   b. Sketch a graph of the equation.

   c. Find the slope of the line.

   d. Make up a problem that can be represented by each equation.

27. a. Graph a line with slope 3.

    i. Find two points on your line.

    ii. Write an equation for the line.

   b. On the same set of axes, graph a line with slope $-\frac{1}{3}$.

    i. Find two points on your line.

    ii. Write an equation for the line.

   c. Compare the two graphs you made in parts (a) and (b).

28. Use the line in the graph below to answer each question.

   a. Find the equation of a line that is parallel to this line.

   b. Find the equation of a line that is perpendicular to this line.

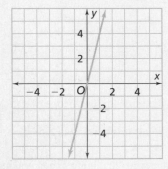

Notes _____

_____

_____

29. a. Find the slope of each line below. Then write an equation for the line.

i.

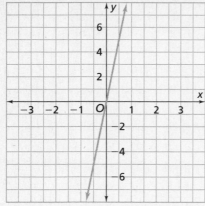

ii.

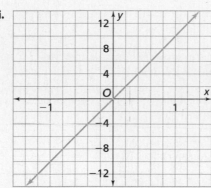

iii.

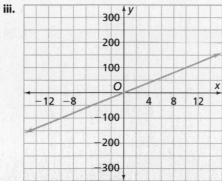

b. Compare the slopes of the three lines.

c. How are the three graphs similar? How are they different?

STUDENT PAGE

Notes _____

_____

_____

30. Descriptions of three possible lines are listed below.

    i. a line that *does not* pass through the first quadrant

    ii. a line that passes through exactly two quadrants

    iii. a line that passes through only one quadrant

  a. For each, decide whether such a line exists. Explain.

  b. If such a line exists, what must be true about the equation of the line that satisfies the conditions?

  c. If such a line exists, sketch its graph. Then write the equation of the line next to the graph.

31. Suppose the slopes of two lines are the negative reciprocal of each other. For example:

$$y = 2x \text{ and } y = -\frac{1}{2}x$$

What must be true about the two lines? Is your conjecture true if the *y*-intercept of either equation is not zero? Explain.

32. Write equations for four lines that intersect to form the sides of a parallelogram. Explain what must be true about such lines.

33. Write equations for three lines that intersect to form a right triangle. Explain what must be true about such lines.

34. Describe how you can decide if two lines are parallel or perpendicular from the equations of the lines.

35. Meifeng is taking a bike repair class. She pays the bike shop $15 per week for the class. At the end of the third week, Meifeng still owes the bike shop $75.

  a. How many payments does Meifeng have left?

  b. How much did the class cost?

  c. Write an equation that models the relationship between the time in weeks and the amount of money Meifeng owes.

  d. Without graphing, describe what the graph of this relationship would look like.

Notes _____

_____

_____

36. Robert is installing a patio in his backyard. At 2:00 P.M., he has 120 stones laid in the ground. At 3:30 P.M., he has 180 stones in the ground. His design for the patio says he needs 400 stones total.

a. When would you predict he will be done?

b. What is a reasonable estimate for when he started?

c. If you wanted to know how many stones he would have in the ground at any time, what would be most helpful to you: an equation, a graph, or a table? Explain.

37. At noon, the temperature is 30°F. For the next several hours, the temperature falls by an average of 3°F an hour.

a. Write an equation for the temperature T, n hours after noon.

b. What is the y-intercept of the line the equation represents? What does the y-intercept tell you about this situation?

c. What is the slope of the line the equation represents? What does the slope tell you about this situation?

38. Damon never manages to make his allowance last for a whole week, so he borrows money from his sister. Suppose Damon borrows 50 cents every week.

a. Write an equation for the amount of money m Damon owes his sister after n weeks.

b. What is the slope of the graph of the equation from part (a)?

Notes

39. In 2000, the small town of Cactusville was destined for obscurity. However, due to hard work by its city officials, it began adding manufacturing jobs at a fast rate. As a result, the city's population grew 239% from 2000 to 2010.

a. What was the population of Cactusville in 2000?

b. Suppose the same rate of population increase continues. What might the population be in the year 2020?

40. Terrance and Katrina share a veterinary practice. They each make farm visits two days a week. They take cellular phones on these trips to keep in touch with the office. Terrance makes his farm visits on weekdays. His cellular phone rate is $14.95 a month plus $.50 a minute. Katrina makes her visits on Saturday and Sunday and is charged a weekend rate of $34 a month.

a. Write an equation for each billing plan.

b. Is it possible for Terrance's cellular phone bill to be more than Katrina's? Explain how you know this.

c. Suppose Terrance and Katrina made the same number of calls in the month of May. Is it possible for Terrance's and Katrina's phone bills to be for the same amount? If so, how many minutes of phone calls would each person have to make for their bills to be equal?

d. Katrina finds another phone company that offers one rate for both weekday and weekend calls. The billing plan for this company is given by the equation $A = 25 + 0.25m$, where A is the total monthly bill and m is the number of minutes of calls. Compare this billing plan with the other two plans.

Notes _____

_____

_____

41. Three students build the following pattern using the least number of toothpicks possible. For example, Figure 2 uses 5 toothpicks. Suppose that this pattern continues beyond Figure 3.

Figure 1 **Figure 2** **Figure 3**

a. The students are trying to figure out the perimeter of Figure 6 without building it. For each student's method, tell whether you agree or disagree. If you agree, explain why. If you disagree, describe what is incorrect about the student's reasoning.

Juan's Method

From one figure to the next, you are adding one unit of perimeter. Figure 3 has a perimeter of 5 units, so Figure 6 will have a perimeter of 5+1+1+1 = 8 units.

Natalie's Method

Figure 3 has a perimeter of 5 units. 6 is twice as great as 3. So Figure 6 has twice the perimeter, or 10 units.

Steven's Method

Figure 6 will have 6 triangles, and each triangle has a perimeter of 3 units. So Figure 6 will have a perimeter of 6 • 3 = 18 units.

b. The students want to figure out a way to calculate how many toothpicks *T* they would need to build any figure number *F*. Which students wrote correct equations? Explain.

Juan's Equation

$T = (F + 1) + F$

There are (F + 1) slanted toothpicks. There are F toothpicks on the top and bottom.

Natalie's Equation

$T = 2F + 1$

There are F of this shape

in each figure plus one extra toothpick at the end.

Steven's Equation

$T = 3F - (F - 1)$

There are F triangles, each with 3 toothpicks. But, there are F – 1 toothpicks double-counted.

Notes

42.

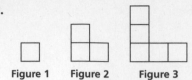

Figure 1   **Figure 2**   **Figure 3**

a. Assume that this pattern continues beyond Figure 3. Write an equation that represents the number of squares S in figure n.

b. Explain how you know your equation will work for any figure number.

c. Write two different equations that represent the perimeter P for any given figure number n.

Connections

43. Some hills have signs indicating their steepness, or slope. Here are some examples:

On a coordinate grid, sketch hills with each of these slopes.

44. Solve each equation and check your answers.

a. $2x + 3 = 9$

b. $\frac{1}{2}x + 3 = 9$

c. $x + 3 = \frac{9}{2}$

d. $x + \frac{1}{2} = 9$

e. $\frac{x+3}{2} = 9$

45. Use properties of equality and numbers to solve each equation for x. Check your answers.

a. $3 + 6x = 4x + 9$

b. $6x + 3 = 4x + 9$

c. $6x - 3 = 4x + 9$

d. $3 - 6x = 4x + 9$

108   Moving Straight Ahead

Notes _____

46. Use the graph below to answer each question.

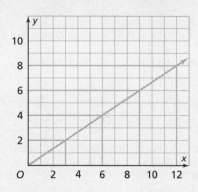

a. Are any of the rectangles in the picture above similar? If so, tell which rectangles, and explain why they are similar.

b. Find the slope of the diagonal line. How is it related to the similar rectangles?

c. Which of these rectangles belong to the set of rectangles in the graph? Explain.

47. The graph below shows the height of a rocket from 10 seconds before liftoff through 7 seconds after liftoff.

a. Describe the relationship between the height of the rocket and time.

b. What is the slope for the part of the graph that is a straight line? What does this slope represent in this situation?

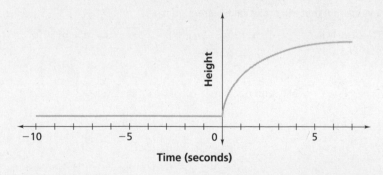

Notes _____

_____

_____

48. Solve each equation. Check your answers.

   a. $2(x + 5) = 18$ **b.** $2(x + 5) = x - 8$

   c. $2(x + 5) = x$ **d.** $2(x + 5) = -15$

49. **Multiple Choice** Which equation has a graph that contains the point $(-2, 7)$?

   A. $y = 4x + 1$ **B.** $y = -x + 5$

   C. $y = 3x - 11$ **D.** $y = -3x + 11$

50. Each pair of figures is similar. Find the lengths of the sides marked x.

   a.

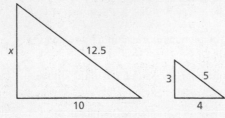

   b.

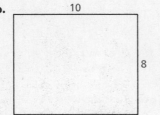

51. Find a value of n that will make each statement true.

   a. $\frac{n}{10} = \frac{3}{2}$ **b.** $\frac{5}{6} = \frac{n}{18}$ **c.** $-\frac{4}{6} = \frac{n}{3}$ **d.** $\frac{5}{18} = \frac{20}{n}$

   e. Write an equation for a line whose slope is $-\frac{4}{6}$.

52. Find a value of n that will make each statement true.

   a. 15% of 90 is n.   **b.** 20% of n is 80.   **c.** n% of 50 is 5.

Notes

Extensions

53. On a March flight from Boston to Detroit, a monitor displayed the altitude and the outside air temperature. Two passengers that were on that flight tried to find a formula for temperature t in degrees Fahrenheit at an altitude of a feet above sea level. One passenger said the formula was $t = 46 - 0.003a$, and the other said it was $t = 46 + 0.003a$.

   a. Which formula makes more sense to you? Why?

   b. The Detroit Metropolitan Airport is 620 feet above sea level. Use the formula you chose in part (a) to find the temperature at the airport on that day.

   c. Does the temperature you found in part (b) seem reasonable? Why or why not?

54. Jada's track team decides to convert their running rates from miles per hour to kilometers per hour (1 mile $\approx$ 1.6 kilometers).

   a. Which method would you use to help the team do their converting: graph, table, or equation? Explain why you chose your method.

   b. One of Jada's teammates said that she could write an equation for her spreadsheet program that could convert any team member's running rate from miles per hour to kilometers per hour. Write an equation that each member could use for this conversion.

STUDENT PAGE

Notes

Mathematical Reflections 4

In this Investigation, you learned that graphs of linear relationships are straight lines. You also learned about the slope, or steepness, of a line. You learned how slope is related to an equation of the line and to a table or a graph of the equation. These questions will help you summarize what you have learned.

Think about these questions. Discuss your ideas with other students and your teacher. Then, write a summary of your findings in your notebook.

1. Explain what the slope of a line is. **How** does finding the slope compare to finding the rate of change between two variables in a linear relationship?

2. **How** can you find the slope of a line from

   a. an equation?

   b. a graph?

   c. a table of values of the line?

   d. the coordinates of two points on the line?

3. For parts (a) and (b), **explain** how you can write an equation of a line from the information. Use examples to illustrate your thinking.

   a. the slope and the y-intercept of the line

   b. two points on the line

Notes

Common Core Mathematical Practices

As you worked on the Problems in this Investigation, you used prior knowledge to make sense of them. You also applied Mathematical Practices to solve the Problems. Think back over your work, the ways you thought about the Problems, and how you used Mathematical Practices.

Hector described his thoughts in the following way.

> It took our group many steps to solve Problem 4.4, Question A. First, since the amount of money Chantal saved from her weekly allowance is the same each week, we reasoned that the amount of money for each of the weeks between weeks 5 and 8 is a constant.
>
> During this time she saved $190 – $175 or $15. So $15 ÷ 3 weeks is $5 per week. To find the amount of money her grandfather gave her, we found the amount of money she saved from her allowance for the first five weeks, which is 5 × $5 or $25.
>
> Then, we subtracted this amount from $175, and this gave us $150. This is the amount her grandfather gave her for her birthday. We think her grandfather is very generous.

Common Core Standards for Mathematical Practice

MP1 Make sense of problems and persevere in solving them.

- What other Mathematical Practices can you identify in Hector's reasoning?

- Describe a Mathematical Practice that you and your classmates used to solve a different Problem in this Investigation.

Notes _____

_____

_____

Looking Back

In this Unit, you explored many examples of linear relationships between variables. You learned how to recognize linear patterns in graphs and in tables of numerical data. You also learned how to express those patterns in words and in symbolic equations or formulas. Most importantly, you learned how to interpret tables, graphs, and equations to answer questions about linear relationships.

Use Your Understanding: Algebraic Reasoning

 Test your understanding of linear relationships by solving the following problems about the operation of a movie theater.

1. Suppose that a theater charges a school group $4.50 per student to show a special film. Suppose that the theater's operating expenses include $130 for the staff and a film rental fee of $1.25 per student.

    a. What equation relates the number of students x to the theater's income I?

    b. What equation relates the theater's operating expenses E to the number of students x?

    c. Copy and complete the table below.

Theater Income and Expenses

Number of Students, x	0	10	20	30	40	50	60	70
Income, I ($)								
Expenses, E ($)								

    d. On the same set of axes, graph the theater's income and operating expenses for any number of students from 0 to 100.

    e. Describe the patterns by which income and operating expenses increase as the number of students in a group increases.

    f. Write and solve an equation that you can use to answer the question "How many students need to attend the movie so that the theater's income will equal its operating expenses?"

    g. Write an equation that represents the theater's profit. Compare your equation to those your classmates wrote.

Notes

   h. Find the number of students that make each of the following inequality statements true.

      i. $E < 255$

      ii. $I > 675$

2. At another theater, the income and expenses combine to give the equation $y = 3x - 115$. This equation relates operating profit and the number of students in a group.

   a. What do the numbers 3 and -115 tell you about:

      i. the relationship between the number of students and the theater's profit?

      ii. the pattern of entries that would appear in a table of sample (*students, profit*) data?

      iii. a graph of the relationship between the number of students and the profit?

   b. Write and solve equations to find the number of students needed for the theater to:

      i. break even (make a profit of $0).

      ii. make a profit of $100.

   c. Write and solve an equation you can use to find the number of students for which the theaters in Exercise 1 and Exercise 2 make the same profit. Then find the amount of that profit.

Notes

Explain Your Reasoning

When you use mathematical calculations to solve a problem or make a decision, it is important to be able to justify each step in your reasoning. For Exercises 1 and 2:

3. Consider the variables and relationships.

   a. What are the variables?

   b. Which pairs of variables are related to each other?

   c. In each pair of related variables, how does a change in the value of one variable cause a change in the value of the other variable?

4. Which relationships are linear and which are not linear? What patterns in the tables, graphs, and equations support your conclusions?

5. For a linear relationship, what information do the slope and y-intercept of the graph indicate about the relationship?

6. For a linear relationship, how do the slope and y-intercept relate to data patterns in the table?

7. Consider the strategies for solving linear equations such as those in Problem 1, part (f) and Problem 2, part (c).

   a. How can you solve the equations using tables of values?

   b. How can you solve the equations using graphs?

   c. How can you solve the equations using symbolic reasoning alone?

8. Suppose you were asked to write a report describing the relationships among the number of students in the group, the theater's income, and the theater's operating expenses. What value might be gained by including the table? Including the graph? Including the equation? What are the limitations of each representation?

Notes

C **coefficient** A number that is multiplied by a variable in an equation or expression. In a linear equation of the form $y = mx + b$, the number m is the coefficient of x as well as the slope of the line. For example, in the equation $y = 3x + 5$, the coefficient of x is 3. This is also the slope of the line.

coeficiente Un número que se multiplica por una variable en una ecuación o expresión. En una ecuación lineal de la forma $y = mx + b$, el número m es el coeficiente de x así como la pendiente de la recta. Por ejemplo, en la ecuación $y = 3x + 5$, el coeficiente de x es 3. También representa la pendiente de la recta.

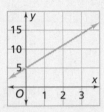

constant term A number in an equation that is not multiplied by a variable, or an amount added to or subtracted from the terms involving variables. In an equation of the form $y = mx + b$, the y-intercept, b, is a constant term. The effect of the constant term on a graph is to raise or lower the graph. The constant term in the equation $y = 3x + 5$ is 5. The graph of $y = 3x$ is raised vertically 5 units to give the graph of $y = 3x + 5$.

término constante Un número en una ecuación que no está multiplicado por una variable o una cantidad sumada o restada a los términos que contienen variables. En una ecuación de la forma $y = mx + b$, el intercepto en y, b, es un término constante. El efecto del término constante hace que una gráfica suba o baje. El término constante en la ecuación $y = 3x + 5$ es 5. Para obtener la gráfica de $y = 3x + 5$, la gráfica $y = 3x$ se sube 5 unidades sobre el eje vertical.

Notes _____

coordinates An ordered pair of numbers used to locate a point on a coordinate grid. The first number in a coordinate pair is the value for the *x*-coordinate, and the second number is the value for the *y*-coordinate. A coordinate pair for the graph shown below is (0, 60).

coordenadas Un par ordenado de números que se usa para ubicar un punto en una gráfica de coordenadas. El primer número del par de coordenadas es el valor de la coordenada *x* y el segundo número es el valor de la coordenada *y*. Un par de coordenadas para la gráfica que se muestra es (0, 60).

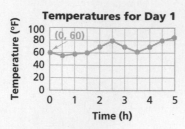

D **dependent variable** One of the two variables in a relationship. Its value depends upon or is determined by the other variable called the *independent variable*. For example, the distance you travel on a car trip (dependent variable) depends on how long you drive (independent variable).

variable dependiente Una de las dos variables de una relación. Su valor depende o está determinado por el valor de la otra variable, llamada *variable independiente*. Por ejemplo, la distancia que recorres durante un viaje en carro (variable dependiente) depende de cuánto conduces (variable independiente).

Notes _____

_____

_____

describe Academic Vocabulary
To explain or tell in detail. A written description can contain facts and other information needed to communicate your answer. A diagram or a graph may also be included.

related terms *express, explain, illustrate*

sample Describe how to solve the equation $3x + 14 = 23$.

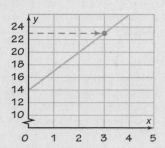

I can sketch a graph of the line $y = 3x + 14$. When y is 23, the value of x is 3.

I can also solve for x in the equation $3x + 14 = 23$ by subtracting 14 from both sides to get $3x = 9$. Then I can divide both sides by 3 to get $x = 3$.

describir Vocabulario académico
Explicar o decir con detalle. Una descripción escrita puede contener datos y otra información necesaria para comunicar tu respuesta. También se puede incluir un diagrama o una gráfica.

términos relacionados *expresar, explicar, illustrar*

ejemplo Describe cómo se resuelve la ecuación $3x + 14 = 23$.

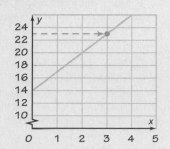

Puedo bosquejar una gráfica de la recta $y = 3x + 14$. Cuando y es 23, el valor de x es 3.

También puedo resolver x en la ecuación $3x + 14 = 23$ restando 14 de cada lado para obtener $3x = 9$. Luego puedo dividir ambos lados por 3 para obtener $x = 3$.

E **equivalent expressions** Expressions that represent the same quantity. For example, $2 + 5$, $3 + 4$, and 7 are equivalent expressions. You can apply the Distributive Property to $2(x + 3)$ to write the equivalent expression $2x + 6$. You can apply the Commutative Property to $2x + 6$ to write the equivalent expression $6 + 2x$.

expresiones equivalentes Expresiones que representan la misma cantidad. Por ejemplo, $2 + 5$, $3 + 4$ y 7 son expresiones equivalentes. Puedes aplicar la propiedad distributiva a $2(x + 3)$ para escribir la expresión equivalente $2x + 6$. Puedes aplicar la propiedad conmutativa a $2x + 6$ para escribir la expresión equivalente $6 + 2x$.

Notes _____

_____

independent variable One of the two variables in a relationship. Its value determines the value of the other variable called the *dependent variable*. If you organize a bike tour, for example, the number of people who register to go (independent variable) determines the cost for renting bikes (dependent variable).

variable independiente Una de las dos variables en una relación. Su valor determina el de la otra variable, llamada *variable dependiente*. Por ejemplo, si organizas un recorrido en bicicleta, el número de personas inscritas (variable independiente) determina el costo del alquiler de las bicicletas (variable dependiente).

inequality A statement that two quantities are not equal. The symbols $>$, $<$, $\geq$, and $\leq$ are used to express inequalities. For example, if a and b are two quantities, then "a is greater than b" is written as $a > b$, and "a is less than b" is written as $a < b$. The statement $a \geq b$ means "a is greater than or equal to b." The statement $a \leq b$ means that "a is less than or equal to b."

desigualdad Enunciado que indica que dos cantidades no son iguales. Los símbolos $>$, $<$, $\geq$ y $\leq$ se usan para expresar desigualdades. Por ejemplo, si a y b son dos cantidades, entonces "a es mayor que b" se escribe como $a > b$ y "a es menor que b" se escribe como $a < b$. El enunciado $a \geq b$ significa "a es mayor que o igual a b". El enunciado $a \leq b$ significa "a es menor que o igual a b".

intersecting lines Lines that cross or *intersect*. The coordinates of the point where the lines intersect are solutions to the equations for both lines. The graphs of the equations $y = x$ and $y = 2x - 3$ intersect at the point (3, 3). This number pair is a solution to each equation.

rectas intersecantes Rectas que se cruzan o *intersecan*. Las coordenadas del punto en el que las rectas se intersecan son la solución de las ecuaciones de las dos rectas. Las gráficas de las ecuaciones $y = x$ e $y = 2x - 3$ se intersecan en el punto (3, 3). Este par de números es la solución de las dos ecuaciones.

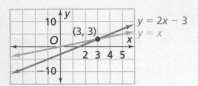

Notes _____

_____

_____

L **linear relationship** A relationship in which there is a constant rate of change between two variables. A linear relationship can be represented by a straight-line graph and by an equation of the form $y = mx + b$. In the equation, m is the slope of the line, and b is the y-intercept.

relación lineal Una relación en la que hay una tasa de variación constante entre dos variables. Una relación lineal se puede representar con una gráfica de línea recta y con una ecuación de la forma $y = mx + b$. En la ecuación, m es la pendiente de la recta y b es el intercepto en y.

O **origin** The point where the x- and y-axes intersect on a coordinate graph. With coordinates (0, 0), the origin is the center of the coordinate plane.

origen El punto en que los ejes de las x y las y se intersecan en una gráfica de coordenadas. Si las coordenadas son (0, 0), el origen es el centro del plano de coordenadas.

P **point of intersection** The point where two lines intersect. If the lines are represented on a coordinate grid, the coordinates for the point of intersection can be read from the graph.

punto de intersección El punto en el que dos rectas se intersecan. Si las rectas están representadas en una gráfica de coordenadas, las coordenadas del punto de intersección se pueden leer en la gráfica.

properties of equality For all real numbers a, b, and c:

Addition: If $a = b$, then $a + c = b + c$.

Subtraction: If $a = b$, then $a - c = b - c$.

Multiplication: If $a = b$, then $a \cdot c = b \cdot c$.

Division: If $a = b$ and $c \neq 0$, then $\frac{a}{c} = \frac{b}{c}$.

propiedades de la igualdad Para todos los números reales a, b y c:

Suma: Si $a = b$, entonces $a + c = b + c$.

Resta: Si $a = b$, entonces $a - c = b - c$.

Multiplicación: Si $a = b$, entonces $a \cdot c = b \cdot c$.

División: Si $a = b$ y $c \neq 0$, entonces $\frac{a}{c} = \frac{b}{c}$.

R **relate** Academic Vocabulary
To have a connection to or impact on something else.

related terms *connect, correlate*

sample Hannah raises $12 for every 3 pies she sells. Write an equation that shows how the total number of pies p she sells relates to the amount of money she raises r.

relacionar Vocabulario académico
Tener una conexión o un impacto en algo.

términos relacionados *unir, correlacionar*

ejemplo Hannah recauda $12 por cada 3 pasteles que vende. Escribe una ecuación que muestre cómo se relaciona el número total de pasteles p que vende con la cantidad que recauda r.

If she raises $ 12 for selling 3 pies, she raises $ 4 for every pie, because $\frac{\$12}{4} = 3$. The equation $r = 4p$ shows the relationship.

Si recauda $ 12 por vender 3 pasteles, recauda $ 4 por cada pastel, porque $\frac{\$12}{4} = 3$. La ecuación $r = 4p$ muestra la relación.

Notes

represent Academic Vocabulary
To stand for or take the place of something else. For example, an equation can represent a given situation, and a graph can represent an equation.

related terms *symbolize, correspond to*

sample A company charges $15 per sweatshirt plus a total shipping fee of $10. Does this represent a linear relationship?

This represents a linear relationship because there is a constant rate of change between the number of sweatshirts and the amount the company will charge.

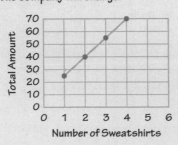

representar Vocabulario académico
Significar o tomar el lugar de algo más. Por ejemplo, una ecuación puede representar una situación dada y una gráfica puede representar una ecuación.

términos relacionados *simbolizar, corresponder*

ejemplo Una compañía cobra $15 por sudadera más una tarifa de envío de $10. ¿Representa esto una relación lineal?

Esto representa una relación lineal porque hay una tasa de cambio constante entre el número de sudaderas y la cantidad que la compañía cobra.

rise The vertical change between two points on a graph. The slope of a line is the rise divided by the run.

distancia vertical La variación vertical entre dos puntos de una gráfica. La pendiente de una recta es la distancia vertical dividida por la distancia horizontal.

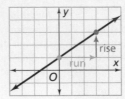

run The horizontal change between two points on a graph. The slope of a line is the rise divided by the run.

distancia horizontal La variación horizontal entre dos puntos de una gráfica. La pendiente de una recta es la distancia vertical dividida por la distancia horizontal.

Notes _____

_____

_____

S **scale** The distance between two consecutive tick marks on the *x*- and *y*-axes of a coordinate grid. When graphing, an appropriate scale must be selected so that the resulting graph will be clearly shown. For example, when graphing the equation $y = 60x$, a scale of 1 for the *x*-axis and a scale of 15 or 30 for the *y*-axis would be reasonable.

escala La distancia entre dos marcas consecutivas en los ejes *x* y *y* de una gráfica de coordenadas. Cuando se hace una gráfica, se debe seleccionar una escala apropiada de manera que represente con claridad la gráfica resultante. Por ejemplo, cuando se grafica la ecuación $y = 60x$, una escala razonable sería 1 para el eje de las *x* y una escala de 15 ó 30 para el eje de las *y*.

slope The number that expresses the steepness of a line. The slope is the ratio of the vertical change to the horizontal change between any two points on the line. Sometimes this ratio is referred to as *the rise over the run*. The slope of a horizontal line is 0. Slopes are positive if the *y*-values increase from left to right on a coordinate grid and negative if the *y*-values decrease from left to right. The slope of a vertical line is undefined. The slope of a line is the same as the constant rate of change between the two variables. For example, the points (0, 0) and (3, 6) lie on the graph of $y = 2x$. Between these points, the vertical change is 6 and the horizontal change is 3, so the slope is $\frac{6}{3} = 2$, which is the coefficient of *x* in the equation.

pendiente El número que expresa la inclinación de una recta. La pendiente es la razón entre la variación vertical y la horizontal entre dos puntos cualesquiera de la recta. A veces, a esta razón se la llama *distancia vertical sobre distancia horizontal*. La pendiente de una recta horizontal es 0. Las pendientes son positivas si los valores de *y* aumentan de izquierda a derecha en una gráfica de coordenadas y negativas si los valores de *y* disminuyen de izquierda a derecha. La pendiente de una recta vertical es indefinida. La pendiente de una recta es igual a la tasa de variación constante entre las dos variables. Por ejemplo, los puntos (0, 0) y (3, 6) están representados en la gráfica de $y = 2x$. Entre estos puntos, la variación vertical es 6 y la variación horizontal es 3, de manera que la pendiente es $\frac{6}{3} = 2$, que es el coeficiente de *x* en la ecuación.

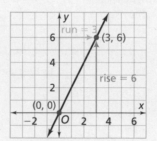

Notes _____

solution of an equation The value or values that make an equation true.

solución de una ecuación El valor o valores que hacen que una ecuación sea verdadera.

solve Academic Vocabulary
To determine the value or values that make a given statement true. Several methods and strategies can be used to solve a problem including estimating, isolating the variable, drawing a graph, or using a table of values.

related terms *calculate, solution*

sample Solve the equation $4(x - 3) = 2x$.

I can solve the equation by isolating x on the left side of the equation.

$4(x - 3) = 2x$
$4x - 12 = 2x$
$2x - 12 = 0$
$\qquad 2x = 12$
$\qquad x = 6$

I can also solve for x by using a table.

x	$4(x - 3)$	$2x$
0	−12	0
3	0	6
5	8	10
6	12	12

The answer is $x = 6$.

resolver Vocabulario académico
Determinar el valor o valores que hacen verdadero un enunciado. Se pueden usar varios métodos o estrategias para resolver un problema, entre ellos la estimación, aislar la variable, hacer una gráfica o usar una tabla de valores.

términos relacionados *calcular, solución*

ejemplo Resuelve la ecuación $4(x - 3) = 2x$.

Puedo resolver la ecuación despejando x en el lado izquierdo de la ecuación.

$4(x - 3) = 2x$
$4x - 12 = 2x$
$2x - 12 = 0$
$\qquad 2x = 12$
$\qquad x = 6$

También puedo resolver x usando una tabla.

x	$4(x - 3)$	$2x$
0	−12	0
3	0	6
5	8	10
6	12	12

La respuesta es $x = 6$.

Notes _____

_____

_____

x-intercept The point where a graph crosses the *x*-axis. In the graph, the *x*-intercept is (−4, 0) or −4.

intercepto en x El punto en el que la gráfica atraviesa el eje de las *x*. En la gráfica, el intercepto en *x* es (−4, 0) ó −4.

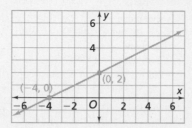

y-intercept The point where the graph crosses the *y*-axis. In a linear equation of the form $y = mx + b$, the *y*-intercept is the constant, *b*. In the graph, the *y*-intercept is (0, 2) or 2.

intercepto en y El punto en el que la gráfica atraviesa el eje de las *y*. En una ecuación lineal de la forma $y = mx + b$, el intercepto en *y* es la constante, *b*. En la gráfica, el intercepto en *y* es (0, 2) ó 2.

Notes _____

_____

_____

Index

Notes

Notes _____

_____

_____

Notes _____

_____

_____

Acknowledgments

Cover Design

Three Communication Design, Chicago

Text

Grateful acknowledgment is made to the following for copyrighted material:

080 National Council of Teachers of Mathematics

From *"Mathematics in Forensic Science: Male and Female Bone Measurements"* by George Knill from MATHEMATICS TEACHER, FEBRUARY 1981.

Photographs

Photo locators denoted as follows: Top (T), Center (C), Bottom (B), Left (L), Right (R), Background (Bkgd)

002 Christina Richards/Shutterstock; **003** Westend61/Westend61/Corbis; **032** Michael Steele/Staff/Getty Images; **087** Dudarev Mikhail/Shutterstock; **088** Les and Dave Jacobs/cultura/Corbis; **105** Christina Richards/Shutterstock; **108** (L) Powered by Light/Alan Spencer/Alamy, (R) Taweesak Jarearnsin/Shutterstock.

Notes _____

Moving Straight Ahead   **Acknowledgments**

1.1 Walking Marathons: Finding and Using Rates

> *Focus Question* What equation represents the relationship between the time and the distance you walk at a constant rate? What are the dependent and independent variables?

Launch

Tell a story about walkathons and ask the class if they know what their walking rates are in meters per second. Student predictions will likely be much higher than their actual walking rates.

Now tell students that they will have a chance to check their guesses. Describe the experiment.

The following suggestions for enriching the experiment might be interesting:

- Let the groups decide whether they want to calculate meters per second or seconds per meter.
- Ask one group to change their walking rate—maybe walk, jog, sprint, and so on.
- Ask some students to walk for 10 seconds rather than 10 meters.

Be sure to discuss these suggestions in the Summarize if you assign them in the Launch.

Key Vocabulary

- linear relationship

Materials

Labsheet
- Generic Grid paper (optional)
- stopwatch
- meter sticks (10 per group)
- transparent grid (optional)
- Data and Graphs Tool

Explore

Give each group 10 meter sticks and a stopwatch or a clock with seconds. Students should do the experiment twice to get an accurate walking rate. They can choose either the rate they want or the average of the two. Make sure there is a person checking the time in each group. As the groups finish collecting their data, they can work on the questions in the Problem.

Look to see how students are recording their walking rates. Some may use unit rates, such as 2.5 meters per second, and some may use ratios, such as $\frac{2.5 \text{ m}}{1 \text{s}}$. Discuss both of these ideas in the Summarize.

Summarize

Ask for some rates. Use one or two of the more typical walking rates to answer the questions in the Problem.

Suggested Questions

If students record their walking rates as both a rate and a ratio, ask how they are the same. You might ask students to write their walking rate in seconds per meter.

- *What information does this rate tell you?*
- *When might you use this rate rather than meters per second?*

- *How does the equation show the relationship between the two variables?*
- *Explain what information the numbers and variables in your equation represent.*
- *Which variable in your equation is the independent variable, and which is the dependent variable?*
- *What does it mean to walk at a constant rate?*
- *Suppose you do not walk at a constant rate for the walkathon. Which of the questions in Problem 1.1 can you still answer? Why?*
- *How is the walking rate represented in these graphs?*

Pick a typical equation from the class and ask students to use this equation to make a table.

- *How does the walking rate show up in the table?*

Pick two different walking rates from the class.

- *If these two students start walking at the same time, how far apart are they after 10 seconds? After $\frac{1}{2}$ hour?*

Assignment Guide for Problem 1.1

Applications: 1–2 | Connections: 15–18

Answers to Problem 1.1

A. Answers will vary. Check that students correctly calculated their walking rates.

B. Answers will vary depending on the student's walking rate. Sample answers are provided for a walking rate of 2 m/s.

 1. Sample answer: A student who walks 2 meters per second will walk 500 meters in 250 seconds, or 4 minutes 10 seconds.

 2. Sample answer: A student who walks 2 m/s will walk 60 meters in 30 seconds. Since 10 minutes = 600 seconds, the same student will walk 2 m/s times 600 seconds, or 1,200 meters in 10 minutes. In one hour, that student will walk six times as far as he or she walked in 10 minutes. Thus, the student would walk 7,200 meters in 1 hour.

 3. Sample answer: In a given number of seconds, you can walk a distance in meters that is twice the number of seconds.

 4. Sample answer: For a walking rate of 2 m/s, an equation is $d = 2t$, where d is the distance in meters and t is the time in seconds.

 5. Using the equation $d = 2t$, you would walk $d = 2(45) = 90$ meters.

At a Glance   Problem 1.2   Pacing 1 Day

1.2 Walking Rates and Linear Relationships: Tables, Graphs and Equations

> *Focus Question* How can you predict whether a relationship is linear from a table, a graph, or an equation that represents the relationship?

Launch

Introduce the three students and their walking rates.

Suggested Questions

- *What effect does a walking rate have on the relationship between time and distance walked?*

- *If you increased your walking rate, what effect would that have on the original equation? The table? The graph?*

- *If you increased the time you walk at a given rate, what effect would this have on your distance walked?*

Explore

Students should each make their own tables and graphs, but they can discuss the questions in pairs.

Suggested Question

- *Which axis should represent time? Which should represent distance? Explain.*

Summarize

Suggested Questions

- *How does the constant walking rate show up in the table, the graph, and the equation?*

- *For those situations in Question C that are linear, compare the walking rates to those of the original three students. Who is the fastest? Who is the slowest?*

Pick one or two of the situations in Question C, and ask:

- *Describe what is happening in each situation. Describe the patterns of change between the two variables.*

> *Materials*
>
> **Labsheet**
> - 1.2 Walking Rates
>
> **Accessibility Labsheet**
> - 1ACE: Exercise 4
>
> **Teaching Aid**
> - 1.2: Tables of Data
>
> - graphing calculators (optional)
> - Coordinate Grapher Tool
> - Data and Graphs Tool

(A)(C)(E)
Assignment Guide for Problem 1.2

Applications: 3–5 | Connections: 19–22
Extensions: 30

Answers to Problem 1.2

A. 1. The greater the walking rate, the more quickly the distance increases for a given interval of time. The walking rate is the amount that the distance (in meters) for each person is changing as time increases by 1 second. For example, Alana's walking rate is 1 m/s; for each increase in time of 1 second, the distance increases by 1 meter.

Walking Rates

Time (seconds)	Distance (meters)		
	Alana	Gilberto	Leanne
0	0	0	0
1	1	2	2.5
2	2	4	5
3	3	6	7.5
4	4	8	10
5	5	10	12.5
6	6	12	15
7	7	14	17.5
8	8	16	20
9	9	18	22.5
10	10	20	25

2.

Walking Rates

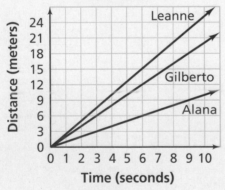

The greater the walking rate, the steeper the graph.

3. Alana: $d = t$; Gilberto: $d = 2t$; Leanne: $d = 2.5t$. The walking rate is represented as the number that time is multiplied by to get distance. (**Note:** Students will discuss later how the expression t is equivalent to $1t$ in the equation for Alana.)

4. In the table, for every increase of 1 unit in x, the value of y increases by a constant amount. Each equation is of the form $y = mx$, which represents a proportional relationship. The graph of a proportional relationship is a straight line that passes through the origin.

5. All three relationships between distance walked and time are proportional. They are all of the form $d = rt$. The value of r is the constant of proportionality for each relationship.

B. 1. Alana: increases by 1 m; Gilberto: increases by 2 m; Leanne: increases by 2.5 m. This change is represented in the table as the difference between the values for distance in consecutive rows. This change is represented in the graph as the steepness of the line. If you start at a point on Alana's line and move 1 unit to the right on the graph, you need to move up 1 unit, the change in distance, to end at another point on Alana's line. The same is true for the lines for Gilberto and Leanne using their changes in distance.

2. If t increases by 5 seconds, d_{Alana} increases by 5 meters, $d_{Gilberto}$ increases by 10 meters, and d_{Leanne} increases by 12.5 meters. In a table, this change is represented by the difference between distance values for any two rows that have a difference in time of 5 seconds. In a graph, this change is represented by the difference in the y-coordinates of two points on the line whose difference in x-coordinate is 5.

3. Walking rates per minute: Alana: 60 m/min, Gilberto: 120 m/min, Leanne: 150 m/min; (walking rate per second × 60 seconds). Walking rates per hour: Alana: 3,600 m/hr; Gilberto: 7,200 m/hr; Leanne: 9,000 m/hr; (walking rate per minute × 60 minutes).

C. Elizabeth's and Billie's relationships are linear. Elizabeth walks at a constant rate of 3 meters every 2 seconds, which you can see in the table. Billie walks at a constant rate of 2.25 m/s, since the equation is in the form $d = rt$, similar to the equations for Alana, Gilberto, and Leanne. The table for George does not show a constant rate of change. In the equation for Bob, the rate is a variable, so the walking rate is not constant. (Some students may make graphs and claim the relationships are either linear or not based on whether the data lie on a straight line.)

1.3 Raising Money: Using Linear Relationships

Focus Question What is the pattern of change in a linear relationship?

Launch

Pick one of the previous examples to review dependent variables and independent variables.

Suggested Questions

- *What variables can affect the amount of money that a student raises?*
- *How can you use these variables to estimate the amount of money each student will collect?*
- *Will the amount of money raised be the same for each walker?*
- *Which variable is the independent variable? Which is the dependent variable?*

Explore

As you circulate, ask students for explanations. Look for students who have interesting ways to explain their thinking. Be sure to discuss these in the Summarize.

Summarize

Suggested Questions

- *How is the amount of money donated per kilometer similar to a person's walking rate in meters per second?*
- *How can you recognize that the patterns in both situations are similar using a table, a graph, or an equation?*

One of the other equations has only a constant term and no x-term: $A = 10$.

- *What is the pattern of change between the two variables? Is it the same for two other points on the line? What rate of change is this?*
- *How is a constant rate of $0 per kilometer related to the graph of a horizontal line?*
- *Describe another pledge plan whose graph is a horizontal line. What is its equation? How does the graph of this pledge plan compare to the graph of $A = 10$?*

Pick some points from each of the three pledge plans.

- *What information does this point represent?*
- *How is this point related to the corresponding table and equation?*

Key Vocabulary

- dependent variable
- independent variable

Materials

Labsheets
- 1.3: Pledge Plans
- Generic Grid Paper

Accessibility Labsheet
- 1ACE: Exercise 6
- transparent grid
- poster paper
- Coordinate Grapher Tool
- Data and Graphs Tool

- *Write two questions that could be answered using this point.*
- *What are the coordinates of the point where each graph intersects the y-axis? What information does this point represent?*

The three graphs intersect each other in pairs. Discuss the coordinates of the points of intersection.

Assignment Guide for Problem 1.3

Applications: 6–9 | Connections: 23–26
Extensions: 31, 32

Answers to Problem 1.3

A. 1. Independent variable: distance walked (in kilometers); dependent variable: amount of money pledged by each sponsor (in dollars)

Pledge Plans

Distance (km)	Amount of Money		
	Alana	Gilberto	Leanne
0	$5	$0	$10
1	$5.50	$2	$10
2	$6	$4	$10
3	$6.50	$6	$10
4	$7	$8	$10
5	$7.50	$10	$10
6	$8	$12	$10

2.

Pledges

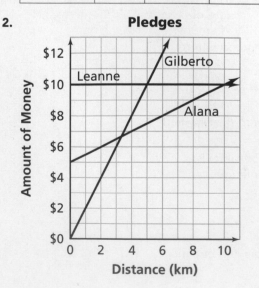

3. Leanne: $A = 10$, Gilberto: $A = 2d$, Alana: $A = 5 + 0.5d$; A is the amount of money pledged by each sponsor and d is the distance in kilometers. The coefficient of d is the amount each sponsor pledges per kilometer, and the term that does not include a variable is the amount each sponsor pledges before the student begins walking.

4. a. Alana's plan: as the distance increases by 1 kilometer, the amount of money she raises increases by $0.50; Gilberto's plan: as the distance increases by 1 kilometer, the amount of money he raises increases by $2; Leanne's plan: no change.

b. Graphs: For Alana's plan, if you start at a point on her line and move 1 unit in the x-direction, you move up 0.5 units in the y-direction to land back on her line. For Gilberto, if you start on his line and move 1 unit in the x-direction and up 2 units, you land back on his line. Leanne's line stays at 10 because the pattern is that amount of money does not change as distance changes. Equations: For all three plans, the pattern of change appears as the coefficient of d. For Leanne's plan, you can write the equation as $A = 10 + 0d$, so the coefficient of d is 0.

c. Leanne's, Gilberto's, and Alana's plans are linear; they all show a constant rate of money raised per kilometer walked. In a table, as the distance increases by a constant amount, the amount of money also increases by a constant amount for each student. In a graph, the graph of each plan is a straight line. In an equation, all three plans have the form $y = mx + b$. (Gilberto's equation has a value of $b = 0$, and Leanne's equation has a value of $m = 0$.)

d. The relationship between amount of money and distance walked for Gilberto is proportional. The relationships for Alana and Leanne are not proportional, because sponsors donate a constant amount in addition to the money donated per kilometer.

This makes the ratio of *amount of money donated : number of kilometers walked* not a constant rate for these two students' pledge plans.

B. 1. Leanne: each sponsor donates $10; each sponsor donates $10 regardless of how far she walks. Gilberto: each sponsor donates $2 × 8, or $16; the amount of money is twice the number of kilometers walked. Alana: each sponsor donates $5 plus $0.50 per kilometer walked, or $5 + 0.5(8) = 9.

2. Leanne: We cannot determine how far she walks; Gilberto: 5 km because $2 \times 5 = 10; Alana: 10 km because $5 + 0.5(10) = 10. You can find the distance by substituting 10 for y in each equation and solving for x, by finding the x-coordinate of the point on each line that has a y-coordinate of 9, or by finding the value in the Distance column of the table for the row that has a value of 9 in the Amount of Money column.

3. The point (12, 11) lies on Alana's graph. This point means that if Alana walks 12 km, each sponsor will donate $11.

4. a. $5 is the amount of money donated before Alana has started walking, or the amount of money donated if Alana walks 0 kilometers.

b. (0, 5) is the point where Alana's graph intersects the y-axis; it is the point on the line for her plan with an x-coordinate of 0.

c. 5 is the term that is added to $0.50d$.

C. 1. $A = 2d - 4.75$; the $2d$ is the money he gets from a sponsor for every km he walks and 4.75 is what he pays for a T-shirt. The variables represent the same values as in Gilberto's original equation. The coefficient of 2 is the constant rate of change, and the number -4.75 is the starting value that represents the amount subtracted to pay for a shirt.

2.   **$A = 2d - 4.75$**

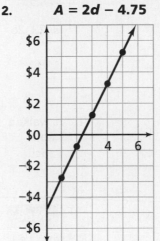

This graph starts at $(0, -4.75)$, whereas the graph of Gilberto in Question A, part (2) started at $(0, 0)$. The graphs have the same steepness, but this one is lower than the one in Question A, part (2). For every value of x, the y-coordinate of a point on this graph is exactly 4.75 less than the y-coordinate of the graph in Question A, part (2).

3. This relationship is linear; it has a constant rate of change. Gilberto raises $2 per kilometer from each sponsor, as he did in Question A. The difference is that he does not raise as much money as he did before giving away a T-shirt to each sponsor. The graph is still a straight line even though it no longer passes through the origin. The starting value is $-$4.75$. The graph looks similar and has been shifted down by 4.75 units.

Moving Straight Ahead **At a Glance**

1.4 Using the Walkathon Money: Recognizing Linear Relationships

> *Focus Question* How can you determine if a linear relationship is increasing or decreasing?

Launch

Display Teaching Aid 1.4. Tell the first story of how one class is going to use the money they raised from the walkathon.

Suggested Questions

- *How can you tell whether a relationship is linear?*
- *What do you think the graph of these data would look like?*
- *Is this a linear relationship?*

Explore

This is the first time that students have encountered negative rates of change or negative slope.

Suggested Question

- *How can you represent this change in a table?*

Summarize

The main goals in this Problem are for students to revisit constant rate and explore negative rates of change in the context of tables and graphs.

Suggested Questions

- *For each class, how much money is being spent or withdrawn each week?*
- *Compare the rates of change in this Problem with other rates that you have studied in this Unit. How do the rates in this Problem show up in a table? In a graph? In an equation?*
- *What are the coordinates of the point where the line intersects the y-axis? What information does this point represent?*
- *What are the coordinates of the point where the line intersects the x-axis? What information does this point represent?*
- *Choose a pair of corresponding values in each table for Questions A and B. What two questions could you answer using each pair of values?*
- *After how many weeks will each account be empty?*

Materials

Labsheet
- First-Quadrant Grid

Accessibility Labsheet
- 1ACE: Exercise 12

Teaching Aids
- 1. 4: Ms. Chang's Class Account

Assessment
- Check Up 1

- Coordinate Grapher Tool
- Data and Graphs Tool

Answers to Problem 1.4

A. 1. $144; this is the amount at the end of 0 weeks.

2. $12; the amount of money withdrawn from the account is the difference between two rows of the table. For example, from the end of week 1 to the end of week 2, the amount of money decreased from $132 to $120, so it went down by $132 − $120 = $12.

3.

Ms. Chang's Class Account

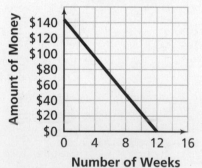

Number of Weeks

4. $A = -12n + 144$; n represents the number of weeks, and A represents the money in the account after n weeks. The rate at which the amount of money is changing is −12 dollars per week, and the starting amount of money in the club's account is $144.

5. Yes; the balance decreases by the same amount every week, and the graph of this relationship is a straight line.

B. 1. The graph shows that the class started with $100, and they withdrew $10 each week. After 10 weeks, the account is out of money.

2.   **Money in Mr. Mamer's Class Account**

Week	Amount of Money at the End of Each Week
0	$100
1	$90
2	$80
3	$70
4	$60
5	$50
6	$40
7	$30
8	$20
9	$10
10	$0

For every 1 week, the amount of money decreases by $10. Since it decreases by the same amount every week, this is a linear relationship.

3. $A = -10n + 100$; n represents the number of weeks, and A represents the money in the account after n weeks. The coefficient −10 is the rate of change of the amount of money per week, and the term 100 is the amount of money initially in the account.

C. 1. In a graph, the relationship is linear if it is a straight line. A linear relationship will show up in a table as a constant increase or decrease in the dependent variable as the independent variable increases by a constant amount. A linear relationship shows up in the equation if the equation is of the form $y = mx + b$. **Note** that this equation still represents a linear relationship even if $m = 0$ or $b = 0$. (A linear relationship can be determined from a verbal description if the verbal description can be modeled by one of the three representations mentioned.)

2. Both of the relationships in this Problem have decreasing rates of changes. As the independent variable increases, the dependent variable decreases. This results in the graph of a line that decreases from left to right, and an equation for which the independent variable has a negative coefficient.

2.1 Henri and Emile's Race: Finding the Point of Intersection

Focus Question When is it helpful to use a graph or a table to solve a problem?

Launch

If you did not pose the following questions at the end of the Summarize for Problem 1.4, ask them now. Begin by having students list several equations from Investigation 1 that represent linear relationships.

Suggested Questions

- *Which relationship has the greatest rate of change?*
- *Which relationship(s) has a graph that crosses the y-axis at a point with a positive y-coordinate? With a y-coordinate of zero? With a negative y-coordinate?*

Tell the story of the race between Emile and his younger brother, Henri. This Problem is intended to show what knowledge students already have concerning linear relationships. Problem 2.2 will serve as a summary of this Problem. Because the Problem asks "how long" the race should be, some students will choose to focus on length and some will focus on time.

Suggested Questions

- *What should Emile do?*
- *What head start should he give his brother, and how many meters long should the race be?*
- *Is giving his little brother a head start sufficient to guarantee that Henri will win?*
- *What strategy do you need to ensure that the younger brother is still ahead at the end of the race?*

This is a nontrivial insight, that the faster rate or the steeper slope will always overtake the lesser rate, given an appropriate domain.

Explore

Some students might use a guess-and-check method to find the answer. Others may use a graph or a table. Look to see if they are choosing reasonable scales for the graphs or intervals for the tables. Some might use an equation, but this may not be as common.

Test students' understanding of how the length of the race depends on the head start and both brothers' walking rates.

Key Vocabulary

- x-intercept

Materials

Labsheet
- Generic Grid Paper
- sticky notes
- poster paper

Summarize

Collect some strategies from the class. Encourage students to explain their reasons for the choices they make. The process of making such decisions is very important.

Students may have informal ways of thinking about the Problem. These informal methods can enhance their appreciation and understanding of what the more formal mathematical processes can tell them.

Suggested Question

- *How did your group interpret the Problem? What strategy did you use?*

ACE
Assignment Guide for Problem 2.1

Applications: 1 | Connections: 29–34
Extensions: 42

Answers to Problem 2.1

A.–B. The race should be less than 75 meters long. Thus, the race should last less than 30 seconds. Strategies may vary. Students may use guess-and-check, graph the situation, generate a table, or write equations.

2.2 Crossing the Line: Using Tables, Graphs and Equations

> *Focus Question* How does the pattern of change for a linear relationship appear in a table, a graph, or an equation?

Launch

Review the questions posed in Problem 2.1. Ask students how they can use a table, a graph, or an equation to answer these questions. Remind students that once they have tables, graphs, and equations for each relationship, they can answer other questions about the race.

Explore

As you circulate, ask questions about features of the graph or table.

Suggested Questions

- How do you represent Henri's walking rate in an equation?
- For the graphs of the two lines, why are the points where the lines cross the y-axis different?
- What does the vertical difference between the two lines on the graph tell you?
- Can you tell from a table how far Henri is from the starting point at 7 seconds? Explain your reasoning.
- Is either relationship linear? Explain.

Summarize

Understanding how an ordered pair appears in each representation of a linear relationship and what the values mean for the situation is very important.

Suggested Questions

- How can you tell how long the race should be using the graph? Using the table?
- What information does the point (20, 50) represent in the situation? Would this be a data point for Henri or for Emile? How does it relate to a table, a graph, and an equation for this situation?
- What does the pair of values (10, 55) mean in this situation? Would this be a data point for Henri or for Emile? How does this pair of values show up on the graph? How is it related to the equation?
- Pick a point on the graph of one of the brothers and write a question that can be answered using this point.
- Describe the two graphs. How can you tell from the graphs who is ahead?

Materials

Labsheets
- 2.2: Henri and Emile's Race
- Generic Grid Paper

Accessibility Labsheets
- 2ACE: Exercise 4
- Coordinate Grapher Tool
- Data and Graphs Tool

Assignment Guide for Problem 2.2

Applications: 2–4, 6 | Connections: 35–37
Extensions: 43

Answers to Problem 2.2

A. 1. Sample table using intervals of 10 seconds:

Distance From Starting Line

Time (seconds)	Henri's Distance (meters)	Emile's Distance (meters)
0	45	0
10	55	25
20	65	50
30	75	75
40	85	100

On the table, the length of the race that ends in a tie is 75 meters. This happens at 30 seconds. For Henri to win, the length of the race should be slightly less than 75 meters.

2. **Henri and Emile's Race**

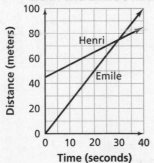

On the graph, the length of the race that ends in a tie is 75 meters. This happens at the point where the two lines intersect. The coordinates of the point are (30, 75). For Henri to win the length of the race should be slightly less than 75 meters or slightly less than 30 seconds long. (**Note** that the line representing Henri's race is above the line of Emile's until the intersection point. Then it is below.)

3. Henri: $d_{Henri} = 45 + t$; $d_{Emile} = 2.5t$; d is the distance from the starting line and t is the time they walked in seconds.

4. The walking rate shows up in the graph as the steepness of the line. In the table, it is the constant change in distance for each second of time. In the equation, it is the coefficient of t.

B. 1. 50 m; since Emile's walking rate is 2.5 m/s, in 20 seconds he walked $2.5 \times 20 = 50$ meters.

2. 15 m; after 20 seconds, the brothers are 15 meters apart. At 20 seconds, Emile has walked 2.5(20) = 50 m and Henri is 65 m from the starting line. So, $65 - 50 = 15$ m. Students may look at a graph for each brother and subtract the two values, subtract the brothers' distances in the table for 20 seconds, or substitute 20 seconds for t in both equations and subtract the distances for the brothers.

3. No; if you substitute 26 for t in Henri's equation you get 71 m, not 70. If you substitute it for t in Emile's equation you get 65 m. If students use a graph to answer this question, they may mistakenly think that the point lies on Henri's graph. The point actually lies very close to Henri's line but not on it. If students use the equation or the table, they will see that the point does not lie on Henri's line.

4. After 75 m, or after 30 seconds; this is the point in the table where the time and distance for the brothers are equal and the point on the graph where the lines cross. Students can talk about the distance or the time it will take for Emile to overtake Henri.

C. 1. In the table, the line is steeper if its rate of change is greater (in terms of negative rate of change, greater means a greater absolute value); in this case the rate is the average walking rate.

2. In an equation, the line is steeper if the coefficient of time, or the number you multiply time by, has a greater absolute value.

D. 1. Emile's line crosses the y-axis at (0, 0) and Henri's line crosses the y-axis at (0, 45).

2. The points represent each brother's starting point in relation to the starting line.

3. In the table, you find the distance values when the time is 0 seconds. In the equations, it is the value of d when $t = 0$.

2.3 Comparing Costs: Comparing Relationships

> *Focus Question* How can you decide if a table or an equation represents a linear relationship?

Launch

You can start by showing the equations from Problem 2.2.

Suggested Questions

- *What do the variables and numbers represent in each equation?*
- *How does the walking rate show up in the equations?*

Explore

Students may use numerical reasoning, tables, graphs, or equations. Be sure to look at what methods students are using to find when the two plans are equal.

Suggested Questions

- *How do the solutions to Question A, part (2) and part (3) show up in the graph and in the table?*

Summarize

Suggested Questions

- *What is the cost per T-shirt under each plan? How would this rate show up in a table? In a graph?*
- *What information does the y-intercept represent in each equation?*
- *How could you use a table to find the cost of producing 100 T-shirts? How could you use a graph? How could you use an equation?*
- *For what number of T-shirts are the two costs equal?*

Key Vocabulary

- coefficient
- solution of an equation
- y-intercept

Materials

Labsheets

- First-Quadrant Grid
- Generic Grid Paper

(A)(C)(E)
Assignment Guide for Problem 2.3

Applications: 5, 7–14 | Connections: 38, 39
Extensions: 44, 45

Answers to Problem 2.3

A. 1. The y-intercept represents the initial payment, and the coefficient of *n* represents the cost for each T-shirt. For Mighty Tee, the initial payment is $49. There is no initial payment for No-Shrink.

The cost per T-Shirt is $1 for Mighty Tee and $4.50 for No-Shrink.

Independent variable: the number of T-shirts bought; Dependent variable: the cost for the number of T-shirts for each company

2. For 12 T-shirts, the cost for Mighty Tee is $61 and for No-Shrink Tee is $54. To find these values, substitute 12 for *n* in each equation. So, $C_{\text{Mighty}} = 49 + 12 = \$61$ and $C_{\text{No-Shrink}} = 4.5(12) = \$54$.

For 20 T-shirts, the cost for Mighty Tee is $69 and for No-Shrink Tee is $90.

3. $120 will buy 71 T-shirts from Mighty Tee and only 26 T-shirts from No-Shrink Tee. Students may guess and check to find the greatest value of n that results in a cost of at most $120. Students may also choose to graph the equations on their calculators and trace the lines to find out which x-coordinate corresponds with a y-coordinate of 120. Other students may use a table.

4. a. The companies have the same cost when you buy 14 T-shirts. It costs $63 to buy 14 T-shirts from either company. Students may make a table and see where the table values for the cost are the same or graph both equations and see where the lines intersect.

   b. On either side of the point where the two lines intersect, there is one line that is above the other (i.e., the cost of one company is greater than the other). Because you want the company with the lower cost, if you know the number of T-shirts you want to buy, you can choose the company whose line lies below the other line for that x-value. If the number of T-shirts is less than 14, No-Shrink Tee costs less. If you want to buy more than 14 T-shirts, Mighty Tee costs less.

5. a. They are both linear relationships because the rate of change for each is constant. For Mighty, the rate of change is $1 per T-shirt. For No-Shrink, the rate of change is $4.50 per T-shirt.

   b. Mighty Tee: as n increases by 1, C_{Mighty} increases by a constant amount, $1. No-Shrink Tee: as n increases by 1, $C_{No-Shrink}$ increases by $4.50.

   c. In all three Problems, there is a linear relationship between an independent variable and a dependent variable, which means there is a constant rate of change. Also, the two equations for T-shirt companies are similar to the equations for the two brothers in Problem 2.2. The equation $C_{Mighty} = 49 + n$ is similar to the equation $d_{Henri} = 45 + t$. The numbers 49 and 45 are the starting values and

the y-intercepts on the graphs. The coefficient of the independent variable for both equations is 1. Henri walks at 1 meter per second and the unit cost at Mighty Tee is $1 per shirt. Similarly, the two equations, $C_{No-Shrink} = 4.5n$ and $d_{Emile} = 2.5t$ are similar. The y-intercepts are 0, and the coefficients of the independent variable represent the cost per T-shirt and Emile's walking rate, respectively.

B. 1. The cost per T-shirt for this company is $2.50 and the down payment, or cost for no T-shirts, is $34. This cost per T-shirt is less than No-Shrink Tee and greater than Mighty Tee.

2. This plan represents a linear relationship because it involves a constant rate of change. The cost of each T-shirt is always $2.50.

3. a. The point (20, 84) lies on the graph because if you extend the table to n = 20, the value for C is 84. So, the point (20, 84) must lie on the graph. The equation of the relationship would be $C = 2.5n + 34$. If you substitute 20 for n, you can see that C = 84, and when you graph the line that this equation represents, the point (20, 84) is on this line.

   b. The coordinates of the point (20, 84) mean that if you buy 20 T-shirts it will cost $84. If you substitute the coordinates into the equation it makes it a true statement.

   c. $C = 34 + 2.50n$.

   d. (20, 80) is not a solution since $80 \neq 34 + 2.50(20)$. (14, 69) is a solution since $69 = 34 + 2.50(14)$. The ordered pair (14, 69) also lies on the line that represents the equation. In other words, the coordinates of a point on a line are also a solution of the equation that corresponds to the line.

At a Glance   Problem 2.4   Pacing $1\frac{1}{2}$ Days

2.4 Connecting Tables, Graphs, and Equations

> *Focus Question* How are solutions of an equation of the form $y = b + mx$ related to the graph and the table for the same relationship?

Launch

Remind students about the three students and their pledge plans from Investigation 1.

Suggested Questions

- *Write a question that could be answered using the point (14, 12). How can you use the equation for Alana's plan to check the answer to the question you wrote?*

- *How can you use a graph to find the number of kilometers that Alana walked if each sponsor donated $17?*

Students should begin to see that there is an infinite number of coordinate pairs that are solutions of $A = 5 + 0.5d$. When they are solving a linear equation in one "unknown," they are looking for the missing coordinate of an ordered pair that is a solution of the linear equation.

- *How far would a student have to walk to raise $8.50 from each sponsor under Alana's plan?*

Explore

Look for interesting explanations of what information each equation represents and discuss these in the Summarize.

Suggested Questions

- *Which relationship has a graph you can use to find a value of x that makes $5 = 5x - 3$ true? Explain.*

- *What point represents the solution for the equation $5 = 5x - 3$? What question could you answer using this point?*

- *Which relationship has a graph you can use to find a value of x that makes $5 = -x + 6$ true? Explain.*

- *What point represents the solution for the equation $5 = -x + 6$? What question could you answer using this point?*

- *Does the table help you decide whether the graph of the relationship is increasing or decreasing?*

Summarize

One goal of this Problem is for students to revisit constant rate in the context of equations and connect the rate to tables and graphs of linear relationships.

Suggested Questions

- *What is the amount raised per kilometer under each plan?*

Materials

Accessibility Labsheet
- PQ: Partner Quiz

Teaching Aids
- 2.4A: Alana's Pledge Plan
- 2.4B: Ali and Tamara's Graphs
- 2.4C: Graph of $y = 5x - 3$
- 2.4D: Troy's Graphing Calculator

Assessment
- Partner Quiz
- graphing calculator
- Coordinate Grapher Tool

AT A GLANCE 2

- *How does each rate appear in a table? In a graph? In an equation?*
- *What information does the y-intercept represent in each plan?*
- *Do the plans make sense? Explain.*
- *How are the equations $12 = 5x - 3$, $-8 = 5x - 3$, and $27 = 5x - 3$ related to $y = 5x - 3$?*
- *For which equation is (2, 4) a solution? Explain your answer.*
- *How is the solution (2, 4) related to a table and a graph of Plan 3?*

(A)(C)(E)
Assignment Guide for Problem 2.4

Applications: 15–28 | Connections: 40, 41

Answers to Problem 2.4

A. 1. Plan 1: A sponsor pays $5 for every kilometer walked, but you pay the sponsor $3. Or you give the sponsor a T-shirt that costs $3.

Plan 2: A sponsor pays $6 and then you give the sponsor $1 for every km you walk. Students will say that the negative rate does not make sense because you give back money. But some may suggest that the walker in Plan 2 collects $6 and promises to walk 15 km. If she does not walk the 15 km, then she pays back $1 for each km not walked. In this case, it is necessary to change what x represents to the number of kilometers not walked.

Plan 3: A sponsor donates a fixed amount of $2 no matter how far you walk.

2. See Figure 1, Figure 2, and Figure 3.

3.

Plan 1

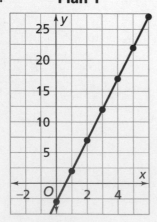

Plan 2

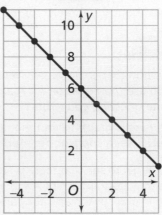

Plan 3

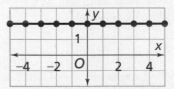

Students may say that the part of the graph that is relevant is the y-intercept and any points to the right of the y-axis. Other students may suggest that the entire graph is relevant because points to the left of the y-axis represent distance walked in the opposite direction.

4. As the x-values increase, the y-values in Plan 1 increase; in Plan 2 decrease; and in Plan 3, stay the same.
Graph: Follow the line to the right and see if it increases (goes up), decreases (goes down), or is horizontal.
Table: As the values of x-increase, see if their corresponding y-values are increasing, decreasing, or staying the same. Just look at the second column.

Equation: Put a value of x into the equation and find the corresponding y-value. Then use a greater value for x and find that y-value. Compare the two y-values. A positive rate of change has increasing y-values, and a negative rate of change has decreasing y-values. If the y-values are the same, the equation is of the form $y = b$, where b is some constant value. Alternatively, you could look at the coefficient of x. If it is positive, the y-values are increasing; if it is negative, the y-values are decreasing.

B. **1.** Plan 2 includes the point (2, 4).

2. The point (2, 4) is a solution for Plan 2; if you substitute 2 for x and 4 for y in the equation, then $-2 + 6 = 4$ is a true statement. In a row of the table, if 2 is the value in the x-column, then 4 is the corresponding value in the y-column.

3. Sample answer: For Plan 2, how much money would you get if you walked 2 kilometers?

C. **1.** Plan 1

2. If you find what value of x makes the statement $8 = 5x - 3$ true, then you know that this point $(x, 8)$ is on the line of the equation $y = 5x - 3$. When you substitute this value, which is 2.2, for x into the equation, $y = 5(2.2) - 3$, so $y = 8$.

D. **1.** 4.8, 10; to find the missing y-value for the point (1.2, ■), you substitute 1.2 for x into the equation $y = -x + 6$ and solve for y. Thus, $y = 4.8$. For the other point (■, −4), you want to find the value of x for which $-4 = -x + 6$. So, $x = 10$.

2. Possible answer: For Plan 2, how much money does each sponsor pledge if you walk 1.2 kilometers?

E. **1.** A point on a graph is an ordered pair. That ordered pair corresponds to the values in two columns of the table and a solution of the equation.

2. **a.** To find the y-value for the equation $y = 5x - 3$ when $x = 7$, you substitute 7 for x and find that $y = 32$. For a graph, you find the value of y for which the point $(7, y)$ is a point on the line of the relationship. For a table, you find the value of 7 in the column for x and look for the corresponding y-value in the other column.

b. If you find the value of x that makes the statement $23 = 5x - 3$ true by solving the equation for x, then you find that $x = 5.2$. You can also find the value of x for which the point $(x, 23)$ is on the line of the equation $y = 5x - 3$. You can find the value of 23 in the y-column of the table and then look at the corresponding x-value in the first column.

Figure 1

$y = 5x - 3$

x	−5	−4	−3	−2	−1	0	1	2	3	4	5
y	−28	−23	−18	−13	−8	−3	2	7	12	17	22

Figure 2

$y = -x + 6$

x	−5	−4	−3	−2	−1	0	1	2	3	4	5
y	11	10	9	8	7	6	5	4	3	2	1

Figure 3

$y = 2$

x	−5	−4	−3	−2	−1	0	1	2	3	4	5
y	2	2	2	2	2	2	2	2	2	2	2

3.1 Solving Equations Using Tables and Graphs

> *Focus Question* How are the coordinates of a point on a line or in a table related to the equation of the line?

Launch

Display Teaching Aid 3.1. Tell students that the graph and table are for Alana's pledge plan, which is represented by the equation $A = 5 + 0.5d$.

Suggested Questions

- *How are the points (3, 6.5) and (30, 20) related to the equation $A = 5 + 0.5d$?*

- *We say that (3, 6.5) and (30, 20) are solutions to the equation $A = 5 + 0.5d$. Find another point on the line whose coordinates are a solution to the equation.*

- *Do you think every point on the line corresponds to a solution to the equation?*

- *Write two questions about Alana's pledge plan that could be answered by the coordinates of the point (14, 12). How can you use the equation for Alana's plan to check the answer to your question?*

- *How can you use a graph to find the number of kilometers that Alana walked if a sponsor donated $17?*

- *How can you use a graph to solve $20 = 5 + 0.5d$? What would the answer mean?*

- *What happens if you choose a point that is not visible on this section of the graph, such as (70, 40)? Does this point lie on the line? Explain.*

Tell students that, in this Investigation, they will explore strategies for finding solutions to equations using properties of operations and equality. This will be useful in finding solutions that are not obvious on a line or in a table.

Explore

Look for interesting solutions. Ask questions to check students' understanding of the connection between tables, graphs, and solutions to equations. Also, check students' understanding of using graphs and tables as viable methods for finding the solution to an equation.

Materials

Labsheet
- Blank Table and Graph

Accessibility Labsheet
- 3ACE: Exercise 1

Teaching Aid
- 3.1: Alana's Pledge Plan

- Coordinate Grapher Tool

- Data and Graphs Tool

Summarize

Go over all parts of the Problem. Question B is particularly important.

Suggested Questions

- *How could you have used a graph (or a table) to find this information?*
- *How could you use the equation? Explain.*
- *Write a question you could ask that could be answered by finding the value of the missing variable in each equation.*
- *Write a general equation that could represent the equations. What are the variables?*

Applications: 1–4 | Connections: 35, 37, 38, 49

Answers to Problem 3.1

A. 1. a. You can use a table by looking for 23 in the independent variable column under d. Then, read across to find the corresponding A-value, or amount of money. To find the amount of money using a graph, go to 23 on the horizontal axis, move up until you intersect the line, then follow straight across to the left to the vertical axis, to read off the money raised.

b. $A = 5 + 0.5(23)$

Substituting 23 in for d (the distance walked), gives $A = 5 + 0.5(23) = 16.5$. The amount of money Alana raised is $16.50.

2. a. Alana is trying to find out how many kilometers she would have to walk in order to collect $30 from a sponsor. You can find the information by completing a table, using the graph, or using the guess-and-check method. She would have had to walk 50 km to raise $30 from a sponsor.

b. You can use a table by looking for 30 in the dependent variable column under A. Read across to find the corresponding d-value, or distance walked. To find the distance using a graph, go up to 30 on the vertical axis, move to the right until you intersect the line, then follow straight down to the horizontal axis to read off the distance walked. You can also solve the equation $50 = 5 + 0.5d$.

B 1. $D = 42.5$; this can be found by multiplying 2.5 by 7 and then adding 25, or by using a table or a graph.

2. $t = 18$; this can be found by using a table or a graph, or by using the guess-and-check method.

3.2 Mystery Pouches in the Kingdom of Montarek: Exploring Equality

Focus Question What does equality mean?

Launch

Remind students that, in the last Problem, they found solutions to equations by using tables and graphs. They also substituted values for the independent variable to find the corresponding value of the dependent variable.

Display Teaching Aid 3.2A and tell the class about the pouches and coins.

- *The number of gold coins on each side of the equality sign is the same, but some coins are hidden in the pouches.*
- *In each situation, each pouch contains the same number of one-dollar gold coins.*
- *The challenge is to find the number of coins in each pouch.*

As the students work on this Problem, you might want to record their work on the table in Teaching Aid 3.2B.

Explore

Encourage students to record their strategies.

Suggested Questions

- *What does equality mean?*
- *How can we maintain equality?*
- *How do you know if your answer is correct?*

Look for interesting strategies to share during the Summarize.

Summarize

If your students recorded their work on poster paper, display the posters and give the class time to examine the various strategies. Have students share all of the correct strategies they used. Display Teaching Aid 3.2C and make sure students understand how the Distributive Property is being used.

Suggested Questions

- *Can you use the Distributive Property on any of the other equations?*
- *Did each group use the same first step in each equation?*
- *What are some common strategies that we can use to maintain equality?*
- *Suppose we let x represent the number of coins in a pouch and 1 represent one coin. Rewrite the equality from Question A, part (4) using x's and numbers.*
- *Write the steps for solving this equation for x.*

Materials

Labsheet
- 3.2: Pouch-and-Coin Situations

Teaching Aids
- 3.2A: Pouches and Coins
- 3.2B: Pouch-and-Coin Strategies
- 3.2C: Nichole's Method
- 3.2D: Symbolic Representation Table

- poster paper

AT A GLANCE 3

Answers to Problem 3.2

A. **1.** 2 coins; check: 10 = 3(2) + 4 or
10 = 2 + 2 + 2 + 4 or 10 = 10
Possible steps: There are 4 coins on the right side. You can take those four away if you take four away from the left side. Now you have 6 coins on the left side and 3 pouches on the right side. There must be 2 coins in each pouch since 3 pouches with 2 coins in each gives you 6 coins. Student work for this part might look like Figure 1.
Description of how to check the answer: You could substitute the number of coins you think are in each pouch for each pouch drawing. Then, add the number of coins in each bag and the number of coins outside the bags on each side of the equality. If the total number on each side is the same, then the solution is correct. **Note:** This description applies to all parts of Question A.

2. 4 coins; check: 2(4) + 4 = 12 or
4 + 2 + 4 + 2 = 12 or 12 = 12
Possible steps: You can use the Distributive Property to split each side evenly into two groups of 1 pouch and 2 coins on the left side and two groups of 6 coins on the right side. Then, divide both sides by 2. The result is 1 pouch and 2 coins on the left and 6 coins on the right. Next, you could remove 2 coins from each side, leaving 1 pouch on the left side and 4 coins on the right side. So, there are 4 coins in each pouch.
You can also regroup the left side and think of it as 2 pouches and 4 coins. Then, you can subtract 4 coins from each side to get 2 pouches on the left and 8 coins on the right. Next, you divide both sides by 2, which leaves 1 pouch on the left and 4 coins on the right. So, there are 4 coins in each pouch.

Figure 1

Original Equation	Strategies
	Remove 4 coins from each side of the equation.
	Divide each side by 3. Each pouch contains 2 coins.

3. 12 coins; check: 3(12) = 2(12) + 12 or 36 = 36

   You can subtract 2 pouches from each side, which leaves 1 pouch on the left and 12 coins on the right. So, each pouch contains 12 coins.

4. 9 coins; check: 3(9) + 3 = 30 or 9 + 9 + 9 = 3 = 30 or 30 = 30

   Possible steps: Take away 3 coins from each side so that you are left with 3 pouches on the left side and 27 coins on the right side. Now you must split 27 coins evenly into 3 pouches, so each pouch must contain 9 coins.

5. 9 coins; check: 3(9) + 3 = 2(9) + 12 or 9 + 9 + 9 + 3 = 9 + 9 + 12 or 30 = 30

   Take away 3 coins from each side so that you are left with 3 pouches on the left side and 2 pouches and 9 coins on the right side. Now take away 2 pouches from each side, and you are left with 1 pouch on the left side and 9 coins on the right side. So, a pouch must contain 9 coins.

6. 6 coins; check: 2(6) + 21 = 5(6) + 3 or 6 + 6 + 21 = 6 + 6 + 6 + 6 + 3 or 33 = 33.

   Take away 3 coins from each side and 2 pouches from each side. You are left with 18 coins on the let side and 3 pouches on the right side. Now you must split 18 coins evenly into 3 pouches, so each pouch must contain 6 coins.

Note: Students may blend fact-family ideas and properties of equality in logical strategies. For example, in part (6), students may say they should subtract 3 coins and 2 pouches from each side, leaving 18 coins on the left and 3 pouches on the right. They may think of this as $3(n) = 18$ and answer $\blacksquare = \frac{18}{3}$. So, each pouch contains $\frac{18}{3}$ coins.

B 1. Yes, Nichole is correct in her thinking. By thinking of the situation as two groups of 1 pouch and 2 coins, each of these groups must be equal to 6 coins.

2. Yes, Noah is correct that Nichole is applying the Distributive Property. The left side of the equation can be thought of as $2(x + 2)$, or two times a group of 1 pouch plus 2 coins. This situation can also be thought of as 2 pouches and 2 sets of 2 coins, or $2x + 2(2)$. The Distributive Property states that these two expressions are equivalent.

3. Nichole's method could work in other situations in which each side can be evenly divided into the same number of groups. For example, the left side of Question A, part (4) can be thought of as three groups of 1 pouch and 1 coin, and the right side can be thought of as three groups of 10 coins.

AT A GLANCE 3

3.3 From Pouches to Variables: Writing Equations

Focus Question How can the properties of equality be used to solve linear equations?

Launch

Start by presenting the example at the beginning of the introduction.

Suggested Questions

- *What should you do to keep the two sides equal?*
- *Summarize what you know about maintaining equality.*

If you did not make the transition from pouches and coins to variables and numbers at the end of the Summarize for Problem 3.2, do so now. Be sure students have a general idea of the procedures. You might want to work through Question A, part (1) as a class or use one of the situations from Problem 3.2.

Key Vocabulary

- equivalent expressions

Materials

Labsheet
- 3.3: Pouch-and-Coin Equations

- poster paper

Explore

Be sure students are recording their methods and checking their answers.

See how students are translating the situation in Question A, part (2). Return to this in the summary and ask if the two expressions are equivalent and why. This will review the Distributive Property.

Suggested Questions

- *What is your equation?*
- *What was the first thing you did with the pictorial equation to begin solving it? How can you show this with your equation?*
- *What was your next step? How can you show this with your equation?*
- *How can you check your answer?*

Summarize

Post the solutions around the room. Make sure you highlight equations in which students may have done something different for the first step.

Suggested Questions

- *What did you do at each step to maintain equality?*
- *Is there another way to make the first step in the solution? Explain.*
- *What general rules were you using to solve the equations?*
- *Describe a general method for solving equations.*

Students should be able to generalize that adding, subtracting, multiplying, and dividing by the same number maintains equality. Be sure to stress that they cannot multiply or divide by 0.

Answers to Problem 3.3

A. 1. $4x + 2 = 18$ (Subtract 2 from each side of the equation.)

     $4x = 16$ (Divide each side by 4.)

     $x = 4$

Check: $4(4) + 2 = 18$

         $16 + 2 = 18$

         $18 = 18$

Note: Students can also start by dividing each side of the equation by 2.

2. $x + 2 + x + 2 + x + 2 = 12$ (Group the 3 sets of $(x + 2)$ together.)

     $3(x + 2) = 12$ (Apply the Distributive Property.)

     $3x + 6 = 12$ (Subtract 6 from each side.)

         $3x = 6$ (Divide each side by 3.)

           $x = 2$

Check: $3(2) + 6 = 12$

         $6 + 6 = 12$

         $12 = 12$

Note: At the second step, students could have chosen to divide by 3 and then subtract 2 rather than apply the Distributive Property.

3. $3x + 3 = 2x + 9$ (Subtract 2x from each side.)

     $x + 3 = 9$ (Subtract 3 from each side.)

         $x = 6$

Check: $3(6) + 3 = 2(6) + 9$

       $18 + 3 = 12 + 9$

          $21 = 21$

4. $6x + 15 = 4x + 19$ (Subtract 15 from each side.)

     $6x = 4x + 4$ (Subtract 4x from each side.)

     $2x = 4$ (Divide each side by 2.)

       $x = 2$

Check: $6(2) + 15 = 4(2) + 19$

      $12 + 15 = 8 + 19$

         $27 = 27$

5. There are 4 possible answers that students can give:

You could write the situation in Question A, part (1) as $4x + 2 = 18$ or as $2(2x + 1) = 2(9)$.

You could write the situation in Question A, part (2) as $3x + 6 = 12$ or as $3(x + 2) = 3(4)$.

You could write the situation in Question A, part (3) as $3x + 3 = 2x + 9$ or as $3(x + 1) = 2x + 9$.

You could write the situation in Question A, part (4) as $6x + 15 = 4x + 19$ or as $3(2x + 5) = 4x + 9$.

B. 1. $30 = 6 + 4x$

     $24 = 4x$

       $6 = x$

Check: $30 = 6 + 4(6)$

         $30 = 86 + 24$

         $30 = 30$

2. $7x = 5 + 5x$

     $2x = 5$

       $x = 2.5$

Check: $7(2.5) = 5 + 5(2.5)$

        $17.5 = 5 + 12.5$

        $17.5 = 17.5$

3. $7x + 2 = 12 + 5x$

     $2x + 2 = 12$

       $2x = 10$

         $x = 5$

Check: $7(5) + 2 = 12 + 5(5)$

       $35 + 2 = 12 + 25$

         $37 = 37$

4. $2(x + 4) = 16$

     $x + 4 = 8$

       $x = 4$

Check: $2(4 + 4) = 16$

         $2(8) = 16$

        $16 = 16$

C. To find a solution to a linear equation, apply the principles of equality repeatedly to the equation until you have isolated the variable on one side and a number on the other side. Then, check the solution by substituting the value of the variable into the original equation to see if the equation is true.

3.4 Solving Linear Equations

Focus Question What are some strategies for solving linear equations?

Launch

Suggested Questions

- *Compare these two equations: 2x + 10 = 16 and 2x − 10 = 16*
- *What property of equality would you use to begin solving these two equations?*
- *In the first equation, instead of subtracting 10 from each side, could we add − 10 to each side?*
- *How can you solve the second equation?*
- *In Question A, part (1), how are the equations alike and how are they different?*

Ask the class to solve the equations, show their work, and check their answers.

Key Vocabulary

- properties of equality

Materials

Accessibility Labsheets
- 3ACE: Exercise 41
- 3ACE: Exercise 58

- poster paper

Explore

Be sure students are making a record of their methods and checking their answers. Encourage students to look for commonalities and differences in each set of equations. This should help them make the shift from equations that had all positive numbers to those that also include negative numbers.

Suggested Questions

- *What operations on x have been used to create the expressions on each side?*
- *How can you get rid of, or "undo," each operation, but still maintain equality?*

Summarize

Go over each part of the Problem.

Suggested Questions

- *What do the equations in Question A, parts (1a) and (1c) have in common?*
- *How else could you find the corresponding values for x?*
- *What about the equations in Question A, parts (1b) and (1d)? What do they have in common?*
- *How is the equation 3.2x + 5 = 16 different from the equations in this Problem? How can we solve this equation?*

Repeat the question above for the equations 3.2x + 5 = 14.6 and 3.2x + 15 = 6.5x + 10. This will lead into the work on finding points of intersection in the next Problem.

Answers to Problem 3.4

Note: Only one possible order of steps is given. Students may decide to solve the equations using different steps. Checking is required but is not included in the answers.

A. 1. a. $5x + 10 = 20$
$$5x = 10$$
$$x = 2$$

b. $5x - 10 = 20$
$$5x = 30$$
$$x = 6$$

c. $5x + 10 = -20$
$$5x = -30$$
$$x = -6$$

d. $5x - 10 = -20$
$$5x = -10$$
$$x = -2$$

e. $10 - 5x = 20$
$$-5x = 10$$
$$x = -2$$

f. $10 - 5x = -20$
$$-5x = -30$$
$$x = 6$$

2. a. $\frac{1}{4}x + 6 = 12$
$$\frac{1}{4}x = 6$$
$$x = 24$$

b. $1\frac{1}{2} + 2x = 6\frac{1}{2}$
$$2x = 5$$
$$x = 2.5$$

c. $\frac{3}{5} = -x + 1$
$$-\frac{2}{5} = -x$$
$$\frac{2}{5} = x$$

d. $3.5x = 130 + 10x$
$$-6.5x = 130$$
$$x = -20$$

e. $15 - 4x = 10x + 45$
$$-4x = 10x + 30$$
$$-14x = 30$$
$$x = -\frac{30}{14}$$
$$x = -\frac{15}{7}$$

3. a. $3(x + 1) = 21$
$$x + 1 = 7$$
$$x = 6$$

b. $2 + 3(x + 1) = 6x$
$$2 + 3x + 3 = 6x$$
$$3x + 5 = 6x$$
$$5 = 3x$$
$$\frac{5}{3} = x$$

c. $-2(2x - 3) = -2$
$$-4x + 6 = -2$$
$$-4x = -8$$
$$x = 2$$

B. Corry's Solution: Corry's method is correct; he is looking for the missing value in the parentheses to solve the equation.
Hadden's Solution: Hadden is incorrect. She added the 2 and 3 incorrectly. The 3 should be distributed over the quantity $(x + 1)$.
Jackie's Solution: Jackie is incorrect. She made an error when she distributed the -2. She did not multiply -2 by -3 correctly. The new expression on the left side should be $-4x + 6$.

C. Answers will vary. For symbolic methods, students' explanations should include keeping expressions equivalent on both sides of the equal sign (e.g., adding 2 to each side, dividing each side by 3, etc.). Students should also include something about using order of operations correctly, although there are some exceptions (e.g., factoring as a first step). Students should also notice that if applying the Distributive Property is possible, then it may simplify the process.
Tables and graphs can also be used to solve linear equations. For example, the equation $2x - 5 = x + 7$ can be solved by finding the point of intersection of $y_1 = 2x - 5$ and $y_2 = x + 7$ on a graphing calculator. Sometimes it is quicker to use symbolic methods rather than spend time entering equations into a calculator. However, if calculators are already being used, and if several questions of this type are being asked, then tables or graphs might be more efficient.

3.5 Finding the Point of Intersection: Equations and Inequalities

> **Focus Question** How can you find when two expressions are equal, or when one expression is greater or less than the other?

Launch

Display Teaching Aid 3.5A and review how to interpret the point of intersection.

Suggested Questions

- *What information do the coordinates of the point of intersection of the two lines give you about this situation?*
- *Show how you could use the two equations to find the coordinates of the point of intersection of the two lines.*
- *For what number(s) of T-shirts is plan C_m less than plan C_n?*

You may want to review inequality statements.

Tell the story of the bakery. Explain what the "break-even" point means. If needed, review income, expense, and profit.

- *In the equations for income and expenses, what information do the y-intercepts give? What information do the coefficients of n represent?*

Explore

Some students may use tables, some may use graphs, and some may use symbolic methods to solve the problems. Make sure that each of these strategies comes out in the Summarize.

In Question B, students determine whether there is a profit for making and selling 100 cakes. The profit is the vertical distance between the two points (100, I) and (100, E) on the graphs. Point out that, in this case, the expenses are greater than the income, so the vertical distance actually represents a loss.

If students are struggling with Question E, suggest that they find when the two expressions are equal and then adjust their answer. Students can graph their solution on a number line or on a graph in the coordinate plane.

Encourage students to check their answers.

Summarize

Discuss all the methods for finding the solutions.

For Question B, display Teaching Aid 3.5B. Use the graph to show that the expenses exceed the for 100 cakes. Mark the difference with a vertical line segment between the point (100, 1,150) on the graph of E and the point (100, 820) on the graph of I. Repeat this discussion for Question E, part (4c).

Key Vocabulary
- inequality
- point of intersection

Materials

Labsheet
- Blank Table and Graph

Accessibility Labsheet
- 3ACE: Exercise 54

Teaching Aids
- 3.5A: Two T-Shirt Plans
- 3.5B: Fabian's Bakery

Assessment
- Check Up 2

- poster paper
- Climbing Monkeys Activity

Suggested Questions

- *How can the vertical distance be interpreted as a symbolic expression? What would this expression mean?*

In Question D, students use the properties of equality to find the coordinates of the point of intersection.

- *How is this similar to the equations in Problem 3.4? To the situation in Problem 2.1?*

A C E

Assignment Guide for Problem 3.5

Applications: 30–34 | Connections: 54, 59

Answers to Problem 3.5

A. 1. The *y*-intercept of the equation $I = 8.20n$ tells you Fabian's income if he makes 0 cakes, which is $0. The *y*-intercept of the equation $E = 825 + 3.25n$ tells you Fabian's expenses if he makes 0 cakes, which are $825.

2. The coefficient of *n* in the equation $I = 8.20n$ tells you the amount by which Fabian's income increases for every cake he makes, which is $8.20. The coefficient of *n* in the equation $E = 825 + 3.25n$ tells you the amount by which Fabian's expenses increase for every cake he makes, which is $3.25.

B. 1. Fabian's expenses are $1,150 because $E = 825 + 3.25(100) = 1,150$. Fabian's income is $820 because $I = 8.20(100) = 820$.

2. No; the expenses are greater than the income for 100 cakes, so Fabian does not make a profit.

3. Kevin could locate 100 on the horizontal axis, which represents the number of cakes Fabian made in January. Then, by moving up on the graph, he can locate a point on each line for which $n = 100$. Kevin can first determine whether the bakery has made a profit by looking at which line is higher on the graph at this point. If the line for income is above the line for expenses, then the bakery makes a profit. If the line for expenses is above the line for income, then the bakery loses

money. In this case, the expense line is higher, so the bakery does not make a profit.
If the income line were the higher of the two, Kevin could determine the profit by finding the vertical distance between the points he located on each line. When the expense line is higher, as in this case, the vertical distance between the points represents Fabian's loss.

C. 1. Profit = Income − Expenses
$P = 8.20n - (3.25n + 825)$
$P = 4.95n - 825$
By substituting the number of cakes sold for *n*, you can calculate how much profit the bakery makes.

2. Yes; this equation comes from subtracting the expense expression from the income expression.

D. 1. To find the break-even point, you could solve the equation:
$$825 + 3.25n = 8.20n$$
$$825 + 3.25n - 3.25n = 8.20n - 3.25n$$
$$825 = 4.95n$$
$$166.\overline{6} = n$$
So, between 166 and 167 cakes, the bakery will break even.
Students could also notice that the break-even point occurs when the profit is 0 and solve the equation $0 = 4.95n - 825$.

2. You could graph the equations for income and expenses and find the point of intersection of the two lines. You could also make a table of values for the relationship between number of cakes and profit using the equation $P = 4.95n - 825$. Then, you could find the break-even point by finding 0 in the column for profit. The number of cakes that corresponds to 0 will tell you the break-even point.

E. 1. $E < 2,400$
       $825 + 3.25n < 2,400$
              $3.25n < 1,575$
                  $n < 484.6$

Note: Because the number of cakes is not a whole number, this is a nice opportunity to ask students whether the exact answer makes sense or if they should round up or down. In this case, we want to keep the expenses less than \$2,400, so we would round down to 484 cakes.

2. $I > 2,400$
       $8.20n > 2,400$
          $n > 292.7$

In this situation, in order for the income to be greater than \$2,400, we would round up to 293 cakes.

3. These methods work because they involve simply substituting the income and expense expressions for the variables I and E, respectively.

4. a. $n < 200$

b. $n > 200$

c. $n > 328$

Some students may record their solutions on a coordinate graph, and some may use a number line. See Figure 1.

Expenses < \$1,475

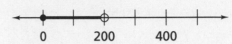

Income > \$1,640

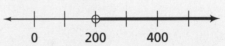

Profit > \$800

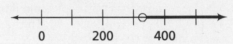

Figure 1

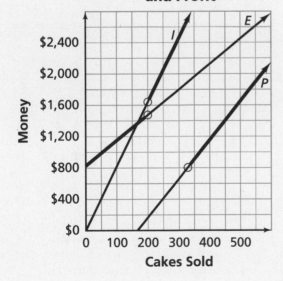

Bakery Income, Expenses, and Profit

AT A GLANCE 3

Moving Straight Ahead   **At a Glance**

4.1 Climbing Stairs: Using Rise and Run

> *Focus Question* How is the steepness of a set of stairs related to a straight-line graph?

Launch

Remind students that they have explored many patterns of change that involve constant rates. They have explored the ways that the rate affects the steepness of the graph, the coefficient of x in a linear equation, and the rate of change between the variables. Tell students that, in this Investigation, they will explore another way to express a constant rate.

Discuss why stair climbing is a popular aerobic exercise.

Suggested Questions

- *Does the steepness of a set of stairs affect the exercise?*
- *Do all stairs have the same steepness? How can we determine the steepness?*

Pose the questions in the Introduction to the Problem. These questions ask students to think about how to describe steepness.

- *How can you describe the steepness of the stairs?*
- *Is the steepness the same between any two consecutive steps?*

For the experiment in Question A, let students go out in groups to measure the rise and the run and then find the ratio of the rise to the run. Tell the groups that they need to measure more than one step in each set of stairs and compare the ratios. Use different sets of stairs for each group if possible.

Materials

Labsheets
- 4.1: Stair Measurement Tables
- Coordinate Grid
- measuring tape in inches
- large sheets of graph paper or poster paper

Explore

For Question A, when the groups have recorded their measures of a staircase in the building, have them organize what they have found out about the ratio of rise to run between several of the steps in the staircase. Also, have them look at the ratios of the rise to the run on the staircases they measured.

For Question B, some students may need help in drawing the line that matches the ratio of changes. Grid paper may help. Suggest that students use the ratio 3 : 5 and the limit of 17 inches to sketch a couple of stairs on the grid paper. Then they can use the same grid paper to make a graph of a line through the origin with slope $\frac{3}{5}$ and compare the graph and the sketch of the stairs. They should see that the stairs align with the slope of the graph.

Suggested Questions

- *What are the measurements for the rise and run that have the ratio of 3 to 5? Explain your reasoning.*

Summarize

Let each group report on stairs they have investigated. Compare the ratios for various sets of stairs.

Suggested Questions

- *Are some stairs steeper than others? If so, how can you tell?*
- *What is the steepest set of stairs in our list? The least steep set of stairs? How do you know?*
- *Can you order the entire list of stairs from least to greatest in terms of steepness?*

If you have not done so already, talk about the carpenters' guidelines with your students. Then ask questions such as the following:

- *How do the ratios of the stairs we measured compare to the carpenters' guidelines? Which ones meet the standards and which ones do not?*

Collect several equations from Question B. You may want to display several of their graphs for the class.

- *What do you notice about these lines?*

Discuss the strategies that students used to answer Question B.

- *How is finding points on this line related to sketching a staircase with a rise to run ratio of 3 to 5?*
- *Sketch a line that does not meet the carpenters' guidelines.*

Use this summary to define slope and to launch the next Problem. Use an illustration of stairs when you define the slope. Help students to make visual connections between these things that they have physically experienced and the lines on a graph representing linear relationships.

ⒶⒸⒺ

Assignment Guide for Problem 4.1

Applications: 1 | Connections: 43–45, 49

Answers to Problem 4.1

A.1, 2. Answers will vary. One possible answer: 7.25 in. to 11.25 in. for the rise to the run, or approximately 0.70 for the ratio of rise to run. The ratio of rise to run is not within the carpenters' guidelines.

B. 1. $3 \div 5 = 0.6$ is just within the range of the carpenters' guidelines. Some students may change this to a unit rate of 0.6 to 1.

2.

3. $y = (0.6)x$

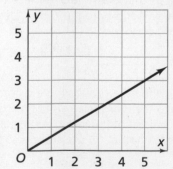

4. a. $y = 0.6x$

b. The coefficient of x is 0.6.

c. The coefficient tells you the line's steepness.

d. The coefficient tells you the stairs' steepness, which is the ratio of the rise of the stairs to the run of the stairs.

4.2 Finding the Slope of a Line

> *Focus Question*   How can you find the *y*-intercept and the slope of a line from data in a table, graph, or equation?

Launch

Display Teaching Aid 4.2A. Tell students that the steepness of the line is the ratio of rise to run, or vertical change to horizontal change, for each step. Tell students that this ratio is called the *slope* of the line.

Suggested Questions

- *Does the slope change if we take two stairs at a time? Explain.*
- *Is the slope the same between any two stairs? Explain.*

Explore

As you move around the room, check to see if students are finding the vertical and horizontal changes correctly. Look for ways that students will find two more points given two points on a line. Refer to these in the Summarize.

Suggested Questions

- *Start at the point where x is 3. What is the corresponding value for y?*
- *Now look at the point where x is −2. What is the corresponding value for y?*
- *What is the change in the horizontal and the vertical directions between these two points? How do you know?*
- *What does this tell you about the slope of the line representing the equation?*
- *If you looked at the ratio of the horizontal change to the vertical change between two different points on the graph of the line, what would the ratio be? How do you know?*
- *How is the coefficient of x in a linear equation related to the ratio of vertical change to horizontal change on a graph?*

Summarize

Be sure to make the connections among the various representations of slope.

Suggested Questions

Use the equation $y = 2x$ to make a table.

- *What patterns do you see in the table? How will this pattern of change appear on the graph of this line?*

Draw the graph of $y = 2x$, using the coordinate pairs from the table.

- *What is the ratio of the change in vertical distance to the horizontal distance?*

Key Vocabulary
- slope

Materials

Labsheets
- 4.2: Linear Relationships
- Coordinate Grid

Accessibility Labsheet
- 4ACE: Exercise 7

Teaching Aids
- 4.2A: A Set of Stairs
- 4.2B: Two Graphs and a Table
- 4.2C: Rate of Change Table
- 4.2D: Mary's Method
- Climbing Monkeys Activity

AT A GLANCE 4

- *What happens to the ratio of vertical to horizontal change when two different, not necessarily consecutive, points, such as (−2, −4) and (1, 2), are measured?*

- *If you know one point on the graph of a line and you know the slope of the line, how can you use the slope to create a set of points that all lie on the line?*

- *How can you find the y-intercept given 2 points on the line, such as (3, 3) and (5, 9)?*

A C E
Assignment Guide for Problem 4.2

Applications: 2–15 | Connections: 46, 50, 52

Answers to Problem 4.2

A.1, 2.

Graph 1: slope: the ratio −3 to 1, or −3; y-intercept: 6; equation: $y = 6 − 3x$
Graph 2: slope: the ratio 3 to 1, or 3; y-intercept: 6; equation: $y = 6 + 3x$
Table 1: slope: 1.5; y-intercept: −1; equation: $y = 1.5x − 1$
Table 2: slope: −0.5; y-intercept: 5; equation: $y = 5 − 0.5x$
Equation 1: slope: 2.5; y-intercept: 5
Equation 2: slope: −3; y-intercept: 20

B. 1. The slope is $\frac{5}{-5}$, or −1.

2. Answers will vary, but they should lie on the line $y = −x + 8$. Some students will find the equation and then use the equation to find two points. Some may use the slope ratio. For example, to go from the point (3, 5), students can go 2 units to the right (+2) and then down 2 units (−2) to reach the point (5, 3). Or they can go right 3 units and down 3 units to reach the point (6, 2).

3. On the graph, you can calculate the slope by determining the rise over the run. Using the two points, you can calculate the slope finding the differences in y-values and differences in x-values. Any two points will work because the slope at two points will be the same ratio as the slope for any two other points on the same line.

C. 1. Yes, John is correct because the y-intercept would be zero, and m represents the rise value for every one unit of run (or x). So, (1, m) will always be on the line. Another way to solve this is to consider that when $x = 1$, then $y = m \cdot 1 = m$.

Note: In the Unit *Comparing and Scaling*, m is called the constant of proportionality.

2. The slope of a horizontal line is zero, or $\frac{0}{1}$. The slope of a vertical line would be $\frac{1}{0}$, which is undefined.

D. 1. To find slope from a table, you can check that the constant changes in x-correspond to constant changes in y. The slope is the ratio of change in y to change in x, and it should also be constant between any two points in the table.
From the graph, you can pick two points. Start at one point to count the distance on the y-axis you move up or down, and the distance on the x-axis you move right or left, to get to the other point. Create a ratio of these values, with the change in vertical distance in the numerator. Be sure to keep the correct sign on each value (up and right are positive; left and down are negative).
In an equation of the form $y = b + mx$, you just read the slope as the coefficient m of x. First, you must adjust the equation so that the coefficient of y is 1 and then arrange it so that x and y are on opposite sides.

2. The constant rate of change is the same value as the slope of a line. The rate of change represents how one variable changes compared to the other. The rate of change, or slope, is constant for any x- and y-values.

4.3 Exploring Patterns With Lines

> **Focus Question** How can you predict if two lines are parallel or perpendicular from their equations?

Launch

Suggested Questions

- *Sketch a line with a slope of 3. Is your line the same as those of your classmates? What patterns do you notice?*
- *How can we predict this outcome from the equations of the lines?*

Ask the class for any observations that they may have about each set of lines in Question A. Tell them they can use their calculators, but that they should keep a sketch of each graph for reference.

Explore

Encourage the students to look for patterns, make conjectures, and think about why their conjectures might work. Suggest that they try a different coefficient (slope) for Question A to test their conjectures.

Suggested Questions

- *What do the graphs of the lines $y = 2x + 5$ and $y = 4x + 10$ look like? Do they fit the patterns in Question A?*

Summarize

Have groups share their conjectures and reasoning. You can refer to the student posters and/or display the graphing calculator screen to show examples from various groups.

Suggested Questions

- *Is the line that passes through the points (0, 6) and (2, 12) parallel to the line $y = 3x + b$? Why or why not?*
- *Are the lines $y = 5x + 2$ and $y = -0.2x$ perpendicular to each other? Why or why not?*

Materials

Labsheet
- Coordinate Grid

Teaching Aid
- 4.3: Pairs of Lines

- graphing calculators
- large sheets of graph paper
- Climbing Monkeys Activity

ACE
Assignment Guide for Problem 4.3

Applications: 16–34 | Connections: 47, 51

Answers to Problem 4.3

A. 1. Groups 1 and 2: Each line has the same slope (the same coefficient of *x*). The lines in Group 1 all have a slope of 3 but different *y*-intercepts. The lines in Group 2 all have a slope of −2 but different *y*-intercepts.

2. Group 1: The lines are parallel.

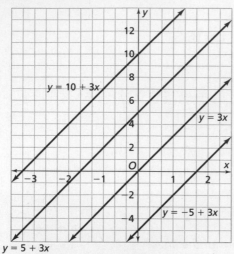

$y = 5 + 3x$

Group 2: The lines are parallel.

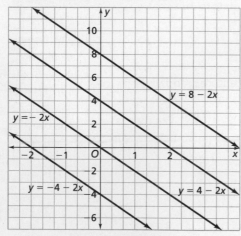

3. Answers will vary. Possible set:
$y = -x + 3$; $y = -x + 7$; $y = -2 - x$;
$y = -x$. All lines have a slope of -1.

B. **1.** The slopes (the coefficients of x) are
negative reciprocals of each other.

2. The lines meet at right angles, so they are
perpendicular.

Pair 1

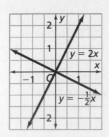

Pair 2

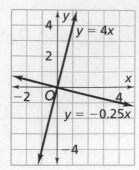

Pair 3

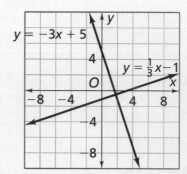

3. Answers will vary. Possible set:
$y = -2 - x$; $y = x$. The lines have slopes
that are opposite reciprocals of each
other.

C. **1.**

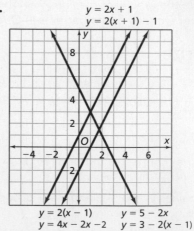

$y = 2x + 1$
$y = 2(x + 1) - 1$

$y = 2(x - 1)$ $y = 5 - 2x$
$y = 4x - 2x - 2$ $y = 3 - 2(x - 1)$

2. The equations in each pair are equivalent,
so their graphs will be the same.

4.4 Pulling It All Together: Writing Equations for Linear Relationships

> *Focus Question* What information do you need to write an equation for a linear relationship? Is the expression for the dependent variable always the same?

Launch

Tell the class that they are to explore several situations and decide whether or not they are linear. If they are linear, students will write an equation that represents the relationship.

Suggested Questions

For Question A, tell the story of Chantal.

- *Do you think this situation will be represented by a linear equation? What cues help you recognize that this is a linear relationship?*

For Question B, present the following scenario about temperature.

- *If you have traveled in Europe or Canada where the temperature is in Celsius and you hear a temperature report on TV that says it is 20° Celsius, how would you interpret how hot or cold it is?*

Then, read Question B with the students.

- *What information do we have? How is this similar to previous problems?*
- *What are the variables?*

Explore

Suggested Questions

- *Why does that make sense?*
- *Can you tell me how this relationship would look as a graph?*
- *Where would the line cross the y-axis? How do you know?*

Look for equivalent expressions. Be sure to ask students to show that the expressions are or are not equivalent.

Summarize

Look for different ways of solving the problem.

Suggested Questions

- *What is the slope? What is the y-intercept? How did you find them?*
- *How did you find the equation?*
- *How many points are on the line? Could we list them all?*
- *What is the x-intercept? What information does it represent?*

> **Materials**
>
> Accessibility Labsheet
> - 4.4: Linear Logic Activity
>
> **Assessments**
> - Notebook Checklist
> - Self-Assessment
> - Unit Test
> - poster paper

Answers to Problem 4.4

A. 1. $5 per week; in three weeks (week 5 to week 8), Chantal will have saved $190 − $175 = $15, and $15 ÷ 3 weeks = $5 per week.

2. Chantal will have saved 5 × $5 = $25 in the first five weeks. So her starting value must have been $175, because 175 − 25 = 150.
Note: Students may have more contextual and less symbolic ways to solve this problem. Or, they may work from a table, applying what they know about relationships with constant rates.

3. $A = 5n + 150$, where A is the amount of money Chantal has saved and n is the number of weeks. Possible explanations: Chantal receives $150 to start with, and she adds $5 a week. Or, every linear equation has the form $y = mx + b$, and in this case m (the rate or slope) is 5 and b (the y-intercept) is 150.

B. 1. $F = \frac{9}{5}C + 32$ or $C = \frac{5}{9}F - \frac{160}{9}$
Note: Students may represent this either way. The first representation will probably be more common.

2. For the equation $F = \frac{9}{5}C + 32$, the y-intercept is 32 and tells us the Fahrenheit temperature when the Celsius temperature is 0. For the equation $C = \frac{5}{9}F - \frac{160}{9}$, the y-intercept is $-\frac{160}{9}$, and it tells the Celsius temperature when the Fahrenheit temperature is 0.

3. Monday: 55°F; Tuesday: 57°F Wednesday: 17°C; Thursday: 21°C Friday: 14°C

C. 1. $P = 4n + 2$, or other equivalent forms, such as $2(2n + 1)$ or $3n + (n + 2)$

2. Students may reason about equivalence either through using the symbols or by transforming one expression into a different one. Students may also use the diagram to reason that two different expressions represent the same relationship.

3. Yes, the relationship is linear because the rate of change is constant. For every increase by one figure number, the perimeter increases by four.

4. a. Some will make a table and claim from the table that it is not linear. Some may just express the relationship in words. They may use the table to say that the number of squares is the square of the figure number plus 1.

b. $T = n^2 + 1$; not all students may write this equation.

c. No, the relationship is not linear. For example, from Figure 1 to Figure 2, 3 squares are added; but from Figure 2 to Figure 3, 5 squares are added. The rate of change is not constant, so it is not linear. This is a quadratic expression.

D. 1. In Question A, the variable on the x-axis would be weeks, and the variable on the y-axis would be money saved. The graph would be a line with y-intercept 150 and slope 5.
In Question B, if Celsius is on the x-axis, then Fahrenheit would be on the y-axis. The graph would have a y-intercept of 32 and a slope of $\frac{9}{5}$.
In Question C, the figure number would be on the x-axis, and the perimeter would be on the y-axis. The graph would have a y-intercept of 2 and a slope of 4.

2. Answers will vary. Different representations have different advantages. For example, looking for a single value or a precise value may best be obtained by an equation. A graph may be helpful if you have lots of information and are looking for intersection points. Tables give a variety of values so you can get an informal sense of how one variable changes with respect to the other one.

At a Glance

Pacing ☐ *Day*

Mathematical Goals

_____

_____

_____

_____

Launch

_____

_____

_____

_____

Materials

Explore

_____

_____

_____

_____

_____

Materials

Summarize

_____

_____

_____

_____

Materials

Notes

Moving Straight Ahead   At a Glance

 **Answers** **Investigation 1**

Applications

1. a. $\frac{10}{3}$, or about 3.3 m/s (The exact answer is 3.33333... m/s.)

  b. 30 seconds

  c. At $\frac{10}{3}$ meters per 1 second, Hoshi walks $50\left(\frac{10}{3}\right)$ meters or $166\frac{2}{3}$ meters (approximately 167 meters) in 50 seconds.

  d. $d = \frac{10}{3}t$

2. Mira's; Milo's walking rate is about 2.7 m/s and Mira's is 3 m/s.

3. a. Jose: $15 \div 3 = 5$ mph;
  Mario: $21 \div 3 = 7$ mph;
  Melanie: $27 \div 3 = 9$ mph

  b. Jose: $7 \times 5 = 35$ mi;
  Mario: $7 \times 7 = 49$ mi;
  Melanie: $7 \times 9 = 63$ mi

  c.

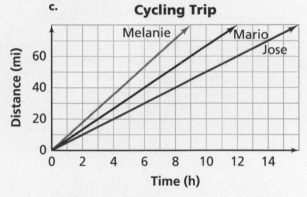

Cycling Trip

  d. Jose: about 33 mi; Mario: about 46 mi; Melanie: about 59 mi

  e. Jose: 14 hours; Mario: 10 hours; Melanie: about 7.75 hours

  f. The faster the cyclist, the steeper the graph.

  g. Let t = the number of hours and d = the number of miles. Jose: $d = 5t$; Mario: $d = 7t$; Melanie: $d = 9t$

  h. Jose: 32.5 mi; Mario: 45.5 mi; Melanie: 58.5 mi

  i. The rate shows up in the equation as the number being multiplied by t.

j. All three relationships between distance cycled and time are proportional. They are all of the form $d = rt$. The value of r is the constant of proportionality.

4. a. $d = 6.5t$

  b.

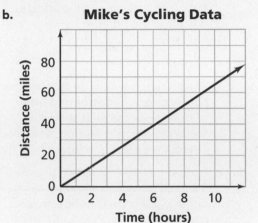

Mike's Cycling Data

Answers will vary. Students may say that they looked at the range of numbers needed for time and for distance and then decided on a reasonable scale.

  c. The table can be extended by adding 6.5 miles every hour (or 3.25 miles for a half-hour) to show 7 and $9\frac{1}{2}$ hours. On the graph, the distances at these points may be approximated. In the equation, the values of 7 and $9\frac{1}{2}$ can be substituted for t, which gives the answers of 45.5 mi and 61.75 mi.

  d. The table can be extended by increments of 1 hour or greater to show values of d that are close to 100 mi and 237 mi. On the graph, the times at these points may be approximated after the graph has been made. In the equation, the values of 100 mi and 237 mi can be substituted for d, which gives the approximate answers 15.4 hours and 36.5 hours.

  e. Answers will vary. Possible answer: If the value is already shown in the table or graph, then these representations would be easy to use. If the values are far from those shown in the table or graph, or if you need an exact amount, it is easier to use an equation to get the answer.

f. In decreasing order, the bikers' speeds are Melanie's, Mario's, Mike's, and Jose's. In the tables, this can be found by comparing the distance biked after 1 hour or by finding the difference between any two consecutive distances for times that vary by 1 hour. In the graphs, the steepness of the line gives this information. In the equations, the bikers' rates can be compared by noting the number by which t is multiplied.

5. a. 7.5 mph

b. Alicia's graph would be steeper than Mike's graph. In decreasing order of steepness, the lines would be Melanie's, Alicia's, Mario's, and Jose's. These lines will all go through (0, 0).

6. a. Plan A: no initial donation and then $3/km; Plan B: The sponsor always donates $5 no matter how far the participant walks; Plan C: $2 initial donation and then $1.50/km (or $2 initial donation and $3 every 2 km)

b. Plan A is $3/km; Plan B is $0/km except for the initial charge; Plan C is $1.50/km.

c. the initial donation for each pledge plan

d. Answers will vary. Sample answers: Plan A: (0, 0) (2, 6); Plan B: (0, 5) (4, 5); Plan C: (0, 2) (4, 8) Each point represents the amount of money that is pledged for a certain distance in km walked. For Plan A, (0, 0) represents that walking 0 km will give you $0 and (2, 6) represents that walking 2 km will give you $6. The points in Plans B and C represent similar situations.

e. The relationship between amount of money and distance walked for Sponsor A is proportional. The relationships for Sponsors B and C are not proportional because the sponsors donate an amount in addition to the money donated per kilometer.

7. a. Fill It Up: $c = 4b$

Bottles by Bob: $c = 25 + 3b$ (where c is the cost and b is the number of water bottles)

b. Independent variable: number of water bottles; Dependent variable: cost

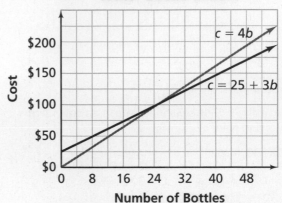

Water Bottle Orders

c. If fewer than 25 water bottles are ordered, Fill It Up has the better offer. If more than 25 are ordered, Bottles by Bob has the better offer. If exactly 25 water bottles are ordered, the companies have the same offer. To decide which company is better, you could look at the point where the lines intersect each other; after this point, the line for Fill It Up is higher than the line for Bottles by Bob.

d. The costs are equal at 25 water bottles. This is where the lines cross.

8. B

Note: The point (0, 5) means that 0 caps cost $5, which doesn't make sense.

9. a. (10, 85) and (3, 60.5); if you substitute 10 for t in the equation, you will get 85. You can apply the same process to (3, 60.5).

b. The coordinate pair (10, 85) represents that after 10 seconds, the cyclist has gone 85 meters from his home. The point (3, 60.5) represents that after 3 seconds, the cyclist has gone 60.5 meters from his home.

10. a. Similarities: In Tables 1 and 2, the x-values increase by one; this isn't true in Tables 3 and 4.

Differences: In Table 1, the value of y doesn't change at all; in Tables 2, 3, and 4, it does. In Table 2, the y-values decrease and then increase; in Table 3, the y-values increase; and in Table 4, they decrease. In Tables 1, 3, and 4, as the x-values go up by 1, the y-value changes at a constant rate; this isn't true in Table 2.

Note: The patterns in Tables 1, 3, and 4 are similar in that, as x goes up by 1, the y-values change by the following patterns: 0, 0, 0 . . . in Table 1; 3, 3, 3, . . . in Table 3; and $-1.5, -1.5, -1.5, . . .$ for Table 4. So, the data in Tables 1–3 are linear.

The graph of Table 2 is nonlinear. (Actually, its graph is a parabola; it is in fact quadratic.) Its table indicates this nonlinearity by the nonconstant rate of change between y-values as x increases by 1.

b. Tables 1, 3, and 4 represent linear relationships. The change in the y-value is the same for each unit change in the x-value, and the graph forms a straight line.

c.

Table 1

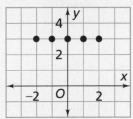

Table 2

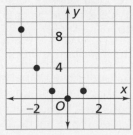

Table 3

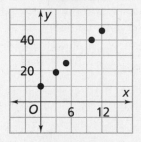

Table 4

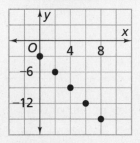

d. Table 1: $y = 3$;

Table 3: $y = 3x + 10$;

Table 4: $y = -1.5x - 3$; In Table 1, the y-value is 3 for any x-value. In Table 3, the x-value increases by 3 for every y increase of 1. When $x = 0$, $y = 10$. In Table 4, the y-value decreases by 1.5 as the x-value increases by 1. The y-value is -3 when $x = 0$.

11. a. $t = 30 - 5h$; The variable t represents the temperature in degrees Fahrenheit, which will be 30° minus the 5° per hour (h) that the temperature is expected to drop.

b. This is a linear relationship. The constant rate of change is -5. That is, as the hours increase by 1, the temperature decreases by 5.

12. a. $20; In the table, "Day 0" represents the start of camp, when Jamal has been at camp for 0 days.

b. $2; As the number of days increases by 1, the amount of money left decreases by $2.

c. Yes; as the values for the days go up by 1 unit, the values for the money left go down by a constant amount.

d.
Jamal's Money

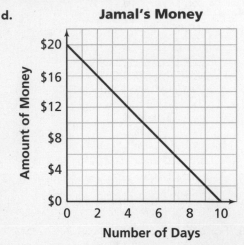

e. $M = -2d + 20$, where M is the money left, d is the number of days, the 20 is the starting amount in Jamal's wallet, and the -2 is the rate at which the money in Jamal's wallet is decreasing.

13. Graph 1: $y = -x$ and Graph 2: $y = -x$

Note: Students are not expected to be fluent at finding the equation from a given graph at this stage.

14. a. Answers will vary. Possible answers:

   i. A cable company charges a family a $100 start-up fee and then $50 per month. The relationship between months that the family has had cable and the total amount they have to pay is linear and positive.

   ii. Another cable company charges a $100 installation fee and no monthly fee. The relationship between months that the family has had cable and the total amount they have to pay to the cable company would be linear with zero rate of change, because no matter how many months they have cable, they would never pay more than $100.

   iii. If the family has $1,000 in their account to pay the first cable company, the amount of money in that account decreases at a constant rate.

   b. Again, answers will depend on the answers to part (a). For the examples above, the first equation is $y = 100 + 50x$, the second equation is $y = 100$, and the third equation is $y = 1,000 - 50x$.

Connections

15. a. His rate started out at 3 m/s for the first 20 seconds, and then slowed down to 2 m/s for the next 30 seconds; he sped up to 3.5 m/s for the next 10 seconds and then walked at a rate of 2 m/s for the last 40 seconds.

   b.
   Jelani's Walking Race

   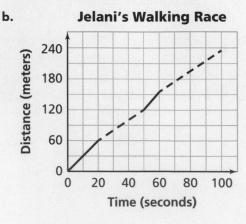

16. a. $2 + (-3 \times 4) = -10$

   b. $(4 + -3) \times -4 = -4$

   c. $-12 \div (2 + -4) = 6$

   d. $(8 \div -2) + -2 = -6$

17. a. True; using the Distributive Property, 20 groups of 410 is the same as 20 groups of 400 plus 20 groups of 10.

   b. True; using the Distributive Property, 20 groups of 308 is the same as 20 groups of 340 minus 20 groups of 32.

   c. True; using the Distributive Property.

   d. Not true; the Distributive Property is not applied correctly. Multiplication should be distributed over addition, not addition distributed over multiplication.

18. **a.** 6

   b. x and 2

   c. x

19. **a.**

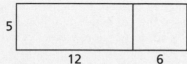

   b. Area equals $5 \times 12 + 5 \times 6$ or 90 units^2.

20. **a.** Unit Rate: 3 dollars per T-shirt or $\frac{1}{3}$ T-shirt for \$1. Equation: $C = 3t$ (C = cost, t = number of T-shirts) or $t = \frac{1}{3}C$.

   b. Unit Rate: 0.23 video games for \$1 or 1 video game for \$4.43. Equation: $C = \frac{31}{7}v$. (C = cost, v = number of video games) or $v = \frac{7}{31}C$.

   c. Unit Rate: 6 tbsp of sugar for one glass or 1 tbsp sugar for $\frac{1}{6}$ glass. Equation: $S = 6g$ (S = total amount of sugar, g = number of glasses) or $g = \frac{1}{6}S$.

21. **a.** $2{,}292 \div 23.66 = 96.87$ hours

   b. $2{,}292 \div 23.56 = 97.28$ hours. So, if his average speed was 0.1 less, it would have taken about 0.41 hours = 41% of 60 minutes, or about 25 minutes longer, to complete the race.

22. **a.** 41 minutes 56.23 seconds = 2,516.23 seconds, and 10,000 m ÷ 2,516.23 s ≈ 3.974 m/s

   b. 86 minutes 52.3 seconds = 5,212.3 seconds, and 20,000 m ÷ 5,212.3 s ≈ 3.837 m/s

23. Possible answer: The relationship between the number of batches b of juice and the number of cups w of water is linear. The relationship between the number of batches b of juice and the number of cups j of juice is also linear. The equations that represent these linear relationships are $w = 3b$, and $j = 5b$.

   Note: Other linear relationships in this table include $w = \frac{3}{2}c$, $j = \frac{5}{2}c$, $j = \frac{5}{3}w$, $b = \frac{1}{3}w$, $b = \frac{1}{5}j$, and $b = \frac{1}{2}c$. Students are not as likely to see these relationships

unless they look at the equations or graphs of *all* relationships between pairs of variables.

24. **a.** 9 cups of soda water; Possible explanation: The recipe calls for 3 times as much pineapple juice as orange juice and half as much soda water as pineapple juice. For 6 cups of orange juice, there would be 18 cups of pineapple juice, and 9 cups of soda water.

   b. 2 cups of orange juice and 3 cups of soda water; Possible explanation: Look at the row in the table that shows the recipe for 12 cups of pineapple juice, and divide each number by 2.

25. For about the first 3 seconds, John ran at a constant rate of l m/s. He then paused for a second and slowly increased his rate for about 3 seconds to run 3 meters, then ran at a constant rate of 2 m/s for one second, paused for 3 seconds, and finished the race at a rate of 3 m/s. He did not run at a constant rate for the entire race.

26. **a.** No, it is not linear; there is not a constant rate of change. There are 4 different rates of change represented in the graph.

   b. Yes; a person starts off walking for 5 seconds at a constant rate, stops for 3 seconds, then walks at a constant rate for 2 seconds, and then walks a little faster at a constant rate.

27. **a.** At 70 seconds, about 20 milliliters has been lost, so an estimated time that the 100-ml container would be full is $70 \times 5 = 350$ seconds, or 5 minutes and 50 seconds.

   b. The relationship between water loss and time is fairly close to linear, but it is not exactly linear. It isn't linear since the rate is not constant. For example, the time is going up by even intervals of 10 seconds. The patterns of change in the water loss for the first few values are $5 - 2 = 3$ and $8.5 - 5 = 3.5$. Since 3 is not equal to 3.5, there is no constant rate.

28. Answers will vary. Possible answer: The difference might be the scale the students used on their axes. Maybe one of Denise's intervals equals two of Takashi's intervals on the *t*-axis.

29. Answers will vary. Possible answers: This could mean that no more water was lost after a certain time, perhaps because the faucet stopped leaking. Or, if *v* refers to the volume collected in the measuring container, the container might have overflowed, so no more water could be collected.

Extensions

30. a. For Deep Valley, as the number of years increased, the population increased at a constant rate of 500. Nowhere's population gradually decreased at a nonconstant rate and then made a quick increase. Swampville's population increased at a nonconstant rate until the fourth year, and then decreased at the same rate it had increased. Mount Silicon's population doubled each year.

b. Deep Valley's population growth represents a linear relationship because it increased at the constant rate of 500 for each year.

c. The populations of Deep Valley, Nowhere, and Swampville are somewhat close and may easily be represented on the same graph. Putting Mount Silicon on the same vertical scale is difficult because its population increased so rapidly. Ranges will vary; students should support their choices. The horizontal scales are the same on the graphs shown below.

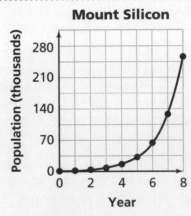
Mount Silicon

d. Answers will vary. Possible answer: The tables may be more appropriate if you want to know the precise population of a city at a certain time. The graphs give a picture of the population over time at a quick glance, and they show overall trends better than tables do.

31. a.

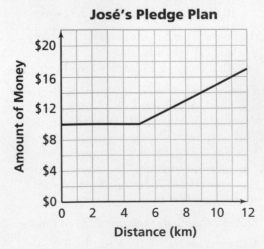
José's Pledge Plan

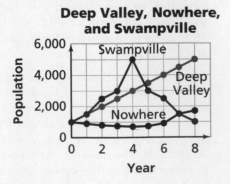
Deep Valley, Nowhere, and Swampville

b. For the first 5 km, this part of the graph looks like Leanne's—a horizontal line that intersects the *y*-axis at 10 and is parallel to the *x*-axis. After 5 km, it goes straight up to the right at a constant rate of $1/km, so it is slightly less steep than Gilberto's graph, which is $2/km.

32. Answers will vary.

a. Possible answer: (4, $40). This coordinate would mean that to make 4 T-shirts, it would cost $40.

b. Possible answer: (1, $30), where 1 is the number of T-shirts made and $30 is the cost for making those T-shirts. This point lies above the line because the cost exceeds that of the original equation. In the original equation, it would cost $25 to make 1 T-shirt.

c. Possible answer: (1, $15), where 1 is the number of T-shirts made and $15 is the cost of making those T-shirts. This point lies below the line because the cost is less than that of the original equation, which is $25 for 1 T-shirt.

33. Answers will vary.

a. Possible answer: He is planning to ask his sponsors for a $20 donation and $3/km. How much money could he earn from each donor by walking 5 km?

b. Possible answer: He is planning to ask her donors for 25¢/km. How far would he have to walk to earn $3 from each donor?

c. Possible answer: He is planning to walk at 4 km/h. How far can he walk in 3 hours?

Applications

1. a. It will take Allie 100 s or 1 min and 40 s. Since Allie's walking rate is 2 m/s, if she travels 200 m, it will take her $200 \div 2 = 100$ s.

b. Grace will reach the fountain first. Since Grace is traveling at 1.5 m/s and she has to go 90 m, it will take Grace $90 \div 1.5 = 60$ s to reach the fountain, which is less time than it took Allie (100 s).

Note: Students may make a table for each girl to find the answer.

2. a. $d = 20 + 2t$

b. Gilberto's graph intersects the y-axis at 20, which is in between the points at which Henri's and Emile's graphs intersect the y-axis. Emile's graph intersects the y-axis at 0 meters and Henri's at 45 meters. Gilberto's graph proceeds from the y-axis diagonally straight up to the right, intersecting Henri's graph at 25 seconds and then Emile's graph at 40 seconds.

3. a. The situation is like the race between Henri and Emile because the question asks when the person traveling at the greater rate will catch up to the other person. In both cases, the person traveling at the slower rate has a head start. In this situation, the head start is given as a time rather than a distance. (This distinction is blurred on the graph because the y-intercept indicates the head start as a distance rather than as a time.) Another difference is that after Ingrid catches up with Tara, they will probably start walking together, which will change Ingrid's and maybe Tara's graph as they adjust their walking rates to walk together.

b. after 4 min

c. 1,000 ft from Tara's house

d. The intersection of Tara's graph at 500 means that when Ingrid started walking fast, Tara was 500 ft ahead of her. The intersection of Ingrid's line at 0 means that Ingrid was at Tara's house when she started walking fast.

e. Ingrid's line is steeper. On the graph, her line is closer to vertical. The faster the person travels, the steeper the line will be.

Note: Later, when students are able to write equations to represent graphs like this, they will see that the steepest line has the greatest coefficient for the variable on the x-axis. It may be interesting to note that the lines continue after Ingrid and Tara meet. Students may want to discuss what this part of the graph means. Some students may be ready to write equations for these graphs.

f. Answers will vary. Possible answer: Their graphs will continue as a single line. If you extend the graphs past that point, the graphs might not be linear because the girls may travel at a new rate that is different from Tara's and Ingrid's original walking rate. So the graphs may not exhibit a constant rate of change.

4. a. Yes, because in each case, as the number of people at the party increases by a constant amount, the corresponding cost of the party increases by a constant amount.

b. Rollaway: $y = 5x$; Wheelies: $y = 100 + 3x$

c. If you continue the table of values for each plan showing Number of People and Cost, then you will look in the Cost column of each plan to see when they are equal. On the graph, you would use the y-coordinate of the point of intersection for Rollaway and Wheelies to tell you where the costs of the two plans are equal. You can decide which company to choose by looking either before the point of intersection or after it (depending on how many people will be attending) and finding the company whose line is below the other. This company will have a lesser cost.

Note: To graph these equations on a graphing calculator, you could use the following window: Xmin=0, Xmax=100, Ymin=0, and Ymax=350 with the X and Y scl=1 and Xres=1.

5. a. $35 is the initial charge for skating. $4 is the price per student to skate.

b. Wheels to Go; on the graph, you would see which line had the smallest *y*-coordinate (cost) when the *x*-coordinate (number of people) was 60. On the table for each company, you would see which one had the lowest *y*-value (cost), when the *x*-coordinate (number of people) was 60. In each equation, you would substitute 60 for the value of *n* and find each cost by solving for *C*.

Rollaway's cost is $300 because 5(60) = 300. Wheelies's cost is $280 because 100 + 3(60) = 280, and Wheels to Go's cost is $275 because 35 + 4(60) = 275.

c. Rollaway: 100 people; Wheelies: no more than 133 people; Wheels to Go: no more than 116 people

d. i. (20, 115) Wheels to Go, because 35 + 4 × 20 = 115

ii. (65, 295) Wheelies, because 100 + 3 × 65 = 295

iii. (50, 250) Rollaway, because 5 × 50 = 250. Also Wheelies, because 100 + 3(50) = 250.

e. Answers will vary. Possible answers: For (20, 115): If you used Wheels to Go and 20 people skated, how much would it cost? For (65, 295): If you used Wheelies, and the cost was $295, how many people skated? For (50, 250): Which coordinate pair would satisfy the equations for Rollaway and Wheelies? Which coordinate pair would show the intersection of Rollaway and Wheelies when graphed? How many people, or at what cost, would there be no difference whether you chose Rollaway or Wheelies?

6. a. about 75 protein bars

Note: Students are reading answers from the graph, so some inaccuracy is expected.

b. $33.50 because 0.67(50) = 33.5; $83.75 because 0.67(125) = 83.75

Note: The 0.67 was derived from the points (0, 0) and (300, 200), showing that each protein bar would sell for $0.67.

c. For an income of $200, the band would have to sell about 300 protein bars. The cost would be $125, leaving a profit of about $75.

Note: Using 300 as the amount of bars and $0.34 as the cost of the bars, the answer is $73. Suggest that students try to write an equation for each line.

7. The graphs in a and b are linear. The equation for a is $y = 3x + 1$, and the equation for b is $y = 2x + 7$. The patterns in c and d are not linear, because there is no constant rate of change.

8. a. 100 brochures; methods will vary. Students may graph the two equations and find the intersection point, they may use a table of values, or may have substituted 100 into each equation.

b. Company A: 500 brochures, Company B: 260 brochures; Students may continue the graph or table to obtain these answers, or they may solve the equation for *n*.

c. Company A: The organizers will have to pay $15 as an initial cost.

Company B: The organizers will have to pay nothing as an initial cost.

d. Company A: The organizers will have to pay $0.10 per brochure.

Company B: The organizers will have to pay $0.25 per brochure.

e. Company A: As the number of brochures increases by 1, the cost increases by $0.10.

Company B: As the number of brochures increases by 1, the cost increases by $0.25.

9. **a.** Tom's Tunes: $y = 60x$; Sabina's Sounds: $y = 40x + 100$; DJ Derek: $y = 30x + 175$

   b. The coefficient of x gives the cost per hour, or the DJ's hourly rate.

   c. The y-intercept gives the initial charge for each DJ.

   d. Tom's Tunes: $510; Sabina's Sounds: $440; DJ Derek: $430

   e. Tom's Tunes: 7.5 h; Sabina's Sounds: 8.75 h; DJ Derek: about 9.2 h

10. **a.** Plan 1: $140.40; Plan 2: $78

    b. Both plans require 25 weeks.

    c. Plan 1: $y = 270 - 10.8x$; Plan 2: $y = 150 - 6x$; y represents the amount of money you owe, and x represents the number of weeks. The 270 and the 150 represent the amount owed after making the down payment (if any down payment), and the 10.8 and the 6 represent how much you pay every week.

    d. The amount of money owed after 12 weeks would increase: Plan 1: $225.40; Plan 2: $163.

    Plan 1 requires the least number of weeks to pay off the skateboard now. It requires a little more than 32 weeks, while Plan 2 requires a little over 39 weeks to pay for the skateboard. The equations are now: Plan 1: $y = 355 - 10.8x$; Plan 2: $y = 235 - 6x$; y represents the money you owe, and x represents the number of weeks. The 355 and the 235 represent the amount owed after making the down payment (if any down payment), and the 10.8 and the 6 represent how much you pay every week.

11. **a.** 1.5

    b. increasing

    c. 0

    d. Possible answers: (2, 3), (0, 0), (4, 6)

12. **a.** -3

    b. decreasing

    c. 10

    d. Possible answers: (0, 10), (−5, 25), (2, 4)

13. **a.** -2

    b. decreasing

    c. 6

    d. Possible answers: (0, 6), (3, 0), (−2, 10)

14. **a.** 2

    b. increasing

    c. 5

    d. Possible answers: (0, 5), (−1, 3), (4, 13)

15. **a.**

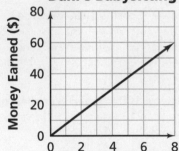

Dani's Babysitting

    b. Answers will vary. Possible answer: The point (6, 45) is on the graph. Two questions: How long must Dani baby-sit to make $45? How much money will she make if she baby-sits for 6 hours?

16. **a.** Trace the graph to find x from the point with 22 as the y-value.

    b. Find 22 in the y column and look at the corresponding value in the x column.

    c. Find the x-value of the point of intersection of $y = 22$ and $y = 100 - 3x$.

17. **a.** Graph 3   **b.** Graph 4

    c. Graph 2   **d.** $y = -2x + 4$

Answers will vary for Exercises 18–21. Sample answers are provided.

18. 0, 1

19. 0, 1

20. 0, 1

21. 0, −1

22. iii

23. Solving $8 = 2x − 6$ gives us $x = 7$; we now know that $(7, 8)$ is a point on the graph of $y = 2x − 6$.

24. ii

25. The coordinates are 6 and 3 for the points: $(−1.2, 6)$ and $(3, −15)$

26. i, iii

27. ii, iv

28. v

Connections

29. **a.** $x × −2 + x × 3 = −2x + 3x = x$

    Note: This is a good opportunity to talk about the form $2x$ for 2 times x and about the Commutative Property of Multiplication.

    b. $(−4 + 2)x = −2x$

    c. $x(1 − 4) = −3x$

30. **a.** True

    b. False; $5(0.7x + 5) = 3.5x + 25$, not $3.5x + 5$

    c. True

31. **a.** $y = 180 − 15x$. In this equation, 180 represents the amount they owe after making the down payment, 15 represents the monthly payment, x represents the number of months after they made the purchase, and y represents the amount they still owe.

    b. The y-intercept is $(0,180)$, the amount they owe as soon as they have made the down payment. The x-intercept is $(12,0)$. 12 is the number of months it will take until they owe nothing.

32. $5(x + 3)$ or $5x + 15$;

    Note: This is an opportunity to revisit the Distributive Property and the role of parentheses in algebraic expressions.

33. **a.** $6 × 15 + 4 × 15 = (6 + 4)15$

    b. $3 × 9 + 3 × 5 = 3(9 + 5)$

    c. $(6 × 10) + (4 × 10) + (6 × 4) + (4 × 4)$ $= (6 + 4)(10 + 4) = 10 × 14$

    d. $8(x + 4) = 8x + 8(4) = 8x + 32$

34. **a.** $0.25 per apple

    b. (See Figure 1.)

    c. 4 apples; Since it costs $0.25 per apple, you could buy 4 apples.

    d. The relationship between the number of apples and the total cost is linear since each apple costs $0.25, which gives a constant rate of change.

35. **a.** $0.75 per bagel (divide 15 by 20)

    b. $C = 0.75n$

    c. $112.50; $C = 0.75(150) = 112.50

Figure 1

Number of Apples	12	6	1	48	10	18
Cost	$3	$1.50	$0.25	$12	$2.50	$4.50

36. Tamara is confused about the order of operations. She is adding $-3 + 5$ to get 2 and then multiplying by -1 instead of doing multiplication first.

37. a and b are false; c and d are true because of the order of operations; e is true; f is false because $\frac{1}{2} + \frac{3}{2} \div \frac{1}{2} = 3\frac{1}{2}$.

38. (See Figure 2.)

   a. 2 cups/day

   b. 50 cups

   c. $f = 50 - 2d$

39. **a.** i and 1; ii and 3; iii and 2; iv and 5; v and 4

   b. Answers will vary. Possible answer: 2; Jalissa started the race fast and then became tired and gradually decreased her speed.

40. a–b.

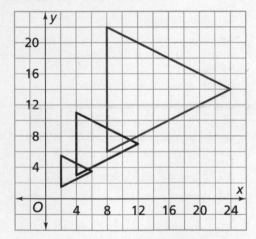

   c. These three triangles are similar.

   d. The areas of the three triangles are 128 square units, 32 square units, and 8 square units, respectively.

e. The corresponding vertices of these similar triangles represent a linear relationship. If you connected these vertices, a straight line would emerge. Also, the relationship between corresponding lengths and scale factor used is linear. (This is easiest to see with the vertical sides.)

Note: The relationship between area and scale factor is not linear.

41. a. **Rectangles With Perimeters of 20 m**

Length	Width
9	1
8	2
7	3
6	4
5	5

   b. 2 times length + 2 times width = 20, ($2L + 2W = 20$) or $L + W = 10$

   c. Yes. As the length increases by a constant amount, the width decreases by a constant amount.

   d. The area of the 1×9 rectangle is 9. The area of the 2×8 rectangle is 16. The area of the 3×7 rectangle is 21. The area of the 4×6 rectangle is 24. The 5×5 rectangle has an area of 25.

Figure 2

Days	0	1	2	3	4	5	6	7	8	9	10	11
Cups of Dog Food	50	48	46	44	42	40	38	36	34	32	30	28

Extensions

42. a. Linear

   b. Nonlinear

   c. Nonlinear

   Note: Students may use graphs or tables to explain their answers to parts (a)–(c). For the equations in part (a), they should say that the table shows a constant rate of change or that the graph is a straight line. For the equations in parts (b) and (c), they should say that the table does not show a constant rate of change or that the points do not lie in a straight line.

43. Answers will vary. Possible answers:

   a. $y = 50$ $y = 2x$ $y = 0.5x$

   b. (See Figure 3.)

   c. No; parallel lines will not intersect and, therefore, cannot form triangles.

44. a. Only $(3, 2)$ is on the line because $3 \times 3 - 7 = 2$. The point $(3, 3)$ is above the line because the line goes through $(3, 2)$. The points $(3, 1)$ and $(3, 0)$ are below the line. (See Figure 4.)

   b. Answers will vary. Possible answer: $(0, -7)$ lies on the line, but $(0, 5)$, $(0, 4)$, and $(0, 10)$ lie above the line.

   c. The inequality $y < 3x - 7$ holds for the points $(4, 2)$ and $(7, 12)$ because $2 < 5$ and $12 < 14$. The inequality $y > 3x - 7$ holds for the points $(4, 7)$ and $(7, 16)$ because $7 > 5$ and $16 > 14$.

45. a. Clear Prints: $C = 2n$
Posters by Sue: $C = 15 + 0.5n$
The cost C to make posters for the walkathon is represented by each equation, where n is the number of posters.

   b. The costs are equal at 10 posters. For 10 posters, Clear Prints and Posters by Sue both charge $20.

   c. If fewer than 10 posters are ordered, Clear Prints has the better offer. If more than 10 are ordered, Posters by Sue has the better offer.

   d. When the cost C is $18, the number of posters is 9 for Clear Prints and 6 for Posters by Sue. Therefore, the class should buy their posters from Clear Prints.

   When the cost C is $28, the number of posters is 14 for Clear Prints and 26 for Posters by Sue. Therefore, the class should buy their posters from Posters by Sue.

   e. The equation for Clear Prints, $C = 2n$, is true for $(9, 18)$, $(10, 20)$, and $(14, 28)$. Thus, the inequality $C < 20$, or $2n < 20$, holds for the point $(9, 18)$.

   The equation for Posters by Sue, $C = 15 + 0.5n$, is true for $(6, 18)$, $(10, 20)$, and $(26, 28)$. Thus, the inequality $C > 20$, or $15 + 0.5n > 20$, holds for the point $(26, 28)$.

Figure 3

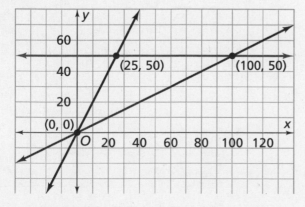

Figure 4

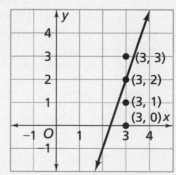

ACE Answers   **367**

Applications

1. a. 25 shirts would cost $70. You could use a table by trying to find the cost *C* for every value of *n*. Thus, the table would reflect values for *n* = 1, 2, 3, . . . , 25. You could use the graph by finding some coordinate pairs and then extending the line formed. You would go over to 25 on the *x*-axis (the axis representing the variable *n*), and then go up on the *y*-axis until you reach the line, and read the value of *C*.

b. The class could buy 30 shirts for $80. You could use a table by trying to find the cost *C* for every value of *n*. Thus, the table would reflect values for n until you reached a value of $80 for *C*. You could use the graph by finding some coordinate pairs and extending the line formed. You would go up to 80 on the *y*-axis (the axis representing the variable *C*), and then go over on the *x*-axis until you reach the line, and read the value of *n*.

c. Taleah is looking for the Cost *C* of 15 T-shirts.

d. Keisha is looking to see if 30 T-shirts resulted in a cost of $80.

2. a. Plan 1: the number of km walked
Plan: the amount of money raised in dollars
Plan 3: the number of km walked

b. Plan 1: Solve for *x*. Divide 14 by 2, which would give you 7 kilometers walked;
Plan 2: Solve the right side of the equation for y. Take 3.5 times 10 (35) and then add 10, thus giving you $45 (the amount raised);
Plan 3: Solve for *x*. Take 100 minus 55 (45), and then divide that by 1.5, which would give you 30 kilometers walked.

3. a. $y = 45$

b. $x = 22$

c. $x = 3$

4. a. $y = -10$

b. $x = 13$

c. You could use a table by trying to find the y for every value of x. Thus, the table would reflect values of x from 1 through at least 13. You could use the graph by finding the coordinate pairs. You would go over to 1 on the *x*-axis, and then go up or down on the *y*-axis until you reach the line, and read the value of *y*. You can do the same thing to find the *x*-value, either by looking at all values in a chart that give you either a particular *x*- or *y*-value or by finding coordinate pairs on the graph. For example, you would go up to 50 on the *y*-axis and move along the *x*-axis until you reach the line. Then read the *x*-value of the coordinate pair, which is 13.

5. 4 coins

6. 5 coins

7. 1 coin

8. 0 coins

9. a.

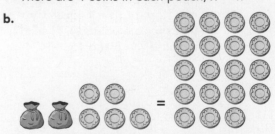

There are 4 coins in each pouch; $x = 4$.

b.

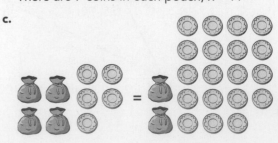

There are 7 coins in each pouch; $x = 7$.

c.

There are 7 coins in each pouch; $x = 7$.

d.

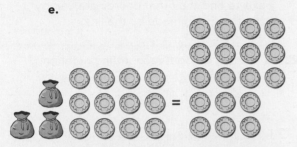

There are 6 coins in each pouch; $x = 6$.

e.

There are 2 coins in each pouch; $x = 2$.

10. a. $y = 5 + 0.50x$. Here x stands for the number of math questions Gilberto gets right, y stands for the total amount of money his grandfather gives him, 5 stands for the birthday money Gilberto gets even if he never answers a single question correctly, and 0.50 stands for the $.50 he gets for every question he gets right.

b. To buy a shirt that costs $25, we need to solve the equation:

$$25 = 5 + 0.50x$$
$$20 = 0.50x$$
$$x = 40$$

So, he will need to answer 40 questions correctly to buy the shirt.

Note: We anticipate that students may use other methods to solve this problem. It might be nice to discuss this exercise as a class to reinforce the idea that solving these kinds of problems algebraically yields the same answer as solving with a table or graph.

c. $y = 5 + 0.50(12)$

$y = 5 + 6$

$y = 11$

So, he will make $11.

Note: Again, students may use tables or graphs to solve this problem. Make sure

they understand that they can also solve this problem by substituting 12 for x.

Note: You can have students compare this to the equation for Alana's pledge plan. They are the same, but each represents a different context.

11. a. $x = 21$; you can use the equation $3x + 15 = 78$ to represent the given information. Subtract 15 from each side of the equation to get $3x = 63$, and then divide each side by 3.

b. $x = 22$; you can use the equation $5x - 27 = 83$ to represent the given information. Add 27 to each side of the equation to get $5x = 110$, and then divide each side by 5.

c. Answers will vary. Sample answer: If you add 6 to 9 times the mystery number, you get 87. The mystery number is 9.

12. a. $x = -3$

b. $x = -10$

c. $x = -\frac{3}{4}$

d. $x = 10$

13. C

14. a. $x = 5$

b. $x = \frac{25}{3}$

c. $x = -\frac{25}{3}$

d. $x = -5$

e. $x = 5$

Note: Students may have various strategies for solving $3x + 5 = 20$, such as:

- Using fact families: $3x + 5 = 20$, so $3x = 20 - 5$. If $3x = 15$, then $x = \frac{15}{3}$.

- Using an "undoing" metaphor: Begin with $3x + 5 = 20$, subtract 5 from each side, and then divide by 3 on each side.

- Using properties of equality: $3x + 5 = 20$, $3x + 5 - 5 = 20 - 5$, and so on.

It would be a good idea to discuss whether each of these strategies will work effectively on ACE Exercise 12 also. Ask students to explain why the strategies will work or why they will not.

ACE ANSWERS 3

ACE Answers

15. a. always equal: $-2(x - 3) = -2x + 6$

   b. never equal (the expressions differ by 12)

   c. sometimes equal (only equal for $x = 0$)

   d. never equal (the expressions differ by 9)

   e. never equal (the expressions differ by 12)

   f. always equal:
$2(3 - x) = 6 - 2x = -2x + 6$

16. Equations A & H: $x = 2$

   Equations B & F: $x = 6$

   Equations C & G: $x = -2$

   Equations D & K: $x = -6$

   Equations E & J: $x = 2.5$

One strategy students might use to match the equations is to solve each equation for x. Another strategy is to simplify each equation in Group 1. For example, dividing each side of equation E by 6 results in equation J. Subtracting 6 from both sides of equation A yields equation H.

17. a. $x = 2$

   b. $x = -12$

   c. $x = -6$

   d. $x = -7$

18. a. $x = -2.5$

   b. $x = 4.5$

   c. $x = -5.5$

   d. $x = -2.5$

19. a. $x = 1$

   b. $x = 2$

   c. $x = 1$

   d. $x = 1$

20. a. $y = -8$

   b. $y = 13$

   c. $y = -2$

   d. $y = 8$

   e. $y = 4$

21. a. $x = \frac{4}{3}$

   b. $x = -\frac{17}{3}$

   c. $x = \frac{19}{3}$

   d. $x = \frac{1}{6}$

22. You can look at either the x-axis or the y-axis to find the other coordinate pair by using the graph made by the line $y = 4 - 3x$.

23. a. Part (a) is about recognizing notation. For example, $-1x = -x$ and $\frac{1}{4}x = \frac{x}{4}$. A & D: $x = 8$; B & F: $x = -8$; C & E: $x = 2$

   b. G, J, M: $x = 7$; H, K, L: $x = -5$

   c. N & P: $x = 4.5$; O & Q: $x = -8$; R & S: $x = -3.5$

24. Student 1 subtracted 6 from the right-hand side, instead of distributing the 6 throughout the parenthesis on the left-hand side (used subtraction to undo multiplication). Student 2 started to distribute the 6 throughout the parenthesis on the left-hand side, but only did it to the first term and forgot to do it to the second one (it should be 24, as opposed to 4). The correct solution is $x = -\frac{26}{3}$.

25. Student 1: The first step is incorrect. Instead of subtracting 6, the student should have added 6. The correct answer is $64.5 \div 3.4 \approx 18.43$.
Student 2: The student's answer is wrong due to incorrect placement of the decimal point. The answer is approximately 18.4.

26. a. To solve $5x + 10 = -20$, use the equation $5x + 10 = y$. To use a table, scan down the table of y-values until you come to -20. The corresponding x-value is the solution. To use a graph, graph the equation $5x + 10 = y$ until you have a point whose y-coordinate is -20. The corresponding x-coordinate ($x = -6$) is the solution.

b. To solve this equation by graphing, graph the lines $y = 4x - 9$ and $y = -7x + 13$. At the point where the graphs cross, the x-coordinate is the solution. To solve using a table, create a table for the left side and right side and look for an ordered pair (x, y) that shows up on both tables. The x-coordinate of this ordered pair will be the solution.

27. a. $P = 2$

b. $c = -30$

c. You could use a table by trying to find the P-value for every value of c. You could use the graph by finding the coordinates of points on the line. You would go over to c on the x-axis (the axis representing the variable c), and then go up or down on the y-axis (representing the variable P) until you reach the line, and read the value of P. You can do the same thing to find the c-value, either by looking up all values in a chart that give you either a particular c- or P-value or by finding coordinate pairs by using the graph.

28. a. i. $m = 79.75$

ii. $m = 15.75$

iii. $m = 25.99$

b. i. $d = 12$

ii. $d = -4.921875$

iii. $d = 26.328125$

29. a. Yes, Khong's method is correct. A factored expression is equivalent to the original expression, and dividing both sides of an equation by the same number results in another equivalent equation.

b. $40x + 20 = 120$

$20(2x + 1) = 20(6)$

$2x + 1 = 6$

$2x = 5$

$x = \frac{5}{2} = 2\frac{1}{2}$

c. Khong is partially correct: his method does not work as well because all the numbers are prime. However, he could still factor out the GCF, which is 1. He could also factor out another number but would get fractions in the new equation. For example, Khong could factor out seven to get $7\left(x + \frac{3}{7}\right) = 7\left(\frac{31}{7}\right)$.

d. Answers will vary. Sample answer:
$12x + 24 = 48$

$12(x + 2) = 12(4)$

$x + 2 = 4$

$x = 2$

30. a. About 71.3 T-shirts must be made and sold to break even. By setting the expressions for E and I equal to each other, you obtain $535 + 4.5n = 12n$. Solving for n gives $n = 71.3$.

b. A loss, because the expenses, which are $535 + 4.5(50) = \$760$, exceed the income, which is $12(50) = \$600$.

c. There is a profit because when the income is $1,200, the number of T-shirts is 100. When the number of T-shirts is 100, the expenses are $985. Whenever the expenses are less than the income, there is a profit.

d. Answers will vary. Sample answer:

For the expenses graph, (10, 580) is on the graph. This means that the cost of making 10 T-shirts is $580. We know this point will lie on the graph because $580 = 535 + 4.50(10)$.
(12, 144) is a point on the income graph. This means that if they sell 12 T-shirts, they will make $144. We know this point will be on the graph because $144 = 12 (12)$.
Note: You can also ask students to find when income is less than expenses or vice versa. They can use the graph to answer this question.

31. a. International Links would be cheaper unless the customer talks more than 625 minutes per month. Students may look at a graph or table of the relationships $C = 50 + 0.10m$ and $C = 0.18m$ to find this answer.

b. International Links is cheaper for $m < 625$. World Connections is cheaper for $m > 625$.
Students could represent the inequalities on a graph. In the graph below, the thicker part of each line below represents when each plan is the cheaper of the two. (See Figure 1.)

Students could also represent the inequalities on number lines.

International Links is Cheaper for $m < 625$.

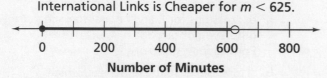

Number of Minutes

World Connections is Cheaper for $m > 625$.

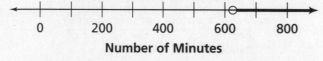

Number of Minutes

32. a. Answers will vary. Students describe how many text messages they send and receive each month on average and calculate the better deal.

b. Possibly, depending on the number of texts that person sends and receives in a month. You can ask students to consider whether their recommendation would be the same for a friend or a parent.

c. The break-even point for the two plans is 400 texts. So, Walby Communications is cheaper for $t > 400$, and Driftless is cheaper for $t < 400$.
Students could represent the inequalities on a graph. In the graph below, the thicker part of each line below represents when each plan is the cheaper of the two. (See Figure 2.)

Figure 1

Long-distance Phone Plans

Figure 2

Text Messaging Plans

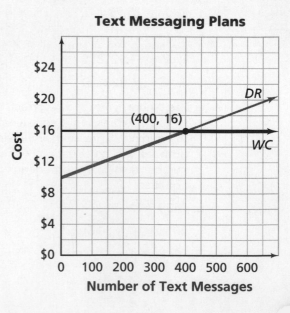

Students could also represent the inequalities on number lines.

Driftless Region is Cheaper for $t < 400$.

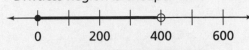

Number of Text Messages

Walby Communications is Cheaper for $t > 400$.

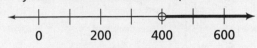

Number of Text Messages

33. a. They must sell 75 roses to break even. By setting the expressions for cost and income equal to each other, you obtain $0.5n + 60 = 1.3n$. Solving for n gives $n = 75$.

b. They do not make a profit, but have a loss of $20, when they sell 50 roses. They make a profit of $20 when they sell 100 roses. They make a profit of $100 when they sell 200 roses.

34.

Cable Television Cost Plans

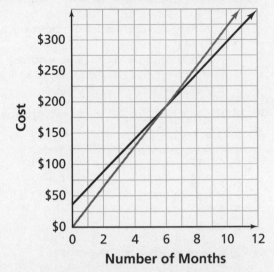

b. (6, 192) is the point of intersection. This tells us that the two cost plans are the same if Ruth uses them for 6 months.

Connections

35. a. multiplication; -32

b. multiplication; -8

c. multiplication and then subtraction; -40

d. multiplication (twice) and then addition; 11

36. a. -4

b. -4

c. 4

d. 0

e. -1

f. -1

g. 1

37. a. No; in the first expression, only 5 is multiplied by 6, but in the second expression, both 5 and 2 are multiplied by 6.

b. No; they are opposites of each other.

c. Yes; they are equal because of the Commutative Property of Addition.

d. Yes; they are equal because of the Commutative Property of Multiplication.

e. No; they are opposites of each other.

f. Yes; both quantities have the same value: $.50.

g. No; 1.5 liters equals 1,500 milliliters, not 15 milliliters.

h. No; 2 out of 5 is 40%, not 50%.

38. a. $n = 30 + -3$ or $n = 30 - 3$, $-3 = n - 30$ or $3 = 30 - n$.
Answers will vary. Some students may think $n = 30 - 3$ is easier, while other students may not.

b. $5 = -36 - n$ or $n = -36 - 5$. Answers will vary. Some students may think $n = -36 - 5$ is easier, while other students may not.

ACE ANSWERS 3

c. For part (a), add −3 to both sides; $n = 27$.
For part (b), subtract 5 from both sides; $n = -41$.
Answers will vary. Some students may find fact families easier; others may find the properties of equality easier.

39. a. $A = x(5 + 4)$; $A = 5x + 4x$

b. $A = 1.5(7 + x)$; $A = 10.5 + 1.5x$

40. a. $x = \frac{3}{14}$

b. $x = \frac{14}{3}$

c. $x = \frac{1}{7}$

d. $x = \frac{10}{9}$

41. a. all numbers greater than −4

b.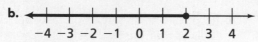

c. all numbers greater than 3

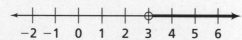

d. $x \le 3$; all numbers less than or equal to 3

e. $x > -3$

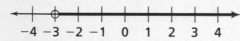

42. a. $n = 4(60) - 160 = 80$ chirps

b. $t = \frac{150}{4} + 40 = 77.5°F$

c. This would be when the number of chirps is 0:
$$t = \frac{0}{4} + 40 = 40°F.$$

d. The y-intercept gives the temperature when the number of chirps is 0. The coefficient of n means the ratio of the change in temperature to the change in number of chirps.

Note: An interesting question to raise is, "If the graph were extended to the left, what meaning would that part have?"

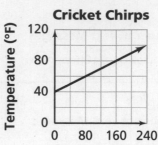

Cricket Chirps

43. a. $T = 0 - \frac{1{,}500}{150} = 0 - 10 = -10°C$

b. $26 = t - \frac{300}{150} = t - 2$; thus $t = 28°C$

44. a. 180°

b. 360°

c. 720°

d. 1,440°

e. 3,240°

45. a. 60°

b. 90°

c. 120°

d. 144°

e. 162°

46. a. 5 sides

b. 8 sides

47. a. $x = 4$, so the three side lengths are 6 cm, 8 cm, and 10 cm.

b. $x = \frac{24}{2\pi} \approx 3.8$ cm

c. $x = 2$, so the side lengths are 2 cm and 10 cm.

d. The area of the right triangle in (a) is 24 cm², and the area of the rectangle in (c) is 20 cm².

48. a. $C = 50 + 0.10t$

b. 10.5 hours = 630 minutes, so $C = 50 + 0.10(630) = \$113$

c. $75 = 50 + 0.10t$, so $t = 250$ min

d. Part (c) should be an inequality. Many phone companies round up the number of minutes used, so the actual number of minutes may be less than what Andrea was charged.

49. a. $h = H - 0.06t$

b. Here, $h = 160$ and $t = 30$, so $160 = H - 0.06(30)$ which gives $H = 161.8$ cm.

c. 6 ft 6 in. = 198.12 cm
$h = 198.12 - 0.06(50) = 195.12$
Therefore, he will be 195.12 cm tall, or about 6 feet 5 inches, at age 80.

d. In part (a), we assumed that a person's height will decrease by 0.06 cm each year. Because the person likely does not decrease by 0.06 cm every year, it could be rewritten as an inequality.

50. a. $h = 61.412 + 2.317(46.2) \approx 168.5$ cm

b. $h = 81.688 + 2.392(50.1) \approx 201.5$ cm

c. femur: 39.1 cm

tibia: 31.4 cm

humerus: 27.7 cm

radius: 20.3 cm

d. femur: 50.9 cm

tibia: 42.4 cm

humerus: 36.8 cm

radius: 28.1 cm

e. The graphs will be straight lines going upward from left to right. The x-intercept tells the value for x (femur, tibia, humerus, or radius length) when the height of the person is 0, and the y-intercept tells the value for y (the person's height) when the length of a bone is 0. These values do not make sense in the context of the problem.

Extensions

51. a. $1,500 = 150A + 40C$

b.
$$1,500 = 150A + 40(10)$$
$$1,500 - 400 = 150A + 400 - 400$$
$$1,100 = 150A$$
$$\frac{1,100}{150} = \frac{150A}{150}$$
$$7.33 = A$$

So, no more than 7 adults can get in.

c.
$$1,500 = 150(6) + 40C$$
$$1,500 - 900 = 900 - 900 + 40C$$
$$600 = 40C$$
$$\frac{600}{40} = \frac{40C}{40}$$
$$15 = C$$

So, 15 children can get in.

52. a. $x = 3$ (x equals an exact number, which is 3, to make both sides of the expression equal.)

b. x = any number. For any value of x, the value of each side of the equation is the same—the two expressions are equivalent.

c. No solution. For any value of x, the value of the left side is 3 more than the value of the right side.

53. a. Frank's method works in general, except for multiplying and dividing by a negative number. This requires flipping the inequality sign, which is the issue in part (b).

b. The inequality $-2x > 4$ is equivalent to the inequality $2x < -4$. One way to see this is to add $2x - 4$ to both sides of $-2x > 4$. Thus, we see that $-4 > 2x$ or $x < -2$. That is, all numbers less than -2 are solutions of the original inequality. In general, multiplying or dividing both sides of an inequality by a negative number reverses the direction of the inequality.

ACE ANSWERS 3

54. a. (See Figure 3.)

b. NY to SF: $d = 270t$; SF to NY: $d = 330t$

c.

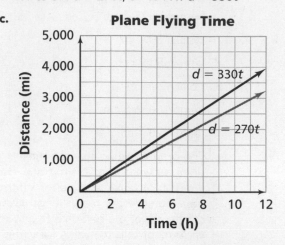

Plane Flying Time

Note: Notice that the graph has time on the horizontal axis and distance on the vertical axis. Students are accustomed to thinking of distance as depending on time. The equations in part (c) show this as well. However, this table is set up in reverse, in a way, as students are asked to find the time given the distance. Some students may think of time as dependent on distance and put time on the vertical axis. The related equations are $\frac{d}{270} = t$ and $\frac{d}{330} = t$, and the graph will show the distance as x and the time as y.

d. Against the wind: $5,000 \div 270 = 18.52$ h; with the wind: $5,000 \div 330 = 15.15$ h

Figure 3

Airplane Flight Times

Distance (mi)	NYC to SF Time (h)	SF to NYC Time (h)
0	0.00	0.00
200	0.74	0.61
400	1.48	1.21
600	2.22	1.82
800	2.96	2.42
1,000	3.70	3.03
1,200	4.44	3.64
1,400	5.19	4.24
1,600	5.93	4.85
1,800	6.67	5.45
2,000	7.41	6.06
2,200	8.15	6.67
2,400	8.89	7.27
2,600	9.63	7.88
2,800	10.37	8.48
3,000	11.11	9.09

55. All three methods are correct. The advantage in Jess's solution is getting rid of the fractions first by distributing. Another way to do this is what Terri did, multiplying the equation by 3. Brian noticed that the expression in both sets of parentheses is the same, so he is correct that he can simplify the left side to $6x - 9$.

56. C is the correct answer. The expression on the right side will always be 6 greater than the expression on the left because the left side is adding 3 to $3x$, whereas the right side is adding 9 to $3x$.

57. C is the correct answer. This equation is an identity. $3(x + 1)$ is equivalent to $3x + 3$.

58. a. $x > 0$

b. any number greater than -3 and less than 3

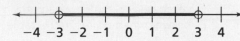

c. $|x| \geq 2$

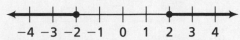

d. any number greater than one, or between -1 and 0.

e. All negative numbers will have negative sums, so those are excluded. Any number greater than 1 will work, but any number between 0 and 1 also works because $\frac{1}{x}$ will be greater than 1.

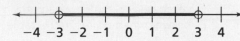

59. a. $C = 0.55 + 0.23(m - 1)$; C is the cost of a call that lasts m minutes. $m - 1$ represents the number of minutes after the first minute of the phone call. 0.55 represents the cost for the first minute. 0.23 represents cost of each minute after the first.

b. $C = 0.55 + 0.23(10 - 1) = \$2.62$

c. $m = 20$ minutes
Note: This equation is a little more difficult to solve. Students may reason through it using words, or they may solve it symbolically or by using a graphing calculator.

$$4.92 = 0.55 + 0.23(m - 1)$$

$$4.92 - 0.55 = 0.55 - 0.55 + 0.23(m - 1)$$

$$4.37 = 0.23(m - 1)$$

$$\frac{4.37}{0.23} = \frac{0.23(m - 1)}{0.23}$$

$$19 = m - 1$$

$$19 + 1 = m - 1 + 1$$

$$20 = m$$

ACE ANSWERS 3

Applications

1. a. No; $2 \div 5 = 0.4$, which is less than 0.45.

   b.

   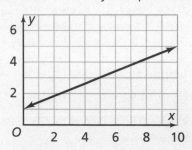

   c. Answers will vary. Sample answer:

   d. Answers will vary based on the graphs that students drew for part (c) and can include any equation of the form $y = \frac{2}{5}x + c$ where c is any constant number. The equation that corresponds to the graph above is $y = \frac{2}{5}x + 1$.

2. a. horizontal distance: -3; vertical distance: 3

   b. Slope $= \dfrac{\text{vertical change}}{\text{horizontal change}} = \dfrac{3}{-3} = -1$

3. slope $= 3$; y-intercept $= 10$

4. slope $= 0.5$; y-intercept $= 0$

5. slope $= -3$; y-intercept $= 0$

6. slope $= -5$; y-intercept $= 2$

7. a. i, iii, iv

   b. ii, vi

   c. i, vi

   d. i, iv, vii

   e. iv, v, vi

8. slope $= 2$; y-intercept $= 0$; equation: $y = 2x$

9. slope $= 1$; y-intercept $= 3.5$; equation: $y = x + 3.5$

10. slope $= 2$; y-intercept can be found by "counting back" in the table: $(0, -1)$; equation: $y = 2x - 1$

11. slope $= -2$; y-intercept $= 5$; equation: $y = 5 - 2x$

12. slope $= -3$; y-intercept can be found by "counting back" in the table: $(0, -5)$; equation: $y = -3x - 5$

13. a. slope $= 1$

   b. The slope is the change in the y-values compared to the change in the x-values between two points in the table. As the x-values go up by 1, the y-values go up by 1. So, the slope is 1 : 1 or 1.

x	-2	-1	0	1	2
y	-3	-2	-1	0	1

14. a. slope $= -2$

   b. The slope is the change in the y-values compared to the change in the x-values between two points in the table.

x	-2	-1	0	1	2
y	7	5	3	1	-1

15. a. $b = 8.5$

   b. $b = 2$

   c. In part (a), the y-intercept is 8.5 and the rate of change is -3.5. In part (b), the y-intercept is -2 and the rate of change is 5.

   d. The x-intercept in part (a) is about 2.4, and in part (b), it is $\frac{2}{5}$. To find the x-intercept symbolically, you need to substitute 0 for y and solve for x: $0 = 8.5 - 3.5x$ and $0 = 5x - 2$. Thus, $(2.43, 0)$ and $(0.4, 0)$ are the x-intercepts.

16. a.

   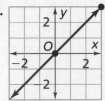

   b. slope $= 1$

   c. y-intercept $= 0$; the y-intercept is where the graph crosses the y-axis, so you could look at the graph.

   d. $y = x$

   e. Possible answers: $(6, 6)$, $(-1, -1)$

17. a.

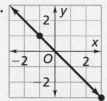

b. slope = −1

c. y-intercept = 0; the y-intercept is where the graph crosses the y-axis, so you could look at the graph.

d. y = −x

e. Possible answers: (0, 0), (−3, 3)

18. a.

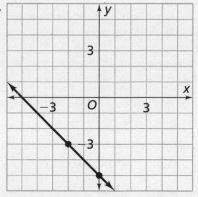

b. slope = −1

c. y-intercept = −5; the y-intercept is where the graph crosses the y-axis, so you could look at the graph.

d. y = −x − 5

e. Possible answers: (1, −6), (−1, −4)

19. a.

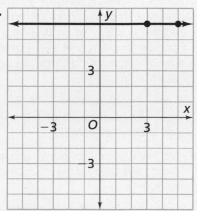

b. slope = 0

c. y-intercept = 6; the y-intercept is where the graph crosses the y-axis, so you could look at the graph.

d. y = 6

e. Possible answers: (1, 6), (2, 6)

20. B, E, and J

21. A, F, and K

22. C, D, G, and H

23. a. y = x − 1 corresponds to graph B

b. y = −2 corresponds to graph D

c. y = $\frac{1}{4}$x corresponds to graph E

24. a.

x	−4	0	4
y	−4	0	4

b.

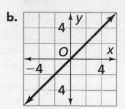

c. slope = 1

d. Answers will vary. Possible answer: The distance y a walker covers in x seconds walking at a constant rate of 1 meter per second.

25. a.

x	−2	0	2
y	−6	−2	2

b.

c. slope = 2

d. Answers will vary. Possible answer: The amount of money y Mary has at the end of x weeks if she starts out owing $2, but she receives $2 each week in allowance.

ACE ANSWERS 4

26. a.

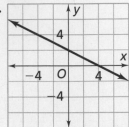

x	−4	0	4
y	4	2	0

b.

c. slope = −0.5

d. Answers will vary. Possible answer: The amount of money, y, Mary has at the end of x days if she starts the week by receiving her $2 allowance, but she buys an apple for $0.50 each day.

27. Answers will vary. Possible answers:

a. Students may graph any line of the form y = 3x + b, where b is any constant, not necessarily the same in both equations.

Possible graph for parts (a) and (b):

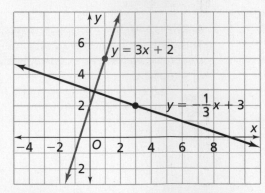

i. Answers will vary based on the graph students drew. For the graph of the equation y = 3x + 2, students could pick (0, 2) and (1, 5).

ii. Since the slope is given, the students just need to find the y-intercept of their graph. Again, they should have an equation of the form y = 3x + b. When students have shared their equations, you may want to ask if it makes sense that their points from part (a) are on the graph of their equation and how they could use their equation to check this.

b. i. Answers will vary based on the graph students drew. For the graph of the equation $y = -\frac{1}{3}x + 3$, students could pick (0, 3) and (3, 2).

ii. Since the slope is given, the students just need to find the y-intercept of their graph. Again, they should have an equation of the form $y = -\frac{1}{3}x + b$. When students have shared their equations, you may want to ask if they notice anything about the angles formed by the two graphs.

c. The lines are perpendicular.

28. a. The equation of the given line is y = 4x. The equation of a line parallel to this one is y = 4x + 5. (Students may choose any line with the same slope of 4 and a y-intercept other than 0.)

b. The equation of a line perpendicular to the given line is $y = -\frac{1}{4}x$.

29. a. i. slope = 10, y = 10x

ii. slope = 10, y = 10x

iii. slope = 10, y = 10x

b. The slopes of the three lines are the same.

c. The three graphs have the same slope and the same equation. The scales on the axes are different, which makes the graphs look different.

30. a. i. Such a line exists, but the y-intercept of such a line must be 0 or negative, and the slope must be 0 or negative. For example, the line y = −2x − 1 does not pass through the first quadrant.

ii. Such a line does exist. The line y = 2 passes through only the first and second quadrants.

iii. No such line exists because a line must pass through at least two quadrants.

b. i. Such a line must have a y-intercept that is 0 or negative and a slope that is 0 or negative.

ii. Such a line must have the equation $y = a$ or $y = ax$, where a is any number not equal to zero.
Note: Students have not been formally introduced to lines of the form $x = b$ for b a constant, so you need not be concerned with these lines at this time.

c. i. $y = -2x - 1$

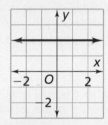

ii. $y = 2$

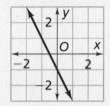

31. Lines whose slopes are negative reciprocals of each other are perpendicular.

Another example would be $\left(-\frac{1}{3}\right)x = y$ and $3x = y$. When these equations are graphed and the angle formed by their intersection is a right angle, these lines are perpendicular. This conjecture is true even if the y-intercept is not zero. For example, if you graph $\left(-\frac{1}{3}\right)x + 5 = y$ and $3x + 5 = y$, the angle formed by their intersection is also a right angle.

32. Answers will vary. Possible answer: $y = 7$, $y = 11$, $y = 2x + 1$, $y = 2x + 15$. Opposite sides of a parallelogram are parallel, so the first two lines are parallel, and the second two lines are parallel. The coordinates are: top left vertex: $(-2, 11)$; top right vertex: $(5, 11)$; bottom left vertex: $(-4, 7)$; bottom right vertex: $(3, 7)$.

33. Answers will vary. Possible answer: $y = -2x + 3$, $y = 1$, and $y = -2 + \frac{1}{2}x$; two of the lines must have slopes which are opposites and reciprocals of each other. The third line must cross the other two lines.

Another type of possibility is $y = 0$, $x = 0$, and $y = x - 1$. The lines $y = 0$ and $x = 0$ are perpendicular.

34. Two lines are parallel if they have the same slope. Two lines are perpendicular if their slopes are negative reciprocals of each other. In addition, two different lines are parallel if they are both of the form $x = a$ and $x = b$, while two lines are perpendicular if they are of the form $x = a$ and $y = b$.

35. a. Meifeng has $75 \div 15 = 5$ payments left.

b. $\$75 + 3(\$15) = \$120$

c. $A = 120 - 15w$, where A is the amount owed, and w is the number of weeks.

d. If you graphed this equation, it would be a line with y-intercept $120 and slope $-\frac{15}{1}$.

36. a. Robert is laying 60 stones in 90 minutes, which is 2 stones every 3 minutes or 40 stones an hour. He has 220 stones left, so it should take about $220 \div 40 = 5.5$ hours at the same rate. So, he should finish at about 9:00 P.M.

b. Because he has 120 stones laid at 2:00 P.M., he is 3 hours into the work, so he would have started at about 11:00 A.M.

c. Answers will vary. Students may say that an equation will allow for a more precise answer but that graphs and tables allow for more visual inspection and estimation.

37. a. $T = 30 - 3n$

b. y-intercept = 30; the y-intercept gives the starting temperature after 0 hours.

c. Slope = -3; the slope tells you the rate of change (decrease) in temperature for each hour.

38. a. $m = 0.50n$ Here, n is in dollars (If n is in cents, the equation becomes $m = 50n$.)

b. slope = 0.50

39. a. About 10,914; since $2.39P + P = 37{,}000$, $P = 10{,}914.45428$. So, the population was approximately 10,914 people in 2000.

b. 125,430; $P = 2.39(37{,}000) + 37{,}000 = 125{,}430$ people in 2020

40. a. $A_{\text{Terrance}} = 14.95 + 0.50m$

$A_{\text{Katrina}} = 34$

b. Looking at the graphs makes it clear that Terrance's phone bill will be cheaper for less than 38 minutes. For example, we can see that for zero minutes (the y-intercept), the cost is $14.95 for Terrance and $34 for Katrina. Despite this early advantage, Terrance's bill will eventually be higher than Katrina's because the rate of change, or slope, is greater.

c. The costs of the two plans will be the same when $A_{\text{Terrance}} = A_{\text{Katrina}}$. Note that the two bills are never exactly equal. They are closest when $m = 38$, at which point Terrance's bill is $33.95 and Katrina's bill is $34.

Students can do this problem on the graphing calculator table, on a graph, or using a paper-and-pencil method. $m = 38$.

X	Y1	Y2
34	31.95	34
35	32.45	34
36	32.95	34
37	33.45	34
38	33.95	34
39	34.45	34

X=38

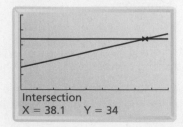

Intersection
X = 38.1   Y = 34

d. The new plan, represented by $A = 25 + 0.25m$, will be cheaper than Terrance's bill if the time charged is more than 40.2 minutes. It will be cheaper than Katrina's bill if the time charged is less than 36 minutes.

41. a. Juan's method is correct; the perimeter increases by 1 each time.

Natalie makes a common mistake. To convince students that she is incorrect, you should be able to apply her reasoning from Figure 1 to Figure 3 by tripling the perimeter of Figure 1. But this would mean that Figure 3 has a perimeter of 9, which we can see is not true.

Steven's method does not work because there are segments that are no longer part of the perimeter when another triangle is added on to the existing figure.

b. All three students are correct in their reasoning and their equations. All the expressions are equivalent. Students may justify each equation separately using the picture, or, if they recognize that the expressions are equivalent, they may justify one from the diagram and then say that the others are true by transforming one expression into a different, equivalent one.

42. a. Possible solutions include $S = 2n - 1$ and $S = n + (n - 1)$

b. Answers will vary. Students might say something about how an arbitrary figure might look, such as having n squares vertically and $n - 1$ horizontally. Another way to describe each figure is to note that each row and column has n squares, but that the corner is double counted.

c. $P = 4n$ (there are n length units on each side)

$P = 2n + 2(n - 1) + 2$

$2n$ represents the edge length on the left and bottom.

$2(n - 1)$ represents the inside corner edge lengths along the top and right sides.

2 represents the two 1-unit sides on the top and right sides.

Connections

43.

$y = 0.3x$

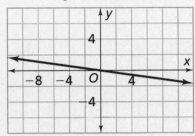

$y = -0.17x$

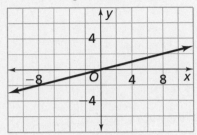

44. a. $x = 3$; $2(3) + 3 = 9$

b. $x = 12$; $\frac{1}{2}(12) + 3 = 9$

c. $x = 1.5$ or $\frac{3}{2}$; $\frac{3}{2} + 3 = \frac{9}{2}$

d. $x = 8.5$; $8.5 + \frac{1}{2} = 9$

e. $x = 15$; $\frac{15 + 3}{2} = \frac{18}{2} = 9$

45. a. $x = 3$; $3 + 6(3) = 4(3) + 9 = 21$

b. $x = 3$; $6(3) + 3 = 4(3) + 9 = 21$

c. $x = 6$; $6(6) - 3 = 4(6) + 9 = 33$

d. $x = \frac{-6}{10}$ or $\frac{-3}{5}$;

$3 - 6\left(\frac{-6}{10}\right) = 4\left(\frac{-6}{10}\right) + 9 = \frac{66}{10}$

46. a. Yes; the ratios of their sides are all 2 : 3, since from smaller to larger the ratios are 2 : 3, 4 : 6, 6 : 9, 8 : 12, which all are equivalent to 2 : 3.

b. $\frac{2}{3}$; the slope of the diagonal line is $\frac{2}{3}$ since the ratio of rise to run is 2 to 3.

The slope is related to the similar rectangles because the ratio of the adjacent sides for each rectangle is the same as the ratio of rise to run, which is the slope.

c. Neither rectangle is in the set, because neither has a slope of $\frac{2}{3}$. However, the first is similar to those shown in the graph; it is just oriented differently.

47. a. Before liftoff, the rocket is stationary (it is on the launch pad awaiting ignition). At time $= 0$, the engines are ignited. It appears that the rocket rises rapidly in the first 2 seconds, and then gradually tapers off.

b. Before liftoff, the slope is 0. The rate of increase in altitude during this time (while the rocket is stationary) is 0.

48. a. $x + 5 = 9$, so $x = 4$.
Check: $2(4 + 5) = 9$

b. $2x + 10 = x - 8$, so $x = -18$.
Check: $2(-18 + 5) = -18 - 8 = -26$

c. $2x + 10 = x$, so $x = -10$.
Check: $2(-10 + 5) = -10$

d. $2x + 10 = -15$; so $x = \frac{-25}{2}$ or $-12\frac{1}{2}$.
Check: $2(-12\frac{1}{2} + 5) = 2(-7.5) = -15$

49. B

50. a. $x = 7.5$

b. $x = 2.5$

51. a. $n = 15$

b. $n = 15$

c. $n = -2$

d. $n = 72$

e. Answers will vary. Sample answer:
$y = -\frac{4}{6}x + 2$

52. a. $n = 13.5$

b. $n = 400$

c. $n = 10$

ACE ANSWERS 4

Extensions

53. a. Temperature should decrease as altitude increases, so $t = 46 - 0.003a$ makes more sense.

b. $t = 46 - 0.003(620) = 44.14°F$

c. Yes; A temperature of 44°F makes sense for Detroit in March.

54. a. Answers will vary. Possible answer: A table because the information would be easy to read.

b. kilometers $= 1.6 \times$ miles; $y = 1.6x$